NIGHT AUTOPSY ROOM:

SEVEN TALES OF LIFE, DEATH, AND HOPE

YOSHIO SAKABE, M.D.

NIGHT AUTOPSY ROOM

SEVEN TALES OF LIFE, DEATH, AND HOPE

YOSHIO SAKABE, M.D.

Translated from the Japanese
by

BROOK NEAL

Cross Cultural Publications, Inc.

CrossRoads Books

Published by **CROSS CULTURAL PUBLICATIONS, INC.**
CROSS ROADS BOOKS
Post Office Box 506
Notre Dame, Indiana, 46556, U.S.A.
Phone: (219) 272-0889
FAX: (219) 273-5973

ISBN: 0-940121-20-4
Library of Congress Catalog Card Number: 94-71050

AUTHOR'S NOTE

The author hopes that through this novel
readers may learn what Japan was like and
what the Japanese experienced during
World War II and thus gain a greater understanding of the all-encompassing tragedy of war. This book was written to create
a better understanding of the Japanese
among the peoples of the world and to
foster friendship between Japan and other
nations.

—Yoshio Sakabe, M.D.

CONTENTS

PREFACE

Night Autopsy Room: Seven Tales of Life, Death, and Hope is primarily the story of people who lived through the turbulent first half of this century in Japan and died amid the chaos that followed Japan's defeat at the hands of the Allies in World War II, or the Pacific War, as it is known to the Japanese. This novel also serves as a forum for me to develop some of my ideas regarding eschatology and to examine the scope of human life, death, and hope.

People are born, live their lives, and inevitably die. But what happens to them after death? The weeping parents prostrated with grief beside the lifeless corpse of the child they cherished; the child wailing with inconsolable sorrow for his mother or father who has just died; the distraught friend who grieves for his dead friend and feels the aching pain of loss at being separated from him; the anguished spouse or lover who has lost his beloved partner and cries his heart out, unwilling to sever his emotional ties; and the people who must somehow bear the unbearable loneliness of knowing that they will never see their dead loved ones again in this world. All these people—the parents, children, friends, husbands and wives, and lovers—ask the same question: Where did my dead loved one go? This question naturally gives rise to mankind's faint but irrepressible desire for eternal life and reunion with loved ones, but is there really any clear answer to this question? Is there really any hope of this desire being fulfilled?

From time immemorial, philosophers and great thinkers have wrestled with, contemplated, and meditated on these questions; and men of religion have prayed to their respective gods seeking revelations from on high. Ordinary people, too, have held their own views on life and death, lived their lives accordingly, and then died.

Buddhist scripture describes in minute detail what happens to people after death. According to one version, after crossing the Sanzu River (the Buddhist counterpart of the River Styx) and arriving on the other side, the virtuous are lifted up into Paradise, and those who committed evil acts during their lives descend into Hell, where they are judged by Enma, the King of Hell, and suffer the torments of whichever particular hell they have been condemned to for eternity. In his book about the afterlife, *Ojyoyoshu*, Genshin gives a considerably concrete, detailed description of the six levels of existence in Buddhism and attempts to prove the reality of Hell. These Buddhist concepts of the afterlife have been set forth to the general public through painting, sculpture, and other arts (in many cases to great and lasting critical acclaim in the art world) and have been a powerful force in the propagation of Buddhism. In addition, the Buddhist concepts of reincarnation and karma have had an enormous effect on how people view life and death. However, are such concepts as these part of the original Buddhist dogma?

There is no record that Shaka, the founder of Buddhism, ever said anything concrete about Paradise or Hell. Wasn't the afterlife set forth by Buddhism essentially a warning to people, used as a means to propagate Buddhism?

I think that what Buddhism seeks to teach, ultimately, is that life and death are one, and that living each moment of life to the fullest is more important than thinking about death, which will take care of itself when the time comes.

The teachings of Shinran were recorded by his disciple Yui'en in the book *Tannisho*. In chapter 2, he is quoted as saying, "*I don't need to know* whether prayers to Amitabha will actually cause a person to be born into Paradise or result in his descending into Hell. Even if I descend into Hell as a result of saying prayers to Amitabha on the advice of the holy priest Honen, still, I will have no regrets" (my italics). In chapter 3 he says, "Since even the so-called virtuous can be born into Paradise, it's only natural that the so-called evildoers should also be born into Paradise. Yet people always say, 'Since even the evildoers can be born into Paradise, it's only natural that the virtuous should also be born into Paradise.'" I would say that Shinran's teachings—which emphasize that it is faith itself, not the doing of good deeds, that is most important, and which utterly ignore the question of what sort of place Paradise is—truly demonstrate the profundity of Buddhism.

The fundamental aim of Christianity is to bring about the creation of Heaven on earth. The Gospels recount the Good News that we, who are all sinners, are forgiven and granted eternal life through the grace of God's infinite love and the atonement of His only Son, Jesus Christ, on the cross. The dissemination of this Good News throughout the world will bring about the creation of Heaven on earth. In the four Gospels, Jesus Christ speaks in numerous parables about what Heaven is like, but never describes it in concrete terms. The subject of Heaven appears to be discussed in the Revelation of St. John the Divine, but it seems to me that the ostensible references to Heaven are actually cautionary scripture directed at the primitive church and early Christians of that period.

Christianity defines sin as the egotism of not putting God first in importance in one's life. Thus, even if we do good deeds, we take pride in them and thereby fall into the sin of asserting our own self-importance, and so we are all sinners before God and cannot receive salvation by virtue of our own efforts. The Christian view of life after death is that people will be granted eternal life because Christ atoned for the sins of all mankind by dying on the cross, thus setting aright the relation between God and mankind, enabling them to receive salvation.

Christians have no idea what concrete form that eternal life will take, but true faith in God as set forth by Jesus Christ is an absolute faith that allows the believer to declare wholeheartedly, "Even if I should descend into Hell, if that were God's will and if God were beside me, that is where I would wish to be." Yet, out of his infinite love and compassion for mankind, God has promised us salvation if we only have faith in Jesus Christ, His only Son. Nevertheless, nowadays even some religious leaders are unable to believe with conviction in the existence of an afterlife or what spiritualism refers to as the spiritual world.

Down through the ages, many people have tried to explain or prove scientifically the existence of an afterlife. Emanuel Swedenborg, Hudson Tuttle, Andrew J. Davis, George V. Owen,

G. D. Thomas, J. J. Morse, and many others have written books from that standpoint. Some of these works, however, are ludicrous in their assertions or theories and are dismissed by most people as works of mysticism or the occult. Some recount near-death experiences (in which a person apparently died, experienced something they believed proves the existence of life after death, and then miraculously revived), but these are not actual experiences of death because the person dies again (this time for real) at some later date. Some do nothing more than use people's feelings and thoughts as a basis for speculating as to what awaits us after death and assert that human wishes, hopes, and desires that went unfulfilled in this world will be realized in the next. Some of these books never get beyond a discussion of such topics as spirit-world communication, spiritual mediums, or other muddled ideas that have no relation at all to the omniscient, omnipotent Creator, the one true God who rules the universe, the everlasting God who is now, always has been, and ever shall be. Though admittedly a Christian influence is apparent in the fundamental concepts of the works of these authors (who grew up in the world of European Christianity), they stray from the path of true Christianity.

The subject of this novel is seven life stories told to a young medical student in a medical school's dissecting room late at night by the spirits of the people who lived those lives. As the subtitle suggests, these tales are intended to be an account of human life, death, and hope.

I, too, may be called a heretic by some religious leaders and a fool or a madman by laymen, but if the publication of this book can be justified by these words from the Bible, "Therefore every teacher of the law who has been instructed about the kingdom of heaven is like the owner of a house who brings out of his storeroom new treasures as well as old" (Matthew 13:52), and afford readers a chance to think about how they live in today's world and to turn their attention to the world of eternity, then as its author I can hope for no greater happiness or reward.

A NOTE ON THE TRANSLATION

Before beginning this novel, readers may wish to take a moment to familiarize themselves with the organization of the educational system in Japan prior to the postwar Allied Occupation. Students attended elementary school for six years. Those who continued their education went to middle school for five years. High school students attended classes for three years (the latter two the equivalent of the first two years of university study in the United States), and graduation from a university required another three years of study. Accordingly, students studying to become physicians took their premedical courses at a high school affiliated with a medical college.

The names of characters in this novel are written in the Japanese style, with the surname first. I included without explanation those Japanese words that can be found in English dictionaries. Bible verses are from the New International Version; although it did not exist at the time of the events depicted in the novel, I feel its superior readability justifies the risk that some readers may find it anachronistic.

I owe a great debt of thanks to Kazuhiko Miyo, my dear friend and former co-worker at Yamaguchi Shoten, Publishers, in Kyoto, who gave unsparingly of his time, scholarship, and linguistic acuity to explain to me the meanings of certain Japanese phrasings. I would also like to thank the persons who advised me on the correct terminology of a variety of subjects: Albert R. Ward, M.D.; Dick E. Richardson, D.V.M.; Dr. Robert M. Brown, Director of the Historical Museum at Fort Missoula, Missoula, Montana; and Reverend David J. Ophus of Saint Paul's Lutheran

Church in Missoula, Montana. My heartfelt gratitude also goes to Alice Cary, M.D., who believed in my ability to translate this novel, and to the author, Yoshio Sakabe, M.D., who gave me the chance to do so.

Most of all, I thank my husband and helpmate, Tatsuo Ishikawa, whose knowledge of Japanese history and culture was an invaluable aid, and who stood by me in good times and bad through the many months I worked on this translation.

Brook Neal

CHAPTER ONE

FIRST ENCOUNTER WITH THE SPIRITS

Scars of Defeat

It was a day he would never forget, that July 7 of 1946, the day of the Tanabata Festival, the one day of the year when the two stars, Vega the weaver and Altair the cowherd, were allowed to meet on their separate ways across the heavens. An unusually long early summer rain had finally lifted. On the morning radio weather forecast, the names of districts where the rainy season had officially ended fell in a monotonous stream from the announcer's lips. As if to prove the accuracy of the forecast, the early morning sun blazed down fiercely on the plants and shrubs in the courtyard, quite the opposite from the day before. The hydrangea in the inner garden, its beauty quiet and subdued under gray skies during the last few days of rain, now triumphantly displayed its gaily multicolored petals in the bright morning sunlight.

Yoshio Umeki, a medical student, put the notebooks for his morning pathology and bacteriology classes onto the rack of his bicycle, which was leaning in a corner of the entryway. On top of these he stacked the cumbersome anatomical atlas by Rauber, the famous German authority on human anatomy, which he would need to refer to during the dissection laboratory that afternoon. He crowned the load with the lunch his mother had packed for him, and then somewhat haphazardly wrapped his folded white laboratory coat around it all, secured it with a cord, and set off for the medical college.

1

Although it had been almost a year since the day Japan's grand aspirations came to their tragic end in defeat, the country had not yet completely recovered from the chaos of its collapse. The food situation had gone from bad to worse and beyond. Even in cities like Kyoto that had not been destroyed by enemy bombs and fire, the housing conditions were very bad and people were struggling to survive from one day to the next. Clothing was scarce, too— most people had nothing but the clothes on their backs.

The houses of Kyoto looked dark and dingy. Much of the plaster had fallen away from outer walls, exposing the dark brown wooden beams of the underlying structure. Economic conditions were so bad that nobody had the wherewithal to attend to mere cosmetic concerns such as broken windows. There was no glass to be had anyway, so plywood boards had been put up instead, but they only added to the seedy, run-down appearance of everything.

"Boy, that blackout sure wrecked my studying last night. I've done hardly any of the preparation for today's classes, especially that dissection laboratory for my gross anatomy course that just started in June—I should've at least glanced over the Rauber atlas a bit by candlelight," Yoshio said, grumbling to himself about the long power failure the night before.

He pedaled north on Fuyacho Street to Oike Boulevard. A few months before the end of the war, the houses lining Oike had been forcibly evacuated and demolished in order to minimize the damage caused by the spread of fire after the American air raids. Though much wider than before, the street remained unpaved, bumpy, and full of potholes, spotted here and there with small vegetable gardens tacitly allowed by the city officials. What scrawny plants managed to grow there despite the lack of fertilizer were more often than not pilfered in the middle of the night, leaving the scanty crops interspersed liberally with weeds. The ground was a reddish brown, covered with fallen plaster from the roofs and walls of mud-and-plaster storehouses that had been razed. Here and there lay jagged wooden planks and huge beams, still awaiting removal. The view to the west stretched wide and open as far as Horikawa Boulevard, its barrenness interrupted only by the stark silhouettes of two or three storehouses that had escaped destruction during the evacuation by proving too much trouble to demolish.

Crossing over these vestiges of the evacuation to the original street, which was at most five meters wide and, despite some potholes here and there, was paved and still recognizable as the pre-evacuation Oike Boulevard, Yoshio turned his bicycle east and headed on. Turning left at Teramachi Street, he crossed Nijo Street and Marutamachi Boulevard, passed between the Kyoto Prefectural No. 1 Girls' High School and the Kyoto Imperial Palace, turned right onto Hirokoji Street in front of Nashinoki Shrine and rode across Kawaramachi Boulevard onto the campus of Kyoto Prefectural Rakuhoku Medical College. Yoshio had made this trip daily except for Sundays since enrolling at the medical college. North of Marutamachi Boulevard at the entrance to Nashinoki Shrine stood a huge stone monument carved with the inscription "Special Government Shrine—Nashinoki Shrine." Massive and prominent, it overpowered its surroundings. The kanji "Special Government Shrine" had been plastered over with cement after the war ended by order of the Occupation Army General Headquarters. Far from erasing them, however, the white cement only made them all the more conspicuous. The irony of this seemed strange and somehow out of place, though, since everything else—the surrounding houses, and the lush greenery and broad expanses of gravel of the Kyoto Imperial Palace grounds—appeared exactly as it had before the war.

As he rode along each morning, catching glimpses of Mt. Hiei and Mt. Daimonji now and then over the rooftops and gazing at the northern range of hills, he felt then more deeply than at any other time the poignancy of the old saying, "Kingdoms may fall, but the mountains and rivers remain."

"Kyoto Prefectural Rakuhoku Medical College" was written in large, bold characters on the wooden board that was hung across the top of the old, time-worn main gate. Inside the gate, Hall No.

1 stood to the right, with its dingy but relatively modern arched entrance. The college library took up the second floor; and Lecture Hall No. 3, where most of the lectures on basic medicine were given, was on the third floor. His home was near the intersection of Fuyacho Street and Takoyakushi Street, so Yoshio could ride his bicycle to school, but the climb to the third floor after his short ride made his legs ache with fatigue, probably because of his chronic malnutrition during and after the war.

The histology laboratory had originally been scheduled for the first class period, but almost all of the college's microscopes were temporarily on loan to Kobe Prefectural Medical School, which needed them to pass the Ministry of Education's inspection in order to receive its college certification, so the lab had been postponed for a month or so. A last-minute notice on the bulletin board yesterday had announced that the first-period lecture would be given by Dr. Arata of the First Department of Pathology.

The lecture was on diseases of the liver, and it provided quite detailed information about cirrhotic lesions, but there was nothing new in what Dr. Arata read from his worn lecture notes. Everything he said came from textbooks and journals published before the war. The war years had been an utter blank as far as the import of new medical knowledge was concerned. Most of the other professors' lectures were just as devoid of new material as Dr. Arata's, but his exams had a reputation for being really tough. Many students flunked them and had to take them over, so Yoshio and the other students took copious notes. Dr. Arata was said to be part of a three-man coalition of great influence in the college, along with Dr. Fujikawa of the Ophthalmology Department and Dr. Yamano of the First Department of Internal Medicine. Collectively, they were known as the Arata Group and had a strong say in faculty meetings. They were even rumored to have been involved in the ousting of two associate professors, Dr. Oyama of the Urology Department and Dr. Takenaka of the Otorhinology Department, for their leftist activities.

The second-period lecture on bacteriology was given by Dr. Ibaragi, who after many years as an associate professor, had finally been promoted to full professor during the war. His forte was really immunology rather than bacteriology, and he had even published several books on the subject. He also had a genius for languages; naturally, being a physician, he had a good command of German, but he was also comfortable with French and English. Recently, his lectures contained tidbits of exciting new material and the latest theories, gleaned from U.S. medical journals he had obtained from one of the Occupation Army doctors—all of which was woefully lacking in the conventional texts. Listening to his lectures, the students got some idea of just how far the astonishing advances in medicine in the United States had surpassed the outdated Japanese and German medical knowledge, which was all that had been available in Japan during the war.

At lunchtime, most students usually stayed in the tiered lecture hall, milling around and talking. Their faces were pale and lifeless; unlike their predecessors before the war, these students did not have any energy to spare for a game of catch. Their lack of physical activity was almost a sort of self-defense, so as to expend as few calories of energy as possible. The students who lived with their families, like Yoshio, brought a lunch—however bland or plain—from home. But it was obvious that the students from outside Kyoto, who were living in boarding houses, skipped lunch altogether, or else made do with nibbling on a piece of coarse bread.

Yoshio's classmates sported a wide variety of clothing. Many wore their old undergraduate university uniforms. There were five or six upperclassmen from the Naval and Military Academies, who had been close to graduation when the war ended; with the abolition of Japan's military forces and the closing of these academies, they had had to take the regular university entrance examination and start their university studies all over again. They, along with a few former naval and military career officers, attended classes wearing their old military uniforms with the collar insignias removed.

In the Dissecting Room

As one o'clock neared, the students rose one by one and started down the stairs toward the dissecting room. The dissecting room was connected to Hall No. 1 by a breezeway off the eastern side of the building. Weeds were growing on the roof of the breezeway, and its soot-covered, dull orange paint was peeling badly and had fallen off in places. Cobwebs covered the ceiling of the breezeway, giving the impression that it hadn't been cleaned in years, and a single bare light bulb poked its head out of the sea of cobwebs. A few fragrant olive trees had been planted along one side of the breezeway, amid which stood a bronze bust of the famous German doctor Scheube, which dated back to the founding of the college. Germany and Japan had joined together to fight the Allies, and together had tasted bitter defeat. The dour, bronze visage of this eminent German doctor now looked somehow forlorn. It was a wonder the bust still remained on the campus, since almost every scrap of iron or bronze had been delivered up to the military as Japan's resources first dwindled and eventually were utterly exhausted during the war. Some wild hydrangeas that had grown up around the bust were blooming, also somewhat forlornly, but at least they brought a little charm to the bleak surroundings.

Yoshio's grandfather, Hidenosuke, had graduated from the medical school which later had become Rakuhoku Medical College. He never tired of talking about the years in the latter part of the Meiji era when Seito University, located to the east across the Kamo River, had been founded. He and a Dr. Irako, Chairman of the Department of Surgery at Rakuhoku Medical School, had left their positions to help found the School of Medicine at Seito University. Clearly, Rakuhoku Medical College had a distinguished history, and had long been held in high regard as one of the outstanding medical schools in Japan. Since Japan's recent defeat, however, it had suffered the same conditions as the rest of the medical institutions in the country—its operating budget had been cut to the bone, and the dilapidation of its facilities had gone unchecked. When Yoshio thought of the many universities destroyed outright by enemy bombardment during the war or those where almost all of the students and faculty had been killed or injured, such as Nagasaki Medical College, laid waste in the blink of an eye by the awesome destructive power of the atomic bomb, he couldn't help thinking that Rakuhoku Medical College had been very fortunate to be located in a city that had escaped with so little damage. In Kyoto, the bombing had been confined to the Higashiyama district, in the southeast corner of the city, and the damage had been so minimal that a police gag order in effect during wartime had prevented most people in other parts of the city from even hearing of it.

Yoshio and the other students made their way across the breezeway to an old, two-story wooden building, which housed the anatomy, pathology, and forensic medicine classrooms. The anatomy and histology laboratories and the dissecting rooms for pathology and forensic medicine were on the first floor; the second floor was divided into research laboratories and offices for professors, associate professors, and instructors.

Entering the building through the open door, the students walked along a hallway lined with shelves packed with glass jars containing specimens that looked as if they had been there since the college's opening day. A ten-watt, bare light bulb hanging from the ceiling cast a dim light on the bottles and their strange contents: specimens of various deformities floating in the glass jars—anencephalic fetuses, Siamese twins, one-eyed fetuses, and the like. They were thought to belong to the Pathology Department. The German lettering on the labels, long since faded, was all the more difficult to make out, covered as it was with a thick layer of dust attesting to the jars' antiquity.

The entire building was permeated with the acrid odor of formalin, but the students attending classes there had gradually become used to it and no longer found it unpleasant. After walking along the dark hallway, on entering the dissecting room Yoshio was momentarily blinded by the dazzling brightness of the summer sunlight streaming in through the windows opposite. Ten dissecting tables were lined up in the room, and cadavers were laid out on seven of them, covered by carelessly draped shiny oilcloth sheets that gave off a glare under the intense light. The students put their texts and notebooks on nearby shelves or empty chairs, slipped on their black oilcloth aprons (some wore their aprons over their white lab coats, others first removed their shirts and wore the aprons against their bare skin), and took their places at the dissecting tables. Six students were assigned to a table, one on each side of the three main divisions of each cadaver, the head, the chest, and the abdomen. By the end of the course, each group of six students would have dissected parts of three cadavers, working on each of the three divisions in turn.

As the students took their seats beside the cadavers, their listless eyes began to shine with mingled curiosity and the desire to learn. Yamaguchi and Aoki, as always, tied headbands around their foreheads, as much to signify their dedication to serious study as to keep their hair from falling in their eyes as they worked. Each student opened his Japanese or German anatomical atlas and laid it on the stool next to him; then, referring constantly to his atlas, each took up a knife, scissors, or thumb forceps and began to dissect. Following the diagram in his Rauber atlas, Yoshio peeled back the skin from the left side of the cadaver's face, and identified the facial muscles and traced the course of the facial nerves. From time to time, one of his classmates using a different atlas would run into some difficulty and call out, "Hey, Umeki, what does Rauber say about this?" Yoshio was proud of owning a Rauber atlas, which was superior to other atlases in clarity of detail and printing quality. It had been left at his house before the war by his first cousin, Ueda Koji, who had also studied at Rakuhoku Medical College on a naval scholarship. After graduating in 1940, he had become a lieutenant commander in the Imperial Japanese Navy Medical Corps. He had served as doctor on the Class I cruiser *Mogami* and was killed in action when she was sunk in the Philippines during the Battle for Leyte Gulf. Even now, Yoshio recalled clearly the day Ueda had dropped by his family's house on shore leave, carrying the heavy Rauber atlas that he had just bought. He could still see Ueda turning the pages with care, one by one, nodding his head appreciatively with an air of satisfaction. Yoshio had been only sixteen at the time, yet his cousin's evident passion for learning had left a deep and lasting impression on him.

Thirty minutes after the start of class, the lean figure of Dr. Noguchi, Professor of Anatomy, entered the dissecting room, wearing sandals and a white lab coat hastily pulled on over his undershirt. Malnutrition had turned his naturally pale complexion even whiter. He walked around the dissecting tables, bending over the students at work and occasionally pursing his lips nervously. "Well, how's it going? Any questions?" he asked each student in turn, his dialect betraying his Kyoto upbringing. A little before four o'clock, the burning afternoon sunlight began to shine in through the west-facing windows, and the stench of the formalin evaporating from the cadavers intensified.

Suddenly the door opened and three Occupation Army officers strode into the room. With them were two Orientals, acting as guides, whose light gray uniforms indicated that they were civilian employees of the Occupation Army. Evidently, they had come to observe the current state of medical training in Japan. Taking a closer look, Yoshio recognized the Oriental guides: they were Dr. Wang and Dr. Su, two Taiwan nationals who had just graduated from Rakuhoku Medical College that spring. They were now employed at the No. 1 Red Cross Hospital in the Higashiyama district, which had been requisitioned by the Occupation forces. Taiwan was one of the Japanese territories that had been liberated by the Allies, and apparently, the Taiwanese in Japan were being accorded special treatment by the Occupation Army, since their government had been on the winning side after Japan's defeat in the war.

Riding around Kyoto in jeeps, the Occupation forces had picked out all the finest residences and requisitioned them for their own use. Kyoto's only truly Western-style hotels, the Miyako Hotel and the Kyoto Hotel, were both being used to billet Occupation troops. The Occupation Army had also taken over the Botanical Gardens, the Okazaki Museum of Art, and the municipal auditorium, just south of which they had even built their own church. Unlike the homes of the Japanese, which were darkened by electrical power failures almost every other night, the living quarters and facilities of the Occupation forces had no blackouts— their glass windows glowed brilliantly every evening. The Daiken Building near the corner of Shijo Street and Karasuma Boulevard in the city center was being used as Occupation Army Headquarters for Kyoto. At Kyoto Station, large signs printed with the letters "RTO" had been hung designating transportation facilities reserved for Occupation Army use. The Occupation Army trains were given scheduling priority over those used by the Japanese, and even arrived at and left from their own platforms. The Occupation Army's power was absolute.

In stark contrast, Japanese children orphaned by the war, carrying shoeshine boxes made from a few scraps of lumber nailed together, roamed the streets around the train stations and the downtown area, crying out "Shoeshine? Shoeshine?" to the Occupation Army servicemen, shining army boots and clamoring for a few copper coins or a pack of gum in payment.

American corn earmarked for livestock feed was distributed among the Japanese, who pounded it into flour and then baked it into hard, rough, barely palatable crackers. The Japanese received a rice ration twice a week, but it amounted to only two days' worth; in an effort to make it last, people mixed the rice with potatoes to make a watery gruel. These were the staple diet of the average Japanese during this time.

Rumors of many Japanese dying of starvation had begun to raise cries of criticism that MacArthur's occupation policy was to blame for the deaths, not only among the Japanese but even back in the United States. The threat of public outrage had resulted in a special distribution of U.S. Army battle rations to the Japanese. These rations came in cardboard boxes about half again as large as the aluminum lunch boxes usually used in Japan. Each box was packed with dark green tin cans of food—soup, corned beef hash, and fruit cocktail for dessert—and a colorful little box of Lucky Strikes, Camels, Chesterfields, or some other American brand of cigarettes.

Once, Yoshio and his family had eaten some black-market, U.S. Army foods; he'd hardly been able to believe such delicious things existed. Knowing that the U.S. soldiers had been eating that kind of food throughout the war, he came to feel that the half-starved Japanese troops had been doomed to lose the war from the very beginning. Although it seemed foolish, Yoshio nevertheless thought it a shame to throw them into the trash, so he kept the little, empty Camel box and a chewing gum wrapper that still smelled faintly of mint, and hid them away in his desk drawer, next to a wrapper from a bar of American soap. The recent scarcity of commodities was so severe that there were almost no cigarettes to be had. Some of Yoshio's classmates, abandoning the normal standards of hygiene and decency, had even taken to picking up and smoking the half-smoked butts thrown down in the street by the Occupation Army servicemen.

The presence of the three officers in the dissecting room filled Yoshio and his classmates with a vague anxiety. The world of the Occupation Army servicemen was utterly different from that of the Japanese. It was the difference between the occupiers and the occupied, the oppressors and the oppressed, the rich and the poor, the well-dressed and the shabby. The worst thing was not being able to understand a word they said, and never knowing when they might speak to you or what they might do next. The students tried to ignore the officers observing them and kept their eyes turned down toward the cadavers they were dissecting. Still, when an occasional lapse of concentration left one of the students open to an awareness of the officers' presence, he invariably felt ill at ease.

Yoshio had heard that a few months before, some U.S. Army doctors had visited the Rakuhoku Medical College Hospital as observers. They had been shocked to see four operations being performed simultaneously on four operating tables crowded into a single, large operating room, with no general anesthesia, by surgeons who were not even wearing surgical gloves, but had merely washed their hands in disinfectant. So now, as these Americans stood observing him and his fellow students, the thought "What do they think of our dissecting class?" flashed through Yoshio's mind amid feelings of mingled anxiety and curiosity. The group of officers left after only a few minutes, perhaps because what the students were doing was self-explanatory or not of great importance or interest to them. As they filed out of the room, the eyes of one of the officers met Yoshio's. The man smiled in greeting, and Yoshio felt his tension and anxiety ease at this unexpected show of friendliness.

The news media had reported that starting next year, the country would switch over to daylight savings time for the summer. This practice of setting the clocks ahead one hour was unfamiliar to the Japanese, but it was being forced on the country by the Occupation Army. But for now, five o'clock was still the same time of day it had been before Japan lost the war, and the blazing afternoon sun had not abated in the least. Now and then, Dr. Noguchi nervously looked at his wristwatch, but despite this, not one of the students started getting ready to leave. With thumb forceps in one hand and scissors or a knife in the other, they continued dissecting, forgetting all else, lost in utter concentration as if every minute of study was precious.

The skin of the cadaver assigned to Yoshio's group had turned dark brown from the formalin used to preserve it, and all the tissues were hard and rubbery. It was the body of a woman in her forties. Her hair had been pulled away from the face and tied in back, yet one could guess from her features that she had probably been of above-average beauty when alive. Her high-bridged, shapely nose seemed to lend her face a certain elegance and dignity.

"Yamada, I wonder what sort of life this woman led when she was alive," Yoshio said quietly to his dissecting partner, who was cutting into the right side of the cadaver's face directly across from him.

"The people who once inhabited these bodies we're dissecting lived their own lives, just like everybody else," Yamada answered, curtly. Yamada wasn't much of a talker, especially when he was absorbed in study. Quite recently, he'd exhibited an unexpected, romantic side to his nature by going ahead with his plans for marriage, knowing full well that his fiancée had contracted tuberculosis of the lungs. At present, Yamada was further burdened with terrible financial worries.

"How's it going with the streptomycin? Are you getting it all right?"

Yoshio had heard that Yamada was buying streptomycin for his wife through an intermediary, one of their classmates, Watanabe, who worked part-time nights doing odd jobs around the Occupation Army quarters. Yamada's predicament always weighed heavily on Yoshio's mind, and now was a good chance to ask him about it.

"It almost never comes when it's supposed to, and when I do get hold of some, it costs an arm and a leg."

Indeed, penicillin and streptomycin were drugs of an entirely new class called antibiotics. These powerful drugs were incredibly effective; the doctors in clinical practice at the Rakuhoku Medical College Hospital across the way had never seen anything like it. Of course, these antibiotics were not being manufactured in Japan yet. They had to be obtained from the Occupation Army through illegal channels. One way or another, you had to depend on an army connection to buy even one or two vials. Streptomycin, in particular, was extremely difficult to obtain, since it was still in the experimental stage even in the United States.

A feeling somewhere between resentment and sadness burned fiercely deep in Yoshio's heart. Perhaps he was being hasty in his judgment, but it seemed that the hardships all Japanese were going through now, some to a lesser and others to a greater extent, were all related to the war that had ended the summer before. God! What had been the meaning of this war, really? He thought of his friends in middle school who had gone on to the Military and Naval Academies and become career soldiers, and friends at university—most of them liberal arts majors—who'd been pulled away from their studies and hustled off to the faraway battlefields during the final stage of the war. A great many of them had died a "hero's death" on the foreign soil of China, at the bottom of the ocean, in a steaming jungle, on a lonely island, or somewhere in the sky—all had died before their time in the name of the Emperor, their brief lives reminiscent of the fragile, short-lived cherry blossoms.

Then there were the hundreds of thousands of civilians who had lost in a single night of fire and terror everything they owned in the world—their possessions, the houses they'd worked so hard to build—and some, their very lives, in the devastating hail of bombs that had fallen on Tokyo, almost all other large cities, and many smaller towns as well. The "Death before Dishonor" dogma had resulted in the deaths of countless Japanese in Saipan and Okinawa. And crowning it all, Hiroshima and Nagasaki had been totally destroyed by atomic bombs, and Japan had at long last accepted the terms of unconditional surrender stipulated in the Potsdam Declaration, thus ending the long nightmare of the war. Yoshio had read in the morning paper that the distribution of food rations had been reduced to twice a week. For so long, it seemed, Yoshio had heard nothing but bad news. One piece of good news was that the demobilization of Japanese troops from China had been completed. However, the Japanese soldiers stationed in Manchuria had been interned in camps in Russia, and it was anybody's guess when they would be allowed to return home. Still worse, the newspaper reported that many Japanese colonists there had been compelled by circumstances to entrust their babies and infants to the care of Chinese friends or neighbors and had escaped to Japan with nothing but their lives.

The scars of this war were etched so deeply in the hearts of the Japanese whose lives it had touched, they would never heal, Yoshio thought to himself. And yet, how much more so that statement must hold true for the peoples of the Southeast Asian countries whose cities and farms had been turned into battlefields for this hideous war! And these cadavers laid out on the dissecting tables—while they were alive they must have been involved in the war in some way or other. Yes, he felt sure that the people these cadavers had once been must have been among society's underprivileged. Although there were some people willing to donate their bodies for medical study, they were quite the exception. It was the underprivileged who were always hit hardest by the harsh realities of war. They were the ones who had to bear the terrible brunt of the tragedy of war.

The Cadaver of a Woman

"In dissecting class recently, I found myself wondering about the lives of the people whose bodies had become material for our medical study, and I thought to myself, 'These people, too, must be saved.'" These were the words of Nishiura Ko, who had entered the Department of Medicine of Seito University after graduating from Yoshidayama High School. Yoshio had become friends with him at church. Yoshio didn't know why, but now, as he worked to unravel the physiological mysteries of the cadaver before him, Nishiura's words came vividly back to him.

Yoshio was seized by the desire to pray to a superior being, someone watching over the world, a Creator, a loving God.

"What sort of life did she have, the woman whose body lies under my knife now? It doesn't really matter, though. Whatever sort of person she was, she, too, must be saved!" Quelling the deep surge of emotion that rose in his heart as best he could, Yoshio did not speak to Yamada, but kept his inner turmoil to himself. Yoshio was in the habit of closing his eyes and praying for a moment with a request for guidance whenever he was in trouble, had to make an important decision, or was confronted with a difficult problem, or in gratitude (whenever he didn't forget to) when something good had happened to him. Now, to appease the emotion that had taken hold of his heart, he stopped dissecting and, unnoticed by his fellow students around him, inconspicuously shut his eyes and prayed.

"God, I am praying for the woman whose body lies here. Please grant her Your divine salvation, and enfold her in Your eternal peace. In Christ's name, Amen."

Immediately afterward, it happened—the unbelievable.

Tears sprang, one by one, from the lachrymal glands near the bridge of the nose of the cadaver. They rolled from the inner corners of both eyes, across the eyeballs as yet untouched by knife or scissors, and down the sunken cheeks—a few, meager tears. Naturally, these few tears on the cheeks of a cadaver already wet with formalin went completely unnoticed by Yoshio and the other students, who would never have dreamed that such a thing could happen.

Despite the lengthening of the days with the approach of summer, the brilliance of the fiery afternoon sun began to subside as six o'clock neared. The shadows of the window frames had become elongated and distorted, and had at last begun to fall on the students and cadavers.

Dr. Noguchi had been walking up and down between the dissecting tables, pursing his lips and shaking his head with a regularity that suggested a mild tic, but by and by he left the room abruptly, without a word. Apparently taking that as their cue, Watanabe and two or three other students packed up their things and left, too. "It must be getting close to the time when they have to report for their part-time jobs," Yoshio thought. By six-thirty, sure enough, dusk had begun to creep into the room, and everyone except Yoshio and Yamada had started for home.

Yoshio was quite pleased with the work he'd done today: he had located the smaller subcutaneous nerves and blood vessels of the face, traced the course of the facial nerves, and identified facial muscles such as the orbicular muscle of the eye and the masseter muscle; he had also examined the superior orbital fissure of the first branch of the trigeminal nerve, the inferior orbital fissure of the second branch of the nerve, and the place where the third branch of the nerve passed through the mental foramen. Getting up from his stool at last, Yoshio stretched himself and lightly pounded his lower back, which ached from his having sat hunched over the cadaver for so long. He retrieved his books from the cupboard under the dissecting table, stacked them on the stool, and placed his Rauber anatomical atlas on top. Yamada appeared to want to continue working, but at Yoshio's urging, he got up and helped Yoshio drape the oilcloth sheet over the cadaver. Then they went to wash up at the sinks on the east side of the room; the light of the setting sun did not reach this part of the room, and consequently it was already dim with the gloom of twilight, its windows a dusky gray. A few of the upper panes of glass still bore the crisscross and diagonal strips of paper that had been glued to them during wartime to keep glass shattered by bomb blasts from falling into the room.

Yoshio's fingers were wrinkled, like those of the cadavers, and white from contact with the formalin. Feeling his senses a bit numbed, he stood beside Yamada and started washing his hands with the misshapen lump of soap they found next to the sinks. The college would never have been able to supply the sinks with soap, so somebody must have brought it from home. It looked like homemade soap or the kind made for sale on the black market. Trying to get rid of the smell of the formalin as completely as possible, Yoshio scrubbed his hands vigorously with the worn-down lump of soap; its oily smell and reddish orange color reminded him of prewar laundry soap. The only thing Japan had in comparative abundance during this postwar period was the water that came rushing out when a faucet was turned on.

Something strange and unbelievable was again happening on the dissecting table at the other side of the room. The left hand of the cadaver that Yoshio and Yamada had been dissecting, its severed muscles, blood vessels, and nerves dangling from it like electric wires, inched its way out from under the oilcloth sheet. If Yoshio and Yamada had noticed it, they would have received the fright of their life and probably fainted. As if it had been waiting for this chance while the two students were busy washing, the cadaver's hand ran its fingers over Yoshio's stack of books and found the one it was looking for on top—the Rauber anatomical atlas. It took the heavy book from the stack and slipped it quietly, though a bit clumsily, into the cupboard under the dissecting table.

"Tomorrow, let's work on the area around the parotid gland a little more and then start on the ear, all right?" Yoshio said to Yamada as he finished washing and dried his hands. He then went back to the dissecting table, picked up his books and put them under his arm without thinking, and went out with Yamada. After checking to see that they were the last ones out, they closed the door, which till then had been left open. The rickety doorknob made of white porcelain was probably an antique from the Meiji era. As Yoshio and Yamada walked past the shelves of specimens and out of the building, the temperature felt a few degrees cooler. The western sky glowed with deep reds and oranges, and silhouetted against those lurid hues, the black figures of birds flying home in the direction of the Kyoto Imperial Palace appeared all the blacker.

After Class

Yoshio's bike was parked in one of the bicycle racks next to the entrance that faced the old, clapboard hospital. After fastening his belongings onto the rack of his bike, he set off for home. It was Yoshio's habit to follow the reverse of the route he took every morning to the medical college. He pedaled west across Kawaramachi Boulevard, south on Teramachi Street, west a short distance on Marutamachi Boulevard, south on Gokomachi Street, across Oike Boulevard, and on down to his parents' house on Takoyakushi Street. To the eye, the streets of Kyoto appeared to be level, but as he rode his bicycle homeward, Yoshio's body registered the slight north-to-south decline in the lay of the land. The homeward trip was definitely an easier, smoother ride and the pedaling did not require much energy. Content that his time at the college, particularly the hours in the dissection laboratory, had been well spent that day, Yoshio pedaled lightheartedly toward home.

His mother would be awaiting his return, with dinner (though, of course, a plain and simple one) ready for him. When he got to the intersection of Gokomachi Street and Oike Boulevard, however, he crossed the boulevard with extreme caution, remembering an incident that had occurred there just before the start of the rainy season. He had been on his way home from the medical college, and at that very intersection, a U.S. Army jeep had come speeding east on Oike and hit the front wheel of his bike, bending it out of shape. No doubt about it, he had had a close call. In retrospect, he realized that if either he or the jeep had reached the intersection a fraction of a second sooner, he would probably have been killed or at least seriously injured. Because the other party involved was an Occupation Army serviceman, he would have had no recourse for compensation.

Whenever Yoshio remembered that brush with death, a chill ran down his spine, and he felt grateful that the near-accident hadn't amounted to anything worse than a bent wheel. Yoshio recalled that the melody of a song immensely popular recently among the Occupation Army servicemen, "You Are My Sunshine," often came naturally to his lips when he was riding his bicycle. He had learned it from Iida, a theology student at Doshin University; the song's English lyrics were simple and relatively easy to remember. Still, this time just a year ago, Yoshio would never have dreamed of singing a song of an enemy nation, least of all a lighthearted love song.

The lights were already on in the house when he arrived, and his father had apparently already begun his evening clinic hours for seeing patients. Softly murmuring a few words of thanks for his father's tireless efforts on behalf of their family, Yoshio opened the private door east of the clinic, which took up the front part of the house, and entered the passageway which ran the length of the clinic and the inner garden to the door of the family living quarters. The passageway was bordered on the right by a corridor linking the clinic and the living quarters, and off of which opened the separate rooms containing the bath, the toilet, and the lavatory. On the other side, the corridor bordered the inner garden. Opening another private door to the family living quarters at the end of the passageway, Yoshio entered and was home. He leaned his bike against the wall of the entryway, took his books and things from the rack and gathered them under his arm, and called out to his mother, "I'm home."

"Welcome back," his mother answered, "you must be tired."

The moment he heard her voice, he felt hungry.

He threw himself down onto a cushion in the dining room, which since childhood he had always called the piano room because it had a piano in one of the corners. His mother set a bowl of chicken mixed with rice on the round table before him. In those days, chicken was luxurious fare.

"Your grandfather brought it back from your uncle who lives in Yagi," his mother said, explaining how such a rarity as chicken had found its way to their table. Yoshio remembered his childhood years before the war as "the good old days," a time when there were always lots of tangerines kept under the round table in winter, sent to the family as gifts from various people, and boxes of fruit or sweets lay stacked in the hallway beyond the piano year-round. Food was always scarce in wartime, but this was especially true of the recent Pacific War; in the final stages of the war and still now, after Japan's defeat, the food shortage was disastrous. Lately, even his father's face had become slightly bloated from long months of inadequate nourishment. During the intervals between his morning and evening clinic hours, his father would try to make their ration of rough, unhulled rice a bit more palatable and as much as possible like the prewar white rice they'd been used to eating by means of a makeshift hulling process. He would put some of the rice into a large, empty sakè bottle and thrust a stick into it through the neck of the bottle again and again and again. Yoshio also often saw his father grinding their ration of corn in a stone mill to make flour for bread or hard crackers.

The dinner prepared by his mother with loving hands was not big enough to make him feel full. After finishing eating, Yoshio switched on the radio that was on a small desk in a corner of the room. He'd been later than usual getting home today, and the "Come, Come, Everybody" English conversation program, which had been broadcast since September right after Japan's defeat, was already over; but the Occupation Army broadcasting station played a string of songs—Doris Day's "Sentimental Journey," Frank Sinatra's "Dream," and Perry Como's "Until the End of Time." Songs such as "It's Been a Long, Long Time" and "You Belong to My Heart," which were wildly popular among the Occupation Army servicemen, were indeed welcome music to the ears of the Japanese radio audience, who, until the war ended the previous August, had been treated to nothing but war songs and marches day and night.

Despite the scarcity of food, clothing, and shelter, Yoshio had believed he could enrich his impoverished life at least through music; before and during the war, he had listened to phonograph recordings of his beloved classical music and endured the abysmal sound quality of records so poorly manufactured that they were like pieces of cardboard covered with Bakelite, playing them on a turntable with a bamboo needle. Ironically, after several years of listening to such "music," he welcomed with something close to longing the postwar American popular music so contrary to his previous taste in music, and had come to think that any American song was good. Recently, he had found himself enjoying the easy-listening music on the radio, which at least offered good sound quality.

When Yoshio had been listening to the radio for about an hour or so after dinner, thoughts of the studying he must do for the next day's classes, particularly the dissection laboratory, began to weigh heavily on his mind. He reluctantly got up and went to his room upstairs.

Ironically enough, as soon as he stepped into powerthe power the power went off almost as if on schedule, and the entire neighborhood was plunged into total darkness. Resigning himself to a period of idleness, Yoshio groped his way to the bed and threw himself down on it. As he lay there in the darkness, he couldn't help remembering the countless times he'd sweated out preliminary air-raid alerts and air-raid warnings during the war. Yoshio's gaze traveled up to a part of the ceiling that appeared blacker than the surrounding darkness, where a big hole still remained. At a time when fire bombs were being dropped on Japanese cities during the American air raids, Yoshio's father, like other heads of households in Kyoto, had been ordered by the authorities to cut a hole in the ceiling so that they would have access to the roof to put out the fire if one of the incendiary bombs packed with jellied napalm fell on their house. However, in practice, this tactic had proved to be nothing more than a childish idea and had been almost useless in other cities that had actually been bombed with incendiaries.

Japan was struggling to recover from its defeat, but the country had been drained of its natural and imported resources by the long war, and recovery was still a long way off, as was evident from the shortage of a basic commodity like electricity. After almost an hour the power blackout, which seemed to symbolize Japan's current state of affliction, finally ended. The power came back on, and the lights came back on in the houses.

Now that Yoshio could start studying, he sat down at his desk and looked for the Rauber anatomical atlas among the books and notebooks he had brought home from the medical college.

"What the—? but it should be right here!" Yoshio murmured to himself incredulously as he realized with growing alarm that his precious Rauber atlas was not there.

Return to the Dissecting Room at Night

"What could have happened to it?" Yoshio asked himself over and over, agonizing over the missing book. A trip back to the college to look for a book at this time of night was no small undertaking. Because he had fastened his books securely to the rack of his bicycle, it couldn't have fallen off on his way home, so he must have left it in the dissecting room. Come to think of it, he couldn't remember with any certainty having had the relatively bulky Rauber with him when he had left class. Yoshio was infuriated at his carelessness. Unless he reviewed the work he'd done in class today and prepared for tomorrow's class, he feared he'd fall irreparably behind in his gross anatomy course. Worse, with the summer vacation coming up, Dr. Noguchi would be giving them an oral test soon, and if he didn't pass it, his final grade for the course would undoubtedly suffer.

He was pretty tired, it was true, but more than that, he felt a strong aversion to returning to the dissection room alone late at night, despite his having gone there regularly now for more than three months and become quite used to its somewhat disconcerting atmosphere. Besides, the Rauber was not the only anatomical atlas to be had. Both the Japanese atlas by Dr. Mori, which was fairly well written (though poorly printed), and Yoshio's father's Spalteholz anatomical atlas, which was somewhat outdated, could probably be found in one of his father's bookcases. Surely, Yoshio tried to persuade himself, he could make do with one of those just for tonight, couldn't he? The upshot of it was that he was used to the Rauber and it was decidedly the best anatomical atlas. He couldn't ignore the possibility, however remote, that the book might be gone by the time he got to the college the next morning.

"I'd better go get it right now," Yoshio concluded. He resolutely got up and started downstairs.

"Mom," Yoshio called on his way out the door, "I'm going to get something I left at the college. I've got a key, so go ahead and lock up for the night. Don't worry, and don't wait up for me. I'll take the streetcar up to the campus; that'll be easier and quicker than riding my bike."

Hurrying out of the house, he jogged over to the intersection of Kawaramachi Boulevard and Takoyakushi Street. Since the end of the war, nighttime Kyoto had become a little brighter, but even the downtown area was still much darker than it had been before the war. The sky above held neither moon nor stars. There was no traffic in the streets, except for the occasional passing of a U.S. Army jeep.

"Boy, it'll be really late by the time I get home and can start studying. It looks like this is going to be another all-nighter," Yoshio said to himself as he waited at the streetcar stop. Just then, the streetcar came rattling up the otherwise empty street at a fast clip, rocking from side to side. The streetcars were packed with people in the daytime, but at this time of night there were very few passengers. Listening to the strange, occasional clanking of the streetcar, Yoshio wondered if there was something wrong with it. The streetcar traveled straight up Kawaramachi Boulevard across Sanjo Street, then Nijo Street, then Marutamachi Boulevard, moving ever nearer to the medical college. At last the west wall of the campus, which ran northward parallel to Kawaramachi and the streetcar line, came into view. Through the streetcar's front windows, the track ahead was visible for only a little way, beyond which it was engulfed in darkness. All of the windows of the building that housed the laboratories in basic medicine were dark, probably because the college was still not up to full staff, and the building itself was shrouded in darkness.

At this point, Yoshio again had second thoughts about going to the dissecting room alone so late at night. Memories of the daytime appearance of the dissecting room and its lifeless inhabitants began to fill his mind, and the more he mulled them over, the more frightened he became. At this time of night, there was probably not a soul around. The living quarters of the old man who worked as an orderly in the Department of Anatomy were quite far from the dissecting room, so Yoshio could hardly go to him and ask him to accompany him on his midnight errand.

Should he just give up the idea and go home? But that would be silly. After all, it wasn't as if the bogeyman were going to jump out and get him. And anyway, he had never done anything to give the cadavers in the dissecting room cause to hold a grudge against him. True, he cut them up with knife and scissors, but even that he did only for the sake of the noble study of medicine. Oh, he'd blundered on occasion and needlessly severed an important nerve or blood vessel, but surely such innocent mistakes would be forgiven. As these thoughts raced through Yoshio's mind, the streetcar started to slow down as it neared the next stop.

"Rakuhoku Medical College Hospital! Next stop, Rakuhoku Medical College Hospital!" As if hurried out of the car by the conductor's booming, no-nonsense voice, Yoshio quickly stepped down into the street. The "Ting! Ting!" of the conductor's signal to the driver rang out clearly in the still night air. The streetcar rattled off northward and almost immediately disappeared into the blackness of the night, leaving Yoshio standing alone beside the track in the street.

He felt there was no going back now. Yoshio resolutely entered the main gate and headed for the dissecting room. In the dark, he stumbled several times on the stepping-stones set between the main building and Hall No. 1, but at last he made it over to the dimly lit breezeway. As he approached the entrance, even the sound of the leather-saving metal taps on his shoes hitting the cement as he walked echoed eerily, and he found himself frightened of his own weirdly elongated shadow. Standing before the door to the building that contained the dissecting room, Yoshio was keenly aware of the rapid beating of his heart. He knew that neither the outer door nor the door of the dissecting room was kept locked. The doorknob of each was so loose and rickety, the doors could hardly have been said to be locked even if the keys had been turned.

Yoshio grasped the doorknob, pushed the outer door open with a loud creak, and stepped into the hallway. In the dim light of the single light bulb hanging from the ceiling, the pale faces and bodies of the deformed fetuses floated grotesquely in their specimen bottles. A one-eyed fetus, which Yoshio was used to seeing in the daytime and usually thought nothing of, now appeared larger and seemed to be staring at him menacingly. Yoshio was scared to death.

In order to get a grip on himself and overcome his terror as much as possible, Yoshio almost completely closed his eyes and confined his gaze to what was directly in front of him as he stood before the door of the dissecting room. In the dim light, the white porcelain doorknob seemed abnormally bright—almost luminous—against the surrounding blackness.

Steeling himself to the task, Yoshio turned the doorknob to the right and threw the door open with a bang. He was convinced that this explosive act would dispel his own fear and, moreover, drive away any ghosts or evil spirits, if there did happen to be any such creatures (incredible as it sounded!) waiting there to do him harm. His frame of mind was similar to that of the samurai in an ancient ghost tale who thundered at the ghost, "Begone!" as he slashed at it with his sword.

Yoshio stepped into the dark dissecting room, and as he was stretching out his right hand to grope for the light switch, a sight not of this world appeared before his eyes—an unbelievable sight beyond all imagining.

First Encounter with the Spirits

Even in the darkness, the west-facing windows of the dissecting room were discernible as gray, hazy, rectangular outlines, probably because of a distant light shining somewhere outside. Yoshio's eyes, wide with terror, were riveted to something in the middle of the room, a vision from another world that defied description by mere word or picture—a shapeless, glowing mass that appeared to be made up of thousands of tiny balls of phosphorescence, like a multitude of fireflies.

Nearly fainting, Yoshio stared as one part of the phosphorescent mass began to move away from the rest of the mass and toward him. In the next instant, he perceived that what had till then appeared as a formless, glowing mass was actually a vaguely human figure. The contours of the face were indistinct but unmistakably human. As the figure came closer, Yoshio thought he recognized its face as that of a middle-aged woman he'd seen somewhere before. With not even the slightest trace of hostility on its face, the figure came toward him, smiling tenderly; it seemed to charge the atmosphere in the room with an exquisite aura of peace.

Even under normal circumstances, let alone in a room full of dead bodies, a person might reasonably be expected to be scared out of his wits if a stray cat suddenly jumped out at him in the dark. Conversely, if something utterly unexpected appeared, perhaps one could remain calm to some extent. Nevertheless, might not the most horrifying experience be if something resembling a human being but clearly not of this world were to appear at such a time in such a place? By means of some power beyond human understanding, however, Yoshio's senses had been completely altered. He felt as if he had been drawn into another world, transported to a realm where the emotion of fear did not exist. His mind was at peace, and he experienced an utterly new sensation: it was as if he were sleepwalking, yet at the same time his power of thought and his physical senses remained acute, so that he perceived everything around him with a preternatural clarity.

Though he had frozen at first sight of the apparition and had not switched on the lights, the part of the room where Yoshio was standing gradually got lighter as the figure came nearer. When at last it stood before him, it spoke softly. Its voice was beautiful, gentle, and dignified, with a tone Yoshio had never before heard in this world. He could not tell whether the voice came from the open mouth of the figure or was being somehow emitted from the figure's entire body.

"Don't be afraid. I'm sorry I frightened you."

Yoshio was unsure whether he was hearing the voice with his ears or perceiving it through some sort of telepathy, but he could understand clearly what the figure said.

"We are the spirits of the cadavers being dissected here."

"Spirits?" Yoshio murmured uncertainly.

"Yes, spirits. Well, it doesn't really matter what we are called, but we are not what people in the world of the living call 'apparitions,' 'ghosts,' or 'evil spirits.' Let's just say that each of us is the collective life force from the trillions of individual cells that made up our bodies when we were alive. As you know, a human being consists of flesh and an intangible essence that dwells within that flesh—life force, soul—call it what you will. But 'spirit' is probably the most fitting term. After a person dies, the life force becomes separated from the flesh and becomes a spirit. The flesh dies and is destroyed: it usually either rots in the earth where it is buried or is burned to ashes during cremation. Or it is reduced to the state of mere matter, as in the case of our bodies, which have been preserved for medical study. The spirit, however, enters a new world after death, the World of the Spirits."

"I see," Yoshio responded hesitantly.

The spirit ignored Yoshio's ambivalent remark, from which it was impossible to determine whether he truly comprehended what the spirit had said, and continued speaking.

"Yoshio, I have come here to talk with you about something of great interest to you, namely, what happens to people after they die. Not just myself but also the spirits of the six other cadavers in this room are going to tell you about their lives on earth and the various hardships they endured. We have come here tonight because I was touched, Yoshio, by your interest in what sort of lives had been led by the people whose cadavers you and your classmates are dissecting; but more than that, I was moved by the fact that this afternoon during class you prayed to God for my salvation and the peace of my soul."

Yoshio was somewhat taken aback that the spirit knew his name.

"Well, I ... uh ... it was really nothing ... I don't have as strong a faith as some. I just couldn't help feeling like praying," he stammered timorously.

"Please come closer to us," the spirit urged him.

With some trepidation, Yoshio advanced slowly toward the center of the room. Now he could discern the individual features and bodies of the figures that before had appeared to make up a single, glowing mass of phosphorescence.

Another of the figures came forward, stepping right up to Yoshio (if such worldly expressions can be applied to otherworldly beings) with its hands outstretched before it, and began to speak.

"I'm really sorry we frightened you. We, the dead who now belong to the World of the Spirits, do not actually appear in this form to each other. This is just a temporary form, a guise to make us visible to people in the world of the living such as yourself, Yoshio. We have been given special permission by the Holy Ghost to appear before you in this form. Later on, I'll tell you a bit about my life. I was president of Eiko Gakuen University in Nishinomiya, of which I am sure you have heard."

"You must be the Spirit of Professor Yuhara of Seito University, who later became president of Eiko Gakuen University and died last fall shortly after the war ended," Yoshio broke in abruptly, thrilled at the prospect of hearing the life story of the eminent Professor Yuhara from his own lips.

"Yes, I am," the Spirit of Professor Yuhara continued, "and I'll tell you all about myself later on, but right now I'd like to give you a general idea of what the World of the Spirits is like.

"At the instant of death, the spirit separates from the flesh, which is destined to decay, and for a while travels through a sort of tunnel, dark and black as a moonless night. The spirit flows along the tunnel oblivious to the passage of time as measured in hours and days in the world of the living, for time as you know it does not exist in the realm of eternity. I use the term 'tunnel,' but this tunnel does not lead the spirit down underground—it goes up, and the spirit feels itself being lifted higher and higher into a new level of existence.

"Meanwhile, family members gather round the earthly remains of the person who once lived among them. The spirit of the deceased has a vague perception of them embracing the corpse and distantly hears their cries of grief, but the soul does not drift about aimlessly over its earthly remains or around the house it used to live in and the people it knew, for it has left the flesh behind and has been lifted far above them. And during the funeral (assuming there is a funeral, of course), the family, relatives, friends, and acquaintances share their grief, make eulogies, and offer up prayers and hymns for the repose of the deceased; but even then, the person's spirit is far away in another world, the World of the Spirits. The same thing happens to the spirits of people who meet their deaths alone and unobserved—for instance, in war. So we might say the funeral is not so much for the sake of the deceased as for the sake of those left behind in the world of the living. But that doesn't mean funerals are futile or meaningless. The prayers offered to God at a funeral are heard in Heaven and confer a blessing on the departed spirit, and the bereaved family and friends on earth receive solace and peace from above. . . ."

"Do you mean that everybody—the virtuous and the wicked, the aged and the infants—all are lifted into Heaven?" Yoshio asked. The spirit's words seemed to contradict one of the accepted ideas of most religions, namely, that the good would be saved and enter Heaven and the bad would suffer eternal torment in Hell.

"Yes," the Spirit of Professor Yuhara replied, "All spirits enter the World of the Spirits after leaving the flesh behind. But the World of the Spirits is not Heaven.

"Almighty God, who created all things, is a loving God. As the Bible says, our Father in Heaven 'sends rain on the righteous and the unrighteous.'"

"Are you saying that it's useless to do good deeds and have good thoughts in this life?" Yoshio again broke in.

"No, not at all! It is written in the Gospel of Matthew that Jesus said, 'I tell you the truth, whatever you did for one of the least of these brothers of mine, you did for me,' and that is true. Good deeds are blessed and please God greatly. By doing these acts of pure love, a person accumulates great riches in Heaven. But people are not perfect, and a person who performs good deeds takes pride in them somewhere in his heart and thus exalts in his own righteousness. Of course, it is only natural that a person be punished for his wicked deeds. But all men are so steeped in sin that no one can efface his ego by doing good deeds, nor can any man stand before God in his natural, unrepentant state of sin. It may sound paradoxical, but the heart that repents its wicked deeds and thoughts is more gratifying to God that the heart that takes pride in its good deeds. As Saint Paul said, 'I do not do the good I want, but the evil I do not want is what I do.'

"Of course, those who have done wicked deeds, turned a deaf ear to the Word of God, and denied God during their time on earth will receive special punishment in the World of the Spirits, along the lines of those in the purgatory described in Dante's *Divine Comedy,* which you probably have read. But you must not forget that the underlying tone of such punishment is, first and last, God's love for mankind and His desire to save us."

"Well, if a person cannot stand before God in his natural state of sin and receive salvation," Yoshio asked, "what should he do?"

The warm glow of a higher love suffused the face of the spirit, and in the forbearing tone of an old friend, he explained.

"In order to save each person who, as a result of free will, has committed wicked deeds as well as good, to restore the rightful relationship between God and mankind, and to redeem the sins of all people, God sent his only son into the world as a man. That man, as you well know, was Jesus Christ."

Realizing that the best chance he would ever have to get a definitive answer to an important question that had been troubling him for a long time was to ask this spirit from the world beyond death, Yoshio dared to interrupt the spirit's discourse again.

"But if God, who is omniscient and omnipotent, wanted to save each of us, couldn't he just forgive our sins outright and grant us salvation, in other words, act directly to save mankind without resorting to such a roundabout means as sending an intermediary, a savior, into the world? And what about the vast number of different religions? There are people who believe in Buddhism, people who believe in Islam, and people who believe in Judaism; and of course, there are believers in Christianity, which includes numerous Protestant and Catholic sects; on top of that, there are other religions with lofty, esoteric doctrines—even paganism and secular religions established for personal gain. What happens to all the people who believe in these different religions?"

"Yes, well, when I was alive," the Spirit of Professor Yuhara began, "I believed that the same moon was visible above the summit no matter which path one followed up the mountain. So while I was working at the university, I organized a club for people interested in religion, where people from various religions and denominations could get together to talk and exchange ideas. But after entering the World of the Spirits, it became clear to me that there is only one path to truth. The path to truth is not something that can exist in multiple forms. But the people who believe in these various religions and have spent their lives humbly and earnestly seeking truth and salvation are accorded special treatment in the World of the Spirits. They have to spend only a short time there, and are soon taken up into Heaven. Of course God can act directly, as you put it, to save mankind. But consider, for example, the faith of the Jews, which does not recognize Jesus as the Savior of Mankind, and does not admit the necessity of an intermediary between God and man and holds that the true savior has not yet appeared on earth. In order for God to save us from sin, to bring about mankind's salvation, the divine mystery was necessary. The Son of God was born in human form, experienced human emotions, and was without sin; He took upon Himself the sins of all mankind by dying on the cross; and He was resurrected and ascended into Heaven. The essential point of Christian faith—the faith that

Jesus, a son of man, is the Savior of Mankind—is the necessity of that divine mystery.

"Well, well, this has turned into something of a catechism, hasn't it?"

At this point, the spirit of the woman who had first spoken to Yoshio addressed Yoshio once more. "As the Spirit of Professor Yuhara just said, when people die and their spirits enter the World of the Spirits, they are grouped according to their beliefs and deeds during their life. In the case of people who have committed wrongs, the person's family upbringing and social environment are given due consideration. This is not the same thing as taking into account extenuating circumstances, as is done in earthly courts; it's a much more just and unerring process, for each person is measured against the yardstick of God's love. As a result, someone who is considered to be a wicked person on earth might be allowed to leave the World of the Spirits after only a short time and enter into Heaven, while a Christian clergyman, Buddhist monk, or other religious leader who is hypocritical might have to spend a long time in the World of the Spirits in order to become sincerely penitent. Those who hear the words of the Gospel during their life on earth and yet do not believe, those who profess to believe in God yet do not live their lives accordingly, and those who do not humble themselves, but instead glorify their own egos—these are the souls that are held in the lowest esteem in the World of the Spirits."

At this point, Yoshio asked another question of utmost importance to him.

"The moment of death is terrible, right? When a person dies, his consciousness grows dim and confused, and even someone who has lived a long life of faith is capable of crazy, incoherent raving. Will even such a person as that be saved?"

The spirit of the woman smiled gently.

"Thanks to God's infinite compassion, a person's mind becomes somewhat dulled at the moment of death to spare him from the terror of dying. So the experience of dying is not really as horrible as the people around the person imagine it to be. Isn't man's fear of death partly the instinctual fear of death as the end of everything, and partly the fear of punishment after death for one's sins on earth? Moreover, the fear of these imagined outcomes is made all the more terrible by the very uncertainty surrounding them."

"May I ask just one more question?" Yoshio again interrupted her, a bit hesitantly. His earlier apprehension in the presence of the spirits had now vanished, and his mind was filled with only one desire—to learn the truth.

"Most people are parted from a loved one by death at some time or another. Let's say that before dying, a husband tells his wife, 'I will go on ahead and wait for you.' She lives another twenty or thirty years, then dies. In what condition will that husband and wife meet again? This may seem a silly, trivial question, but assuming that people are allowed to be reunited with their loved ones after dying and entering the World of the Spirits, wouldn't the husband in this example find himself reunited with a wife old enough to be his mother? And what about a mother whose baby dies? She is beside herself with grief, and lives only for the day when she will be reunited with her child in Heaven. But if the young mother dies fifty or sixty years later and, as hoped, is then reunited with her beloved child, their reunion would be like that of a seventy- or eighty-year-old woman and her great-grandchild, wouldn't it? And what if a husband remarries after his wife dies? When the time comes and all three of them are dead and have entered the World of the Spirits, what will be the relation between the two wives? And one more thing... there are probably some husbands and wives who don't want to see each other again after they die, let alone spend eternity together—what happens to them?"

"These are reasonable questions, Yoshio." This time, it was the Spirit of Professor Yuhara who addressed Yoshio's questions. "In the World of the Spirits, things are quite different from what people in the world of the living may think or hope they will be.

A mother whose child dies is permitted to be reunited with her beloved child in the same condition as when she was parted from him: she will feel the same emotions and appear the same to her child. Parents, brothers and sisters, friends, and any persons with some intimate relation are able to recognize each other immediately when they meet again in the World of the Spirits. Earlier, I touched briefly on the subject of appearance in the World of the Spirits. Let's say a person has a disfiguring wound on his face when he dies. Now, you would think that if he entered the World of the Spirits in that condition and met his loved ones, they wouldn't recognize him and might even be frightened of him. But you would be thinking in the terms of your own, limited human understanding. How we appear at the moment of death is irrelevant; in the World of the Spirits, we appear to each loved one in the most appropriate form for that person. And these reunions with our loved ones bring us great joy. Naturally, you in the world of the living are not permitted to see or hear what goes on in the World of the Spirits.

"I have one more thing to say in relation to these reunions with loved ones in the World of the Spirits. Life is so hard, one might say that man's capacity for forgetting is truly one of life's blessings. If a person felt for the rest of his life the piercing sadness and emotional pain of losing a loved one, he probably wouldn't be able to endure it and would go mad. So, fortunately, the pain lessens and gradually fades away, but still, if the person desires to meet the loved one again in the World of the Spirits, that wish is heard in Heaven.

"At any rate, faith means believing in something that one has never seen. The visible passes away, but the invisible exists forever.

"Well, it's getting late. Time, as it exists in your world, has no meaning for us, Yoshio, but we must not keep you from studying for your classes tomorrow. Let's stop here, for now, and leave further discussion of these matters to another occasion. Starting tonight, Yoshio, with your permission, we seven propose to take turns telling you about our lives on earth—one spirit's life story each night. All of us took different paths through life: some of us lived lives that will seem dull and ordinary, some lived lives full of ups and downs, and some had lives of mingled joy and sadness, hope and despair. But all of our lives had one thing in common— none of us could see what lay ahead, not even a few seconds ahead. And what's more, each of us spent his entire life without even being aware of that fact. It's as if you are suddenly enveloped by a mist while walking along a ridge. You continue walking. Then the mist clears a bit, you look down to see where you are stepping, and a chill runs down your spine as you realize that you are walking along the edge of a sheer cliff.

"In the world of the living, the only certainty is that death will come, sooner or later. Yet people behave as if they think it is always some other person ('Not me! Surely, never me!') who will die, and that they alone will be spared the inevitable coming of death.

"I have talked in general about what happens after a person dies, Yoshio. What is important for you is to live to the best of your ability the life that has been granted you. Become the sort of person that will please both God and your fellow men and women. Worldly honor, material goods, work, and pleasure—all these things amount to nothing when you stand at the door of death. But the life of a person who believes his life is part of God's plan and puts his trust in God, will be a full, meaningful life. Strive to become perfect, Yoshio, in order to attain the level of perfect virtue realized in Jesus Christ.

"The Buddhist idea that life and death are one, and the saying 'Create Paradise on earth,' have more or less the same meaning as Jesus' words in Luke 12:31, 'Seek His kingdom.'

"Each person lives but one life. Please remember these things, Yoshio, and live your life accordingly."

The Spirit of Professor Yuhara fell silent, his narrow, earnest face full of love and compassion.

As if taking over where the Spirit of Professor Yuhara left off, the spirit of the woman who had first spoken to Yoshio now addressed him.

"The other spirits here will introduce themselves later when they tell the stories of their lives on later nights. Now, I guess I'll start us off. Mine is a rather dull story, but please hear me out."

The seven spirits and Yoshio seated themselves around one of the dissecting tables, and all eyes turned to the spirit of the woman who was about to speak. Each of the spirits had his own individual face and form, of course, but together they created a unifying atmosphere of gentleness and peace that filled the room.

The first spirit softly began to speak.

CHAPTER TWO

FIRST NIGHT:

The Tale of a Woman Who Was an Atomic-Bomb Victim

The Awakening of Love

I will be the first to speak, but before I begin, Yoshio, let me apologize to you once more. Today when you expressed interest in the sort of life I had led and prayed for my soul, even though I had already left the flesh of the cadaver you were working on and was far away in the World of the Spirits, I sensed your thoughts and actions clearly. Those in the World of the Spirits are endowed with such powers. Normally, we are not permitted to do such things, but using the body I once inhabited, I hid your precious book under the dissecting table. There was no other way I could get you to return to the dissecting room tonight. In order to do that, I had to ask for special permission from the Holy Ghost, and it was granted just this once, because He was moved by the purity of your feeling. Jesus once said, 'If you have faith as small as a mustard seed, you can say to this mountain, "Move from here to there," and it will move. Nothing will be impossible for you.' Our presence here tonight, Yoshio, is proof that this is true.

I haven't told you my name yet. When I was alive, I was called Shiono Yoshiko. I was born on June 18, 1900, into a family that had been in the wholesale pharmaceutical supplies business in the Doshumachi district of Osaka for many years. My mother's father was a professor in the Department of Pharmacy at Seito University. Her parents lived in Shimofusa-cho in the Kamigyo Ward of

38

Kyoto, and because my mother went home to them to be taken care of just before, during, and after my birth, it happened that I was born in Kyoto. I grew up surrounded by material comforts and showered with love by my parents. After graduating from an elementary school near our house in Osaka, I entered the newly built Naniwa Girls' High School. The Russo-Japanese War was fought during my childhood, from 1904 to 1905, but I have no recollection of it. After that came a period of relative calm, in which the days passed uneventfully, tranquilly, blessed with all the material and social advantages of living in a well-to-do family. Those years brought a strike by the factory workers and the rise of the proletarian movement, but such matters were not to be comprehended by such as I, raised as I was to be a young lady. For me, it was to all appearances a time of freedom and peace. It was the era of the so-called Taisho Democracy.

I had one brother, younger than me, named Hiko'ichiro. At the time these events took place, he was attending the middle school affiliated with the Osaka Normal School.

After graduating from Naniwa Girls' High School, I began the premarital training considered de rigueur for an *ojo-san* such as myself, a young woman of family and means. My days were filled with lessons in tea ceremony, ikebana, and the koto, as befitted my position as an *oito-han*, the term for 'rich miss' in the Osaka dialect.

During this time my grandfather, in Kyoto, died of a stroke, but beyond that I experienced no particular sadness or trouble in my life; or rather, I simply lived from day to day without ever thinking very deeply about my life or what was going on in the world around me. This will sound like an excuse, but in those days women took little interest in the problems of society and had a low social status. I was no different from all the other young women around me. If I had continued on the course my parents had laid out for me and married a man of their choosing, I would probably have lived the placid, uneventful life of an ordinary woman of means. But something happened that turned my world upside down and changed my life irrevocably.

It was still unusual in those days, but my father owned a country house in Suma, which stood a little way up toward the mountains above the pine groves that bordered the coast. Starting the year I entered Naniwa Girls' High School, we spent our summer vacations there. The turning point in my life came during the second summer after my graduation. My little brother Hiko'ichiro was with me at the house in Suma as usual, but that summer our parents could only come down from Osaka on the weekends. The live-in caretaker, a man named Takino, who had been wounded in the Russo-Japanese War, and his wife were also there. Their son, a young man who was working his way through the Hyogo Commercial College in Kobe, often came to stay with them. The son's name was Sei'ichi, and he was about my age. He helped his parents with the household chores, and during the summer vacation he was always about doing something or other. Beyond returning his polite "Good morning" each day, for years I took no particular notice of him, had no special feeling toward him, and was indeed oblivious to his existence. Ours was nothing more than a master-servant relationship between the daughter of the employer and the son of the employee.

But that summer, all that changed. Suddenly, I began to see Sei'ichi in a different light. To the eyes of a sheltered *ojo-san* such as myself, this youth working his way through college now appeared somehow wonderful, with his grown-up ways and his muscular, manly physique. In short, I began to regard Sei'ichi as a man. From late July to just after the Bon holidays in mid-August, Sei'ichi often took me, and on occasion my little brother, swimming, rowing, and fishing. We also went climbing from time to time in the mountains behind my parents' house.

In those days, the white sands of the Suma Coast were so beautiful, with the view along the shoreline stretching off into the distance and the deep, cool greens of the pine groves resplendent under the midsummer sun. Of course, the sea was beautiful, too.

The waves of the Inland Sea gently lapped the beach with a soft murmur, almost as if they were saying something. Sometimes we would see the local fishermen turn out in full force to pull in a large fishing net with its catch, full of jumping, silvery sardines.

Those were happy days, full of joy and contentment. All the usual summer activities which, until that year, I had come to regard as rather run-of-the-mill, now presented themselves to me as fresh, new experiences. The whole world seemed transformed into something rare and precious—all because of Sei'ichi.

In those days, boys and girls attended classes together through the third grade of elementary school, but in the higher grades the sexes were segregated. Consequently, there was little opportunity for friendships to develop between boys and girls, and it was unimaginable for male and female students of middle school age or older to be seen even walking along the streets side by side. Middle school students were not permitted to walk through the shopping district alone, they could not enter a movie theater unescorted by an adult chaperone, and they were forbidden to go to coffee shops, which were just becoming popular at that time. This climate of segregation of the sexes during youth probably had something to do with my having such a strong interest in Sei'ichi as a member of the opposite sex.

Even now, how clearly I remember the night Sei'ichi and I first declared our love to each other! The summer had come to its inevitable end, and my brother and I were to return to Osaka in three days' time. Now that the autumn school term was drawing near, Hiko'ichiro was preoccupied with completing his summer homework. After dinner, feeling unbearably lonely and longing to talk to someone, I was able to slip out of the house unnoticed by Hiko'ichiro and go looking for Sei'ichi. Sei'ichi was chopping firewood behind the house, in the fading light of the long summer day. He stopped working and nodded to me in greeting. I told him I felt like going for a walk and invited him to come along. It was probably inconvenient for him to leave off chopping before he had finished, but he leaned his ax against the stacked bundles of firewood and came with me. As usual, he was slightly reserved in his attitude toward me, as if there were a clear, though invisible, line drawn between him and me.

When we got down to the beach, Sei'ichi started throwing flat stones out into the sea, aiming at the sinking sun. The small stones he threw traveled quite far, skipping smoothly across the surface of the water. Copying Sei'ichi, I too threw some stones, but mine sank out of sight after only one or two skips at best. Although simple and somewhat childish, this game nevertheless set us laughing and giggling with abandon. After a while, the sun vanished below the western horizon and we could no longer see where the stones fell, so that after leaving our hands they appeared simply to be swallowed up by the steadily deepening dusk. Giving up our idle play, we threw ourselves down on the sandy beach.

After a long silence, I looked up longingly at his finely chiseled profile, which stood out clearly from the surrounding dusk in the fading light reflected by the sea.

'Sei'ichi, what was that German song you were singing a few days ago when you were climbing up the hill behind the house? It was really beautiful.'

'Hmm . . . I wonder which one you heard me singing. I only know the three songs that my German teacher taught me during my first year at college: "The Linden Tree" and "Serenade" by Schubert, and a lullaby by Weber,' he answered softly.

'Sing them!' I fairly commanded him. As usual in those days, the tone of my request was a bit peremptory.

Despite his busy schedule of classes and part-time work, Sei'ichi managed to find the time to sing in the men's chorus at his college. The previous autumn, they had taken second place in the Kansai Choral Competition, so as might be expected, Sei'ichi had a wonderful tenor voice. He sang in German, first "The Linden Tree," *"Am Brunnen vor dem Thore, da steht ein Lindenbaum ..."* and then "Serenade," *"Leise flehen meine Lieder durch die Nacht zu dir. . . ."*

The exquisite melodies flowed from his lips out over the waves that were gently breaking on the shoreline with a brilliant flash of white foam, out to sea and into the all-engulfing embrace of the advancing night.

'Ah, I know the first one. We learned "The Linden Tree" at my high school. So the one you were singing the other day on the hill must have been "Serenade" by Schubert. I can sing "The Linden Tree" in Japanese. Sing it again and I'll join in.'

I sang the melody, and Sei'ichi sang harmony.

> By the well before the doorway, there stands a linden tree.
> How oft beneath its shadow, sweet dreams have come to me;
> Upon its bark, when musing, fond words of love I made,
> And joy alike and sorrow still drew me to its shade.

All at once, I felt myself blushing and stopped singing.

'Shall I sing the Schubert "Serenade" in Japanese?' Sei'ichi offered.

'Oh yes, please do!'

I was thrilled that he had finally spoken to me on his own, without my having to prompt him with a question. I listened raptly as he sang,

> Warm entreaties gently pleading through the night to thee
> Say, while all is calm and silent, 'Dearest, come to me!'
> Whisp'ring branches softly murmur in the moonlight clear;
> None may watch thee, none can harm thee, wherefore dost thou fear?
> Hear the nightingale so tender; would her strain were thine!
> Ev'ry note lamenting echoes some fond sigh of mine.
> Ah! she knows the lover's wishes, mourns when hopes depart,
> Moving with her silv'ry cadence every drooping heart
> Let thy pity then restore me, Dearest, art thou near?
> Oh! I tremble lest I lose thee! Come, and bless me here!

His beautiful voice . . . that romantic song . . .

By now, the veil of night had completely enfolded the two of us and the surrounding coast. The only sound was the soft murmur of the waves as they rushed in to shore and then receded, lulling us with their rhythmic repetition. Till then, I had never noticed how white the foamy crests of the waves shone at night, but that night they impressed me so vividly it was as if I were seeing them for the first time. The briny scent of the sea seemed to intoxicate me, and a gentle sea breeze softly brushed my burning cheeks like a caress.

Suddenly, almost without our knowledge, our hands had found each other's and my cheek was resting against Sei'ichi's shoulder. My heart felt near to bursting with an excitement I had never known before—the first spark of passion, perhaps—my mouth was dry with anxiety, but despite the lump in my throat, I murmured softly,

'Sei'ichi, I love you!'

'*Ojo-san*, what are you saying? Don't even joke about such a thing. Don't you realize we come from two totally different worlds? Get hold of yourself.' As he spoke, his eyes filled with tears.

'No, no, the difference in our circumstances doesn't matter. I love you! I will marry you!'

Having once begun, my confession of love gushed out in a torrent, and though the words were spoken in my customarily peremptory tone, they were nevertheless sincere.

'I know I'm not good enough for you, *ojo-san*, but I love you, too. I've been in love with you for a long time now.'

Though he pretended to be calm and was obviously trying hard to control his feelings, he suddenly took me in his arms and held me tight.

Eventually, I got up and returned to the house, on the way brushing the sand from my feet and my light cotton, summer kimono, and went to my room. Hiko'ichiro was apparently still working on his homework in the next room.

Drawing open the mosquito net, I got into bed. As I lay thinking about Sei'ichi, who was even now probably lying down to sleep next to his parents in another room under the same roof, my heart ached with longing. The light of my small lamp was already obscured somewhat as it passed through the fine mesh of the mosquito net, and my tears blurred it all the more. Turning my face in the direction of Sei'ichi's room, I softly whispered, 'Sei'ichi, I love you. Good night.'

One week after my brother and I had returned to Osaka, Sei'ichi and I sat before my parents as we had planned together beforehand. We knew all too well that they would never sanction a marriage between us. We had thought about it from every conceivable angle, but the outcome was always the same: my parents would never permit us to marry. For my part, I was willing to keep our relationship secret for the time being, and sneak out to meet Sei'ichi when I could, and I once even suggested as much to Sei'ichi.

'For now, it's enough if we can just continue to see each other,' I said. 'We can marry later, when the time is right.'

However, I was nineteen at the time, and I knew that my parents had already started talking about my marriage prospects and were looking for a suitable match for me. Besides, I was willful by nature and used to having my own way as a result of my *ojo-san* upbringing; once I had made up my mind that Sei'ichi was the man I wanted for my husband, I could not wait for us to be together. Moreover, Sei'ichi was a man of great integrity, and it was not in him to hide in the shadows and meet the woman he loved on the sly. I believe it took great courage for him to make his decision, but in the end, he said, 'I will go with you to ask them for permission to marry.'

My father was more stubborn than most people. He believed that his opinion was always the most sensible one and therefore the only right one. In addition, the social and family structure then, midway through the Taisho era, was vastly different from that of today. Marrying for love was considered preposterous at best, and at worst a shameful, immoral sin against one's social class.

As we had feared, my father was dead set against our relationship. He wouldn't even listen to our side of the matter.

'How dare you, a nobody, a son of one of my servants, take advantage of the daughter of your master's house! First of all, just how do you intend to put food in her mouth? You little upstart, with your gentle, innocent-looking face—you're nothing but a despicable seducer of young girls!'

My father continued in this vein for some time, becoming more and more incensed by his own invective and heaping all manner of abuse and insults on my poor Sei'ichi.

Sei'ichi just hung his head, maintaining an attitude of earnest appeal.

My mother appeared to feel utterly powerless to intervene on our behalf. She knew my father's character only too well, having lived with him for many years, and realized, no doubt, that it was useless to try to advise him. Besides, when it came to the question of my marrying Sei'ichi, she too seemed to feel strongly that she could not go along with such a thing. Once in a while, she put in a word or two, asking us to reconsider, but she did not offer us support or encourage us in any way. Then again, she may have hoped that the love we professed to feel would prove no more lasting than a transient fever, and would eventually cool and dissipate of itself if given time. With all the desperation of young lovers on the brink of that abyss worse than death—life without each other—Sei'ichi and I implored my parents to recognize the importance of our feelings for each other and let us marry. But when all was said and done, they remained adamantly opposed to our union.

My father said our love was filthy and disgusting, and concluded the discussion with a cold, curt command: 'If you insist on being with him, get out of my house!'

Shocking to us as this terrible scene was, we had been prepared for opposition, and our relationship was too precious for us to give up, even in the face of the worst possible outcome. I was painfully cognizant of my filial disobedience. During the discussion with them, I had heard for the first time that they had already arranged for me to marry the son of a distinguished family that owned a prestigious pharmaceutical company. In those days, it was still usual for the parents to decide on their own whom their children would marry.

But to Sei'ichi's and my way of thinking, the decision of such an important and intimate matter as our marriage belonged to us and us alone. In a black moment of despair, I even asked Sei'ichi to commit suicide with me. In those days, love relationships were quite rare, but not unheard-of. From time to time, the newspapers would report a double suicide at such-and-such waterfall or cliff, the so-called *shinju* of lovers for whom things just hadn't worked out in this world and who thought they would be better off spending eternity together in the next. Like them, I, too, was seriously thinking about dying. But Sei'ichi insisted that we must continue living and persevere through whatever hardships came our way.

Having been brought up as a sheltered and pampered *ojo-san*, I had never experienced any sort of hardship and wasn't overly keen on the idea of starting to even then. But I was by nature strong-willed—my determination was probably the positive side of my selfishness)—and with Sei'ichi's love and encouragement, I began to feel I might be able to endure a life of adversity with him by my side. Gradually, I even came to look forward to our new life together.

A New Home

I left a one-page farewell letter for my parents and moved with Sei'ichi to the Sangenyanishi area in the Taisho Ward of Osaka. We lived on the second floor of a dilapidated row house, directly behind which ran the Japan National Railways Loop Line. Our room was truly wretched, even worse than those allotted to the live-in employees in the house where I'd grown up.

Sei'ichi, who had quit his studies, faced great difficulties in finding work, but by chance he was able to get a job at a factory where our landlord's son was employed. The 'factory' was actually a medium-size workshop that made steel ball bearings.

The neighborhood was populated by common people, and they were warmhearted, kind, and friendly. Perhaps they guessed there were extenuating circumstances behind our living there, but they never mentioned the subject and did all they could to help us.

Nevertheless, this new lifestyle was hard on me. After Sei'ichi left for the factory each morning, I would carry the washtub down narrow, rickety stairs, through the gloomy, dirt-floored kitchen, out to the four-meter-square backyard to do our laundry, then carry the wash back upstairs and hang it out to dry on a pole outside our window. I had to wait for the landlord's wife to finish in the kitchen before I could use it to prepare our meals, and then I had to carry all the dishes up to our room. We couldn't even go to the toilet without having to worry about whether we might disturb the landlord's family. This sort of life, so different from what I was used to, depressed me and often drove me to tears.

But my husband, Sei'ichi, was good to me. He really loved me with all his heart. His love cheered me and gave me strength.

On Sundays, we would sit enjoying the morning sunlight that poured in through the window and leisurely talk over our plans for the future. The subject of my alienated parents weighed heavily on our minds, but of course we did not make any move to get in touch with them, and there was no indication that they were making inquiries as to our whereabouts. My younger brother, Hiko'ichiro, was another concern of mine; but however much I longed to contact him, I knew that doing so would only cause trouble for him with our parents.

Though we were poor, our hearts were full of the incomparable joy that comes from being with the one you love. When I recalled the sterile coldness and lovelessness then so prevalent in affluent households, I had to ask myself, 'What, really, is happiness? What are the truly important things in life?' Except for their lack of money, our neighbors, too, seemed to have found contentment and happiness in their lives of humble means.

About a year and a half after our move to Taisho Ward, our first son, Kunio, was born. Before the birth of our second son,

Hideo, we were able to rent a small house of our own in Sakuragawa; though our new neighborhood was just five hundred meters farther east, across the Kizu River, we now lived in Naniwa Ward.

Time and again I longed to contact my parents, especially my mother, and say, 'You have a grandchild!' But because of my stubbornness, I simply could not bring myself to do it. My father's parting words of bitter reproach still rang in my ears.

By that time, my maternal grandmother, in Kyoto, had died. At the time of our marriage, Sei'ichi's parents had left their position as caretakers at my family's villa in Suma and returned to their hometown, Hiroshima. At Sei'ichi's request, his mother came and stayed with us to help out when Kunio was born. After that, however, we merely corresponded from time to time.

The next ten years were difficult, but they were also years full of love, and even now it feels as if those best and happiest years of my life flew by in the wink of an eye. In addition to Kunio and Hideo, a third son, Takao, and a daughter, Atsuko, were born, making me the mother of three boys and one girl. Sei'ichi was intelligent and diligent by nature. At the factory, he was respected and trusted by his superiors, co-workers, and subordinates alike. In time, he was promoted to head of the accounting section, and so, despite having six mouths to feed, we had more than enough money to live a humble, plain life and could even start saving a little.

Life is such a sad business! My husband's company, like all the others, was hit hard by the chronic, worldwide depression that followed the prosperity of World War I. Sei'ichi had an uncommonly strong sense of responsibility; day after day, he worked till late at night and went all over the city getting loans to tide the company over until business got better. Probably because of the stress and long hours, he caught a severe cold, which developed into pneumonia, and in hardly more than a single night, he was gone. When we sent for a doctor, it was already too late. Besides, at that time even sulfa drugs had not yet been developed, and the only treatment for pneumonia was aspirin for the fever, then rest and nutritious food. The doctor could only stand by and watch as the disease followed its inexorable course and drained away Sei'ichi's life. There was absolutely no way to save my poor husband.

My Sei'ichi died and went to Heaven. We were reunited in the World of the Spirits, and through the mercy of God, we enjoyed a truly wonderful time together. His spirit had already finished the preparation of the soul in the World of the Spirits, been granted permission by the Holy Ghost, and ascended into Heaven, but his spirit descended from Heaven to the World of the Spirits in order to meet me again. One is not allowed to enter Heaven while one still belongs to the World of the Spirits, but one may descend from Heaven, if it is deemed necessary. I shall say more about the World of the Spirits later, but it is getting quite late, so I'll continue my story.

I always felt that Sei'ichi should have asserted himself in life a bit more. After we left our respective homes and got married, he always seemed to carry a heavy burden of guilt about our breach of filial duty to my parents and the life of hardship he had brought me.

When Sei'ichi died, Atsuko, the youngest of the four children, was a baby only six months old, who still had to be nursed. The next youngest, Takao, was four years old; he was at that troublesome age where I could not let him out of my sight even for a moment, and compared with his elder brothers at that age, he was in many ways a rambunctious little rascal.

I knew it wouldn't do to keep on crying and grieving about the sudden death of my beloved husband, but when I thought about the future of my children, I couldn't help feeling hopeless. For the sake of the children, many times I wondered whether I shouldn't abandon my willful hardheadedness and implore my mother and father for help. I believed that my parents would forgive me, their daughter who had endured so many hardships and was now in such a dire predicament. But the bitter memory of being cursed and called worse than a dog still prejudiced my feelings toward them. I could not forget. And so, come what might, I could never go home to them.

A Widow's Life

After resigning myself to the fact that there was no one else to help me and I would have to do whatever I could for myself, I withdrew my meager savings from the bank and opened a small candy shop.

It was really tough in the beginning. I didn't even know how to get stock from a wholesaler. All I wanted was to be able to give my children a chance to grow up decently. They were sweet children, each of them bright and clever. From then on, everything I did was for the sake of my children. Perhaps because they sensed the many hardships I faced, the elder children were obedient and well behaved, and helped looked after the younger two. Once when Kunio, the eldest, was eight years old and in the second grade of elementary school, he said to me, 'Don't worry, Momma. I'm going to grow up to be a great man someday.' His words touched me so deeply, without thinking I clasped him in my arms and wept. Ah! that moment! when even my child wept in sympathy with me. I remember his little voice pleading anxiously, 'Don't cry, Momma, please don't cry!'

Because my candy shop was in a neighborhood where plenty of young children lived, the business eventually managed to bring in enough money to feed our family of five. All the same, I was still worried about how I would be able to provide my children with a decent education. On the basis of my own experience and that of my dead husband, I wanted to see that the boys at least graduated from middle school and got some professional training and that Atsuko finished a girls' high school.

When my youngest child, Atsuko, was a bit older and I didn't have to spend so much time looking after her, I started taking knitting lessons in the little spare time now available to me. The avocational knitting I had learned as an *ojo-san* during my days at Naniwa Girls' High School was of no use to me whatsoever. I had to start over from scratch. Nevertheless, two years later people were coming to me with requests for knitting, and I was able to earn a bit of income that way.

As time went by, many more orders came my way than I had ever expected, since in those days not everyone could knit. I remodeled some of the candy display racks, lined the shelves with skeins of woolen yarn, and started selling yarn in addition to sweets. This was another unexpected success, and my income doubled. The yarn sold well compared with the candy, which sold with no effort but had already reached the upper limit of its income potential. Moreover, the people who bought yarn often came back asking me to help them learn how to knit. I taught them as patiently and genially as I could, and that brought a new sense of purpose and fulfillment to my life, in addition to assuring steady yarn sales. It was not at all unusual for me to be up knitting till one or two o'clock at night, working on the things that people had ordered.

I persevered and spared no effort for the sake of my children— my dear, sweet children. At long last, it seemed the time had come when my efforts would be rewarded.

In 1941, Kunio, my eldest, turned twenty-four; after graduating from Naniwa University of Commerce, he had enlisted in the Imperial Army, gone through officers' training, and received a commission as second lieutenant. Hideo, twenty, was in his third and final year at Settsu Preparatory Academy. Takao, seventeen, had just started his first year of premedical study at the high school affiliated with Okayama Medical College. Atsuko was already twelve years old and a freshman in a girls' high school; like her brothers, she always got good grades. She understood the difficulties I faced, and helped me quite a bit with the housework; I was thankful that I had been blessed with a daughter in addition to my fine sons. In spite of our relative poverty, things seemed to be going pretty well.

Meanwhile, terrible events tied in with Japan's escalating warfare were occurring, the real significance of which went unnoticed by ordinary people like me—the February 26 Incident, the Manchurian Incident, and the Sino-Japanese Incident—but they did not have much effect on everyday life. Cotton undergarments were being rationed, and little by little the stock of woolen yarn available became limited, but there was no serious shortage of commodities yet.

The Tragedy of War

On December 8, Japan rushed headlong into the nightmare of the Pacific War. Even now, I remember clearly that early morning radio news report. 'This is an announcement from Imperial Headquarters: The Imperial Army and Navy engaged in battle with American and British troops in the western part of the Pacific Ocean early this morning!'

At first, this war was the stage for many glorious military achievements for Japan, but things gradually started to go wrong shortly after it entered its second year. Of course, announcements from Imperial Headquarters never referred to it as anything but a sweeping victory for our side, but . . .

Kunio was sent into action at the battlefront, first in Singapore and later in Burma. After graduating from Settsu Preparatory Academy, Hideo had entered the economics department of Naniwa University; but during his third year there, his graduation had been accelerated as a result of student mobilization and he had been drafted into the Naval Air Force. He was now undergoing flight training in a squadron at Tsuchiura Naval Air Base northeast of Tokyo.

Both of them often sent me letters. The letters would begin 'Dear Momma,' then ask how I was getting along, tell me to take good care of myself, and conclude with a few words of greeting to Atsuko.

The war became increasingly fierce. On April 18, 1942, Doolittle led his squadron in the first air raid on Tokyo. Then there were more air raids, first on Kitachishima far north of the Home Islands in August 1943 and then on Kitakyushu in June 1944. In

November of 1944, the Americans sent a new type of plane to attack Tokyo and Nagoya, a heavy bomber called the B-29 Superfortress. The Home Islands of Japan now became targets for the enemy's terrible bombs and incendiaries.

Letters from my two sons away at war suddenly stopped coming, and Atsuko and I became increasingly anxious as one day after another passed with no word from either of them. Since Takao was a medical student, he had a draft deferment and was continuing his studies, but he was living in a boardinghouse in Okayama, some distance from our home in Osaka, and this was another source of worry for me. But at least he had won a naval scholarship in order to help out with the family budget as much as possible, and I didn't have to worry about paying his college expenses.

By this time, there were hardly any candies or sweets to be had, and it was impossible to obtain woolen yarn. I kept the shop open, but did no business. However, I had anticipated this development and hoarded away some of my stock; I secretly traded these meager remaining stores of sweets and yarn, a little at a time, for rice, fish, and vegetables. It was certainly lucky for me that I ran a shop dealing in sweets and woolen yarn, which were two of the most precious commodities at that time, and had had the foresight to hold back a small supply of these goods in reserve. In those days of governmental regulation and national mobilization, it was a crime to restrict the sale of goods or keep a secret cache, but my shop was quite small, so it did not come under close scrutiny by the authorities.

But then the day came that I had secretly feared would come sooner or later. Never will I forget that day, October 30, 1944, when I was notified that Hideo had died in action crashing his plane into an enemy ship on a suicide mission. My high-spirited, headstrong Hideo! In a small corner of my heart, I had been secretly afraid that such news might come one day, but I wonder if you can imagine the depth of my grief and sorrow at that moment. The room seemed to darken around me and I nearly fainted. Atsuko and I took each other's hands and wept together all through the night.

We never again heard from Kunio, in Burma, either. Hearsay had it that the fighting was fierce in Burma; the war was going badly for our side, and our troops were suffering heavy combat casualties. Each day was filled with unrelenting anxiety, the memory of which even now makes me shudder.

By this time, more and more U.S. aircraft were flying in to attack inland Japan, and the bombing had become indiscriminate. Our homeland was truly a battlefield. Day after day, the people in each neighborhood worked together constructing air-raid shelters in the streets in front of houses or in the few vacant lots available, but this heavy labor had to be done by women and children and old men, since almost all of the young people had been rounded up and sent off to fight in the war or work in the munitions plants. Air-raid drills were conducted frequently. A state of blackout was ordered: at night each electric light had to be covered with a sack of black cloth, leaving only a tiny circle of light directly beneath, and black curtains had to be hung inside all doors and windows. Our nights were black as pitch, like the hearts of people without hope.

Women wore baggy cotton work-pants and jackets, and put on air-raid hoods of heavily padded cotton even when stepping out of the house for just a moment. Things had come to such a pass that a woman was considered unpatriotic if she had her hair done in a permanent wave, and you never saw young women wearing skirts anymore. The men all had close-cropped hair and wore the khaki uniform and gaiters for civilians. The scanty food rations left everyone constantly hungry, and yet, believing the Emperor to be a living god, people spoke with conviction of the indestructibility of Japan, known since ancient times as 'the Land of the Gods,' and did not doubt that Japan was fighting a holy war—such was life on the home front. Anyone who cast the slightest doubt on this set of patriotic beliefs by word or deed was soon hauled away by the *Tokko*—the special secret service section of the police—or by the Military Police. It was a time of severe constraint.

In 1945, the B-29s started dropping bombs on Osaka, and the preliminary air-raid alert sirens blared daily. At first the planes came only in small numbers, but late on the night of March 13, the B-29s attacked in force.

A large formation of B-29s had already attacked Kobe in earnest a little over a month before, on February 4, and I knew it was only a matter of time before Osaka came under full-scale attack. On the night of the thirteenth, the radio warned us to expect an air raid sometime that night or the next. But even knowing that destruction was close at hand, all we could do was make sure a bag of emergency provisions was ready and waiting by the door in case we had to flee for our lives.

The Firebombing of Osaka

I will never forget it. That evening, I had put aside my knitting to sew a few stitches in a 'thousand-stitch waistband' that was being passed around the neighborhood to be sewn a little by everyone and, when finished, sent to one of the neighborhood men stationed at the front, as a sort of talisman and in the hope that the densely sewn fabric might protect him from enemy bullets. As my fingers moved the needle and thread, I was thinking vaguely about the past and our future course.

But my reverie did not last long. Soon the radio announcer was excitedly reading a bulletin from the Civil Defense Headquarters for Central Japan: 'A large formation of B-29s is at this moment crossing the Kii Channel, heading north.' At almost that very moment, the air-raid sirens began to blare and the neighborhood fire alarm started clanging.

A few minutes later, I heard the booming of explosions toward the southwest. It was impossible to distinguish between the sounds made by bombs dropped from enemy planes and those of our side's anti-aircraft guns. The booming gradually became louder and louder, until it seemed to reverberate through the pitch-black darkness and fill the entire sky with its man-made thunder.

Clearly, this air raid was different from the ones we had experienced so far.

The frenzied clanging of the fire alarm drove us into a panic and then seemed to pull us out of the house. Grabbing the bag of valuables and emergency provisions I had already packed, I ran with Atsuko to our neighborhood air-raid shelter. Just as we entered the shelter, I looked up. The western sky was a deep red; the beams from searchlights on the ground were busily crisscrossing the sky, but the lights could not pick out any enemy planes and bounced blankly off the clouds, only adding to the confusion.

Before long, incendiary bombs began to fall like hail, with an odd, plashing sound. Earth and sky were indistinguishable, filled with fireballs. As these horrible fire bombs poured down, the fire alarm continued its demented clanging. Men carrying buckets ran pell-mell into the midst of the flames, but in all the confusion they could not locate the water tanks and no water would come out of the hydrants, so all their fire-fighting training proved utterly useless.

I gave Atsuko strict orders not to set foot outside, then dashed out of the air-raid shelter and ran toward our house some fifty meters away. I was seized by an impulse: I didn't want to try to save something from the house, but merely wanted to witness the end of the house where I had shared a few precious years of happiness with my husband, Sei'ichi.

The house was engulfed in a seething mass of flames that encompassed the walls, tatami mats, roof, and even the trees and shrubbery in the garden. When the incendiary bomb had hit, jellied napalm had splattered into countless fiery clumps, setting the whole area ablaze almost instantly. As the roof collapsed before my eyes, I instinctively clasped my hands together in a gesture of supplication, and they remained so as I hurried back to the air-raid shelter, for at this point I could no longer stay there because of the searing heat from the inferno, which had kept me dodging from spot to spot. My padded-cotton air-raid hood and baggy work-shirt had been scorched to a crisp, and sparks clung to them and were beginning to smolder. Still worse, a whirlwind of heat had sprung up, fed by the many fires, and flames were beginning to overflow out of the blazing houses on either side into the streets.

Once back in the air-raid shelter, I crouched motionless on the ground with Atsuko for a while, but the heat soon began to reach us even there in the dugout shelter. From what I had just seen outside, I knew that even this place was not safe. With us in the shelter were seven or eight people from the neighborhood and several others I'd never seen before. With bated breath they waited, their faces full of terror and anxiety. I briefly explained the situation outside and tried to convince them of the danger we were in.

'We haven't a moment to lose! If we don't get out of here and take refuge somewhere else, we'll all be killed!'

But none of them would listen to me. Perhaps they were paralyzed with fear, or perhaps they overestimated the safety of the air-raid shelters because of what they'd been taught during air-raid drills. But I had never had much confidence in those flimsy, makeshift shelters built by inexperienced elders, women, and children, who had simply dug a hole in the ground, braced the walls with wooden beams, laid on a flat wooden roof, and then heaped the dirt onto the roof. In fact, that shelter seemed to me one of the least likely structures to withstand the intense heat steadily bearing down on us. Rather than stay there and be baked alive, I urged Atsuko forward and ran with her out of the shelter, tightly clutching my bag of emergency supplies.

We ran to the north, where the fires appeared to be relatively less intense. The Horie district was a sea of flame. We came across a water tank along the way, and I gave Atsuko a good splashing. After I dunked my cotton hood in the water and poured some over myself, we ran on with but one thought: to stay alive.

In the houses we passed, we saw people trapped under collapsed pillars that were blazing furiously, but we were in no position to try to help them. We ran from block to block for . . . oh,

I don't know . . . several hundred meters, but it took quite a long time because we had to run first east, then north, zigzagging whichever way appeared to have the fewest fires, all the while brushing off the sparks that landed on us and being chased by the furious whirlwind. At last we came to a wide thoroughfare that I recognized, Midosuji Boulevard, but it too was an absolute sea of flame. The splats of the fire bombs and the blasts of explosions continued with no letup, as the second or third wave of enemy planes dropped still more incendiaries over the sea of roiling flames.

In the direction of Umeda, a business district to the north, the sky was still dark. Stepping over wounded people and charred bodies, we ran straight north for all we were worth, the fire storm still raging behind us.

It started to rain, and the heat was so intense that the rain freakishly turned to steam the moment it touched our clothes. I thought that if there really was a Hell, it must surely be like this.

We crossed over the Yottsu and Higo Bridges, glancing over the side at the hapless people clinging to perilously overcrowded small boats or rafts floating in the river below, their pitiful struggles made visible by the lurid glow of the flames. When we finally reached Umeda, my watch said four o'clock. Although by this time the hideous splats of falling fire bombs were no longer heard, we had to watch out for burning debris—fiery futons, clothing, and even parts of smashed furniture—which had been carried aloft by the powerful whirlwinds and now was swirling down around us.

Survivors of the holocaust arriving at Umeda with nothing but the clothes on their backs slumped to the ground, dazed and exhausted, their faces and clothes black with soot. Some had sprained ankles; some were crying out in pain from other injuries; some had horrible, oozing burns all over their faces and bodies.

Before long the gray light of dawn began to steal over what was left of Osaka. Now, in stark contrast to the burning heat of the night's inferno, the icy chill of mid-March began to make itself felt. To the south lay nothing but blackened, smoldering ruins as far as the eye could see.

I took some hardtack from our emergency bag, and as Atsuko and I chewed it, I thought about what we should do next.

There was no need to go back and check on our home. My last sight of the house had left no doubt in my mind: it had been burned to ashes. The emergency bag that I had clutched so tightly throughout the long night contained my postal savings passbook, my personal seal, a little cash, and a small supply of emergency food such as the hardtack. Atsuko was carrying an emergency bag, too, containing her certificate of school enrollment and other necessities.

I felt there was nothing to keep us in Osaka. Not that I was unconcerned about the safety of my parents, but Sei'ichi's mother and father in Hiroshima had been writing to me once a month or so to ask how we were getting on, and they had always said we should come to them if things got too bad to stay in Osaka. As I huddled next to Atsuko in the morning chill and gazed vacantly over the smoldering wasteland that had been my home, their kind offer came to mind and seemed to me our best course of action, all the more so since it would take me closer to Okayama, where Takao was.

Atsuko agreed to the plan, and we hurried to catch the first train from Osaka to Hiroshima, which did not follow the inland route but went by way of the seaport of Kure.

We had to ride in a third-class car so jammed with people there was not even any extra standing room, but the train arrived in Hiroshima on schedule. As the train passed through Okayama Station, I thought, 'Takao is here!' and was seized by an impulse to jump off the train and go to him, but I resisted the urge, telling myself that we must first get ourselves settled in a new home.

After arriving at Hiroshima Station, we set out on foot for Sei'ichi's parents' house, using the return address from one of their letters. It was already evening by the time we at last found our way to their house in Minamimachi. My father-in-law, a worker at the Mitsubishi Shipyard in Kannonmachi, was not home yet, but my mother-in-law was there. When she opened the door, I was glad to see her looking well. I hadn't seen her since the two times she came to Osaka for Kunio's birth and Sei'ichi's funeral. At first, she had no idea who we were or what we wanted and looked suspiciously at our bedraggled, soot-blackened figures. But when she realized who we were and heard what had happened, she welcomed us with all her heart. My father-in-law returned home from the shipyard by and by. He listened to our account of the ordeal we had gone through, consoled us, and said, 'At least you came out of it alive and unharmed. That's what counts.'

Next, we went to the public bath in their neighborhood. Atsuko and I washed off all the soot and dirt, and at last we began to feel like ourselves again. In those days, the hot water in the tubs at the public baths was remarkably dirty, the water was lukewarm as there was little wood for fuel available to heat it properly, and people had precious little soap—of course, the situation was the same in Osaka and the rest of Japan.

For dinner we had salted dried fish and rice, which my parents-in-law had probably been saving for a special occasion. How good it tasted! Even now I remember that meal and how grateful we were to have it. We hadn't had a real meal since the previous night, just hardtack to gnaw on.

My father-in-law said that he would go the very next day and see about getting Atsuko enrolled in Hiroshima Prefectural Aki Girls' High School as soon as possible.

That night, even though we'd found a new place to live, I couldn't hold back my tears and I wept all night long.

The next day, knowing it wouldn't do for me to remain idle and be waited upon like a guest, I started looking for work. Luckily, I found a job at a military clothing warehouse nearby. The shortage of manpower was so great that even with the mobilization of students the demand for workers could not be met. At the ward office, I applied for assistance as a refugee from the Osaka firebombing and was issued some rice-ration tickets, and filed the necessary documents for Atsuko's transfer to her new school. These activities kept me quite busy, and before I knew it, three days had passed.

I also wrote to my youngest son, Takao, in Okayama, who would no doubt be worried about us after hearing about the Osaka firebombing, and soon received a reply from him.

My impression of the Osaka air raid was that the entire area from near the shoreline north to the center of the city—which included the wards of Naniwa, Nishi, Minato, Minami, Taisho, Higashi, and Nishinari—had been almost completely destroyed. But in Hiroshima, although there were reports of an air raid in Osaka, they said that the damage was minor and our side had shot down seventy-seven of the ninety enemy planes. I was amazed at these erroneous reports from the military authorities, whose intention was probably not to worry the population. Indeed, neither Takao nor my husband's parents in Hiroshima were very worried by the official reports of the Osaka air raid, and anyway, they would never have thought it possible for a city as large as Osaka to be so devastated in a single air raid.

Graduation was accelerated in the girls' high schools, too, during the war, and students graduated after only four years instead of the usual five. Atsuko started going to her new school in April, but due to the worsening war situation, regular classes were out of the question. An emergency mobilization was imposed, and more days than not the girls were ordered to report for labor service in munitions plants. They commuted to work from their homes, and sometimes entire classes of students were even assigned to live at the factory where they worked.

About this time, the American troops started landing at Okinawa amid heavy fighting. The air raids became more and more frequent throughout Japan, until the preliminary air-raid alert sirens seemed to blare constantly. The naval base at Kure, not far from Hiroshima, was under frequent attack by Grumman fighters and other planes flying in from enemy aircraft carriers that were cruising offshore.

Nevertheless, once every two weeks or so we made the journey to get food from my father-in-law's elder brother, who lived in Kamigurose in Kamo County across the mountains to the northeast. Despite the great effort involved in getting there and back—and on a day off from work, no less!—we were very fortunate and thankful to be able to supplement our meager food rations with a bit of rice and some potatoes or other vegetables. Under the care of my dead husband's parents in his stead, Atsuko and I led a life which, though hard, was fulfilling in its own way.

But that, too, was to be short-lived.

Suddenly, on the evening of August 3, I received a telegram from the professor in charge of Takao's class at the medical school in Okayama: 'Takao critical. Come immediately.'

I could not imagine what had happened. My legs felt weak and I thought I was going to collapse; it was as if I'd been cast into a bottomless pit. Summoning up all my strength, I dropped everything and hurried to Hiroshima Station.

I arrived just in time to catch a night train. The words 'Osaka-Bound'—in stark, white kanji on a blue background—on the side of the train made a vivid impression on me, filling my distracted mind with fleeting images of my childhood, my life with Sei'ichi, and the terrible holocaust that had driven me out of my home.

Atsuko had come to the station with me to see me off. Her eyes were filled with tears, yet she managed to put on a sunny smile to bolster my spirits. As the train pulled out of the station, she waved good-bye to me and called out, 'Take care, now! Take care!'

Dear, young Atsuko! She was being subjected to one terrible experience after another, and at such a tender age—the firebombing of Osaka, our life of wartime austerity, Hideo's death in combat, and now Takao's unexplained critical condition. It was more difficult than I can say to wrench myself away and leave her alone with her grandparents. Though only God knew it, that was the last time I ever saw her alive.

I spent the several hours on the train in a state of silent prayer, all the while crying in my heart, 'Takao, you can't die, you mustn't die! Hang on!' I was surprised when we pulled into Okayama Station on time, but apparently the American planes did not strafe the trains at night.

My mind tried to deny the real significance of the telegram's dire words 'Condition critical.' The professor at the medical school who had sent it was a medical doctor, and if he said Takao was in critical condition, then . . . But no, my mind would not accept the obvious, and my head rang with the thought 'It's not true! It can't be!' Still, anxiety enveloped my heart like an ever-widening storm cloud, black and ominous.

I rushed to the Okayama Medical School Hospital and found Takao in an utterly weakened condition. Even to a mother's hopeful eye, the shadow of death was plain on his wan, bloodless face. The professor who had sent me the telegram sympathetically and gently explained what had happened: Appendicitis had led to rupture of the appendix, and now general peritonitis had developed. The medical school, which for a long time had maintained its regular classes relatively unaffected by the war, had at last succumbed to the pressure of worsening circumstances and started sending students to work at the aircraft factory in Mizushima. Apparently, the day before, Takao had ignored a severe pain in the abdomen and continued working. He always did have a 'never-say-die' attitude and was, besides, a naval scholarship student, which probably instilled in him a strong sense of duty to help the war effort as much as possible, even to the point of continuing to work despite the pain. Anyway, by the time he was taken to the medical college hospital for emergency surgery, it was already too late; the surgeons had found his abdominal cavity full of pus, and he was in a serious condition. Moreover, the drugs needed to treat him were not available, and, like most Japanese then, his health was poor from the outset due to long months of malnutrition. In no time at all, his condition had deteriorated from serious to critical.

On August 5, my son Takao spoke his last words as I sat beside him.

'Momma, forgive me for dying before you. Take good care of yourself, and have a good life. Say good-bye to Atsuko for me. . . . Momma! . . .'

Then he was gone, and I had lost yet another child, the fruit of all my years of striving.

It was a Sunday, but by special arrangement I was able to have the body cremated. Clutching the container of ashes tightly, I boarded the Hiroshima-bound night train, which passed through Okayama at three o'clock on the morning of August 6. I couldn't catch an earlier train because I had to go through Takao's things and clear out his room at the boardinghouse before leaving.

I think you can imagine how desolate I felt as I rode in that train hurtling through the night back to Hiroshima. I seriously contemplated suicide, so weary was I of the seemingly endless series of tragedies that made up my life. If not for Atsuko, how easy it would have been to throw myself from the train!

As the sky began to grow light, the train was passing along the Inland Sea. I could see a large Japanese battleship moored offshore; an electrical line stretched between it and the land—there was no fuel left to run its generators—and the deck was covered with potted pine trees, probably for camouflage.

It was obvious even to me, ignorant as I was of military matters, and a woman, to boot, that Japan was fighting a lost war. A mood of defeat seemed to be flickering vaguely across the hearts and minds of the Japanese. Though people still mechanically repeated those catchphrases of the war—'the indestructibility of Japan, the Land of the Gods,' 'doing one's duty in the holy war,' and 'for the sake of the Emperor,'—their hearts were not in it. The words sounded hollow and meaningless, like prayers mindlessly droned over and over for form's sake.

From the window of the train, I could see that enemy air raids had utterly destroyed the Kure Naval Base, the navy yard, and the city of Kure. The early morning sun of midsummer shone down brightly and mercilessly on the ruins, as if to expose the shameful end of Japan's bid for the domination of Southeast Asia.

Even as I sat holding the ashes of my son Takao on my lap, the thought of seeing Atsuko again in Hiroshima in just another thirty minutes or so filled me with new strength. My long, lonely journey on the night train, which I had spent recalling fond memories of Takao and crying till I thought surely I had no more tears left, was drawing to a close.

The thought that I would soon be with Atsuko again was my sole strength and comfort, but at the same time my heart ached at the thought of having to tell her of her brother's death.

A little after seven o'clock, the brakes suddenly squealed and the train began to slow down. In those days, enemy planes from aircraft carriers in the coastal waters were constantly flying in and firing on trains, so for a moment I thought the train's slowing down was an evasive measure against such an attack. But then I heard the familiar whine of the preliminary air-raid alert sirens in the distance and understood that was why the train had stopped. I sighed with relief, for by that late stage of the war, preliminary air-raid alerts were an everyday occurrence.

The Dropping of the Atomic Bomb on Hiroshima

The moment after the all-clear was sounded and the train began to move again, suddenly there was a flash of light brighter than anything I had ever seen before, many times more intense than the early morning glare of the midsummer sun. And the next instant, the train was hit by a tremendous blast of air and a shock wave, and I was flung from my seat into the aisle.

The other passengers looked around bewilderedly, wondering what on earth had happened, some of them moaning in pain from the blows they had received from being knocked this way and that. One by one we picked ourselves up, jumped down from the train, and gathered in small groups by the side of the track. When I turned my face instinctively toward the direction the light had come from, my God! what a sight! A gigantic cloud was billowing skyward over the place where I knew Hiroshima must be. Then the top of the rising column began to expand horizontally, and it looked just like a mushroom. The billowing cloud gradually changed from white to yellow to purple, and within it red tongues of flame shot in and out of sight—I felt as if I were being given a glimpse into Hell itself.

Judging from the appearance of Mt. Ogon to the left and the Enko River, I determined that the train had stopped near Fuchu-cho and figured it was about four kilometers to Sei'ichi's parents' house in Minamimachi. I began to run single-mindedly alongside the track in the direction of Hiroshima Station, holding the box containing the urn of Takao's ashes tightly in my arms.

I went across the Higashi Bridge and passed through the Kaita district. I didn't understand what had actually happened, but I realized that Hiroshima had been utterly destroyed by a force of mind-boggling proportions, though I had no idea what sort of weapon could have wreaked such massive damage.

The center of the city was blanketed under roiling clouds of smoke and dust, and fires were raging everywhere. My progress into the city was impeded by one group of people after another, some of them work gangs of high-school girls, fleeing to the south away from the terrible flames behind them. The clothes had been burned off of most of them, and they were almost naked. Some of them had angry red burns all over their bodies, with flaps of burned skin hanging down from their cheeks or arms. Others had their eyes staring out of faces of raw bone, the flesh completely burned away from the top of their heads to their cheeks. Still others were unscathed on the front of their bodies, but had no clothes on their backs from head to toe—only red-glistening, raw flesh where there should have been skin.

These poor wretches were helping each other along, holding each other up by the shoulders and gasping under the effort. Some people fell in their tracks before my very eyes and lay motionless, pushed beyond the limits of their physical and emotional endurance. Many of them begged in a feeble voice, 'Won't you give me

some water? Water . . . please . . . water . . .,' but there was nothing
I could do for them. When I tried a few times to help some
stumbling victims who appeared to be on the verge of collapse,
their burned skin slipped off in my hands wherever I tried to take
hold of them. It was hard for me to bring myself to look directly
at these poor people with such repulsive injuries, and at the same
time I dreaded finding Atsuko among them—yet I had to find her,
so I forced myself to keep my eyes wide open as I ran on, and
examined each blistered wreck of a human being to see if it was
my daughter.

In the Midorimachi district, all of the houses had been flat-
tened by the blast. As I realized that Minamimachi, which lay still
closer to the center of the city, must be in a similar state of ruin,
a tragic certainty closed around my heart like a fist, but still I
continued north against the endless stream of people in flight.

Civilian air-defense wardens were instructing the fleeing
throngs to go to the Deshio-cho district, where a medical-relief
station had been set up. Each one I met tried to stop me from going
north, commanding, 'Don't go that way! It's dangerous!' But I
ignored their injunctions and struggled on toward Minamimachi.

The buildings of both Hiroshima Women's College and
Hiroshima High School were smoldering heaps of debris, and
many people were huddled on the ground on the adjacent athletic
fields.

When I at last made my way to the house in Minamimachi, out
of the corner of my eye I saw a huge crowd of people fleeing across
Miyuki Bridge. But my attention was focused on the corpses of
my father- and mother-in-law, which lay before me in the debris
of the collapsed house, pinned under a great wooden beam.

The backs of their heads had been crushed by the thick, heavy
beam, and thin trickles of blood ran down their lifeless faces. They
appeared to have been hit the instant they had turned and started
to run for the door, for their bodies were facing that way.

My first impulse was to get their bodies out of the ruins, but
what with all the weight of other timbers and the caved-in roof on

top of it, the beam would not budge an inch when I plied my frail strength against it. There was no way I could remove the debris and carry their bodies out of the wreckage. And even if I had been able to do so, where could I have taken them?

I was wild with anxiety about what had happened to Atsuko. I combed the wreckage of the house and its environs, but I couldn't find her body anywhere. For the past week or so she had been going out daily with her classmates, as ordered by the school authorities, to help build a firebreak by demolishing houses around the government-office quarter. I knew she must have left the house early that day, for the work began at seven o'clock each morning, even on Sunday. That meant that Atsuko had probably suffered the same fate as those poor girls I had seen earlier staggering away from the center of the city like a ghastly parade of the walking dead.

I turned away from the ruins of the house and bolted off again toward the north, running like a scared rabbit. Of course, I didn't know the exact location of her work site, but I had to try to find her as soon as possible, for I realized that soon the increasing heat of the fires would prevent me from going any farther.

About that time, a strange, black rain began to fall, in drops so abnormally large that they didn't seem to be drops of water. The farther north I got, the more charred bodies I saw lying sprawled on the ground, frozen by death in their final postures, some clutching up at the sky, others contorted and tearing at their chests in the extremity of their agony. Many of the dying had dragged themselves into clusters around outdoor water taps, driven by a desperate craving for water, only to find the taps dry. Occasionally one of the blackened figures would move a little—how could such a creature still be breathing, I wondered—and in a voice as thin and small as the buzz of a mosquito beg for 'Water . . . water . . .' Other people, their faces twisted into grimaces of horror and desperation, hurried past the fallen figures of the dead and dying, carrying the severely injured in pushcarts.

How many dead and injured did I run past on that tragic day? No matter how long and hard I called out, 'Atsuko! Atsuko!' the only reply was the moaning of countless people on the brink of death.

Unfortunately, it had been only about four months since Atsuko had transferred to her new school. I didn't know any of her classmates well enough to recognize them now and ask them about her; and they, for their part, probably hadn't known her long enough to remember her. I knew it was useless to ask injured and gasping girls about the same age as her, 'Do you know Atsuko? Have you seen Atsuko?'

Thinking that she might have been admitted to a hospital, I went round to all the major ones, including the Red Cross Hospital, the Mutual Aid Association Hospital, and even the military hospital at Hesaka. After that, I checked every place I could think of: the armory at Kasumi-cho, the elementary schools, and any sort of camp or relief center where victims of the disaster might have been taken. But if Atsuko had been burned to death like so many others—her face blistered and swollen, her blackened skin and clothing fused into a slimy crust that slipped off in large pieces at the slightest touch—how could I ever hope to recognize her, even though she was my own child?

When it turned completely dark, I found an empty corner in the No. 1 Elementary School, the last place I had come searching for Atsuko, and spent the night there, weary and dazed by the horror and misery I'd witnessed that day. Through it all, I had kept Takao's ashes close to me, the boxed urn nestled on my breast in a cloth tied around my neck.

The next day I heard that there were many injured and evacuees at the port of Ujina, so I set out for it immediately. Although I'd eaten nothing and felt exhausted to the point of collapse, I gathered up what strength I had left and plodded on, wearily but resolutely. But there, too, I found no one, dead or alive, who appeared to be Atsuko.

Then someone at Ujina told me that many people had been taken by boat to Ninoshima, and I managed to jump aboard a boat headed there that was just leaving the harbor.

Ninoshima, too, was truly Hell on earth. And it was there that I at last found Atsuko's body. She'd been brought there by army truck and boat along with three of her classmates from the girls' high school. Her face was swollen but free of any trace of suffering, and she looked peaceful in death. The familiar indigo and white pattern of her baggy work-pants and blouse, and the name badge still pinned on her chest brought home the grievous certainty that this lifeless form was indeed my dear Atsuko. Poor child! The skin of her back had been burned off from neck to waist, and her spine was clearly visible amid the glistening raw flesh. The mother of one of the other girls, who had found out that they had been brought to Ninoshima and who had arrived the previous night, told me that Atsuko had remained alive, though just barely, until that morning, moaning constantly, 'Momma, Momma!' Then suddenly, with her last breath she'd sung a line from an old nursery song and died: *"Gin-gin gira-gira yuhi ga shizumu"* (Shimmer-glow, dazzle-gleam, the evening sun is sinking).

When I heard that Atsuko's last words had been that line from the nursery song I had often sung to lull her to sleep when she was a baby, I buried my face against her body and sobbed until I thought my heart would break.

I have no recollection of anything that happened to me in the world of the living after that. The death of my one remaining child must have pushed me beyond the limits of my endurance, for I soon lost my mind.

I seem to have spent several days muttering incoherently in front of Hiroshima Station, though the building itself lay in ruins. Then one day, I boarded a train bound for Osaka. I don't know why. Perhaps my deranged mind was somehow drawn there by memories of the happy days with Sei'ichi and our children, or perhaps somewhere deep in my deranged mind I was worried about my parents and wanted to go to them.

When the train arrived at Kyoto, some people around me who had noticed my abnormal behavior notified the conductor, and I was taken off the train and transported to a mental hospital in the Kitayama district of Kyoto.

Weakened in both body and spirit, I came down with acute radiation sickness, which was only to be expected, I suppose, in light of the many hours I'd spent walking through the radiation-blasted ruins of Hiroshima and circulating among its countless injured and dead.

I died in the hospital one week later.

In all the confusion immediately following the end of the war, my nameless corpse was brought here to the dissection laboratory of Rakuhoku Medical College for anatomical study.

After Hearing the First Night's Tale

The Spirit of Shiono Yoshiko fell silent and closed her eyes, shaking her head sadly as if pondering the days of her life once again.

"Well, you certainly had more than your fair share of troubles," Yoshio said. "Your husband died an early death, your beloved children died before you, and on top of all that, you lived through the terrible firebombing of Osaka and the dropping of the atomic bomb on Hiroshima—just one blow after another. You seem to have suffered every misfortune imaginable. I'm sorry you had to go through all that."

Yoshio could say nothing more. For indeed, what words of solace could there be for someone whose life had held such depths of misery and hardship that human language was at a loss to describe them adequately. He felt that any words of solace he might offer would fall empty and futile on the ears of the Spirit of Shiono Yoshiko.

"Well, then, what became of your eldest son, Kunio?" Yoshio asked, anxious to learn the fate of the son stationed in Burma whose letters had suddenly stopped coming.

"When Hideo was killed during a suicide mission, I resigned myself to the likelihood that Kunio had also died in battle. After all, rumor had it that almost all Japanese servicemen in Burma were dead. But on entering the World of the Spirits, the first thing I asked for was news of Kunio. I learned that he had been captured by British troops and imprisoned since that time in a POW camp in Burma, and that he was soon to be repatriated to Japan. If I had known that while I still lived, I would have had at least something to hold on to—the hope of seeing Kunio again—and I might not have lost my mind.

"You must forgive me for having talked at such length about my tiresome troubles. My life was indeed full of turmoil- 'Nothing more than a series of sorrowful events,' one might be tempted to say. But I say again, in the end all people live their lives without knowing what is going to happen next. There is a saying, 'Look before you leap,' and indeed, fortunate are those whose hearts are prepared for the unexpected and fortified by their faith in God, for they can cope with life's trials. What happens to people is not so important as how they face each new turn of events.

"Well, as the hour is now quite late and you have classes to attend tomorrow, you must go home now. And don't forget your Rauber anatomical atlas!" The Spirit of Shiono Yoshiko smiled sweetly at Yoshio.

The Spirit of Professor Yuhara, who had till now been so moved by the words of the Spirit of Shiono Yoshiko that he could only nod his head silently in agreement, now turned to Yoshio and said, "Yoshio, over the next six nights the remaining six of us will tell you our life stories, too, one each night. Please return here tomorrow night at ten o'clock."

The shapes of the spirits, indistinctly visible as if hovering in the midst of a nimbus of light, slowly began to fade and shortly disappeared before Yoshio's amazed eyes.

Yoshio took the Rauber atlas from the shelf under the dissecting table, ran his hand fondly over its cover, then put it under his arm and left the dissecting room.

Though mentally and physically exhausted, Yoshio nevertheless felt himself sustained by some greater power outside himself. Feeling strangely exhilarated, he looked u at the late-night sky, his mind superimposing an image of the World of the Spirits upon the vast expanse of myriad twinkling stars, and then started for home.

CHAPTER THREE

SECOND NIGHT:

The Tale of a Korean Man Who Was a Victim of Lifelong Discrimination

Separation from His Homeland

When I was alive, my name was Kim Han Sik. I was born in Hadong County, Kyungsangnam Prefecture, Korea—*Chosen*, as the Japanese called my country before their defeat in World War II. The third son of a poor farmer, I was born January 7, 1900, about ten years before the annexation and colonization of Korea by Japan. According to what my parents told me, life in precolonial Korea had never been what you could call prosperous, but it had been peaceful and imbued with four hundred years of the tradition and culture of the Ri Dynasty. The people who lived in farming villages enjoyed a pastoral, quiet life free from care.

Suddenly, we farmers had our land taken away from us by the Japanese—land which had been handed down from our forefathers for generations. We were forced to work as tenant farmers, cultivating only a small piece of land, thus driven into greater poverty than ever before. Under the pretext of the Land Survey, Japan made the Korean farmers issue a formal declaration of their forest and farmland holdings. Fearing that their land would be confiscated or taxed, some farmers intentionally underestimated their holdings; others unwittingly submitted erroneous declarations because they could not read or write well enough to do it correctly. But whatever the reason for the underestimation, all land not reported in the official declarations was seized and became the property of the Japanese government. Those who made honest, accurate declarations did not fare much better, because all land above a designated amount was confiscated by Japan. So, either way, the Land Survey was simply a ruthless means to ensure that all the Korean farmers were left with only a little land of their own.

In addition, Japanese farmers began to immigrate to Korea, and since we Koreans were unable to understand the Japanese language sufficiently—indeed, some could not even read Japanese documents—many sold their ancestral lands and homes for a fraction of their value. Some of the deals were so bad, the land was as good as confiscated. In the end, having lost all their ancestral holdings in Korea, many Koreans were forced to leave their native land and go to Japan or Manchuria to eke out a living.

Being the third son, I was the one in my family whose lot it was to sail for Japan with the help of a labor-recruiting agent, so that my family would have one less mouth to feed. I was sixteen at the time.

It was really hard for me to leave my father and mother and two elder brothers, but I consoled myself with this thought: 'Everything will be all right in the end, because I'll make lots of money working in Japan, and I'll come back to Korea, and then I'll take good care of Momma and Poppa and see that they want for nothing.'

The family is an especially strong social unit in Korea, family members being bound to each other by deep emotional ties, and so it was very painful for me to bid farewell to my beloved family and the fields and mountains of my native village.

I traveled to Japan with twelve other Koreans gathered together by a Japanese labor-recruiting agent. I left Korea with nothing but ten yen, which I'd been given to cover expenses until

I got my first wages and which I kept concealed on my person at all times, and a cloth-wrapped bundle of a few changes of clothes that my mother had prepared for me.

Contrary to the pretty picture that the labor-recruiting agent had painted of our life ahead, a harsh fate awaited us poor Koreans who took the Shimonoseki-Pusan ferry over to Japan. On board the ferryboat, and later in Japan riding in a train for the first time, my heart was filled to bursting with curiosity and great hopes for the future—after all, I was an inexperienced youth of sixteen. But my wonder and hopes were all too soon snuffed out, as I came to know firsthand and to the fullest extent just how harsh life can be.

I had been told enticing stories about the good jobs available in turneries, glass factories, shipyards, iron foundries, and so on, jobs where I could learn a skill. But those stories were all lies, every last one of them. Not being able even to speak the language of the country where we hoped to work, we uneducated Koreans were fit for nothing but low-paying physical labor. The only types of work open to us were those that involved hard labor and hazardous working conditions and were shunned by the regular Japanese laborers: jobs in coal mines, road and railway construction crews, and river conservation outfits.

So you see, for the many Koreans who had lost their source of income and food in their homeland, there was no alternative; like it or not, they had to go to Manchuria or Japan to try to earn a living. It happened that more and more Koreans came to Japan to fill in the gaps in the labor force produced by the shortage of Japanese manpower, at wages much lower than Japanese laborers were paid.

Because of the exceedingly bad working conditions and the unscrupulousness of the labor-recruiting agencies, it was only natural that the Government-General of Korea should issue the Regulations for the Recruitment of Korean Laborers to control such practices, which were implemented a year after I came to Japan. These regulations, however, did not seem to have much effect on the exodus of workers from Korea. Even after the new regulations went into effect, Koreans were permitted or denied unrestricted passage to Japan depending on the needs of Japan at any given time. For example, when Japan needed workers during the economic prosperity immediately after World War I, Korean workers were allowed unrestricted passage, and when the Depression hit causing widespread unemployment even among Japanese workers, the Japanese government instituted restrictions to halt the influx of Korean workers. When we Koreans were allowed to enter Japan to work depended on Japan, but basically we went not because we really wanted to, but because we had lost our land and livelihood and had no alternative.

In the Coal Mines of Chikuho

After arriving at Moji on the Japanese island of Kyushu, the first place I was taken to was the coal mines of Chikuho, where Korean laborers were usually sent in those days.

During the burgeoning industrial revolution that followed the Sino-Japanese War of 1894–1895, Mitsui, Mitsubishi, and Sumitomo, three of the big zaibatsu, the powerful family-controlled financial groups with massive capital, had branched out into mining in Chikuho, a region in northern Kyushu. I ended up working as a coal miner in the mine owned by Toyota, a company that had entered the mining industry somewhat later. Of course, since I had no real freedom of choice in the matter, I simply went along with whatever the labor-recruiting agent said, my heart full of mingled anxiety and hope.

Many of my fellow Korean workers were married and had brought along their wives. I believe I was the youngest there. The single men were housed together in large, crudely built shanties, called *Chosen-naya* by the Japanese, which were rough, ramshackle huts with thatched-straw roofs. We were forced to live in those wretched shacks in squalid living conditions, ten men crammed into each room no bigger than six tatami mats.

Our traditional Korean clothes of white cotton were soon permanently soiled to a black luster by our work in the mine, but with our physical strength and endurance, we Koreans made short work of the heavy jobs that the Japanese workers did not want to tackle. We were strong and we worked for low wages that were less than half those of the Japanese laborers—the Japanese companies that hired us must have been chuckling with delight over the good deal they were getting.

Our awful working conditions were pretty hard to take, it's true, but for me what was even worse was the discrimination against Koreans. I'm not saying that the Japanese manager of the mine and all the Japanese laborers were bad people, but it surely seemed that deep in their hearts the majority of them looked down on Koreans and discriminated between us and themselves. Actually, some Japanese made an effort to provide places for the Korean laborers to rest and relax, such as clubs and night schools, and we had access to those where I worked, too. I drove my exhausted body to go to night school so that I could learn Japanese. Thanks to my youth, I learned the language faster than the other Korean laborers.

The skimpy portions and inferior quality of the food we received were a great hardship for me, since the strenuous work burned up a great deal of energy and I was at the age when a growing boy most needs to eat his fill. If we were served a bit of fish on top of our bowls of *mugimeshi,* boiled rice and barley, we considered ourselves lucky. We would put soy sauce on the *mugimeshi* and then douse the mess with hot water, trying to fool our hungry stomachs by increasing the quantity of food as much as we could.

It was customary for the Korean laborers to be assigned exclusively to work the dangerous coal faces, so many of us were the victims of mining accidents such as cave-ins, gas explosions, or being crushed between two handcars. And if a Korean exhibited the slightest recalcitrance, he was deemed insubordinate by the Japanese miners, who would then set upon him with blows, sometimes beating the poor wretch half to death. Those of us who were foolish enough to try to run away were hunted down, brought back to the mine, and, as an example to the rest of us, beaten savagely and dragged away God knows where. I saw it happen more times than I care to remember.

Of course, in the beginning, I was absorbed in the novelty of it all: living in a foreign land, working underground, being on my own. I didn't know what the real situation was, and although the work was grueling, at least it afforded me the joy of being able to send money home to my parents, which made me feel it was all worthwhile. After two years, however, the Japanese miners' discrimination against us became more than I could bear. The work was hard, we were forced to work longer hours than had been agreed upon in our work contract, and we were given barely enough food to keep us going; I realized that if I continued to work there, I'd just be slaving my life away with no hope for a better future. My discontent at this dismal prospect deepened with every day of back-breaking labor and abuse at the hands of the Japanese.

About that time, a fellow worker told me that he'd heard on the outside that there were easier ways of earning a living if one went to Osaka or Kyoto in the western region of Kansai, or farther east to Tokyo in the Kanto region.

Escape

When I couldn't take it any more, one night I escaped from the mine. Having seen other runaways brought back and beaten to within an inch of their lives, I planned my escape with great care and made it safely to Hakata. My command of Japanese had improved a fair bit by then; I could understand most of what was said to me and converse easily enough about everyday matters, but every Japanese I spoke to could tell that I was from Korea the minute I uttered a single word, and they reacted to me strangely. The intense stress and uncertainty of that escape journey taxed my nerves to their utmost limit. I had no idea which way led to Kyoto or Osaka or Tokyo, or how far away these cities were. On top of that, I was afraid that a posse might be hot on my trail; it was just my imagination, but I seemed to feel their eyes on me every minute of the day and night. Whenever someone looked at me closely or suspiciously, or of course, when I caught sight of a policeman, I would melt into the shadows and make myself scarce. To make matters worse, the only money I had on me was the previous month's wages, which I had not sent home to my parents.

Chance led me to board an east-bound train, and when I finally got off at the end of the line, I found myself at Kyoto Station. Before I left Korea, my father had given me the address of a Korean living in Kyoto and told me to look him up if I ever went there. Now, with the worn scrap of paper on which the address was written held tightly in my hand, I started walking toward the western part of the city where the Korean residential district lay.

At last I arrived at the block of dilapidated row houses in which Park Eut Kyun and his family lived. Park was from a neighboring village in Kyungsangnam Prefecture and was a friend of my father's; he'd come to Japan right after the annexation of Korea by Japan. Since he had been part of the first wave of Korean immigrants to Japan, he'd managed to make a better—though by no means affluent—life for his family than most of the Koreans who came over later.

The next day, I started working as a construction helper on public works projects, such as building embankments along the Katsura River and road construction in various parts of the city. But if a day began with rain, construction halted and I was out of a job until the weather permitted us to resume work. On those rainy days, I stayed at the house, killing time as best I could, but feeling ill at ease about inconveniencing Park and his family. He and his wife and their three children lived in a small row house that consisted of only two six-tatami-mat rooms and a tiny, dirt-floored kitchen. Each night when it came time for bed, I had to spread out a straw mat on the dirt floor of the kitchen to sleep on.

The more hospitable Park and his family were to me, the more constraint I felt about continuing to accept their kindness. One day, almost exactly a year after coming to their house, I borrowed a small amount of money from Park, promising to repay it someday, and despite the family's magnanimous protests that I was welcome to stay with them however long I wanted, I left and headed for Tokyo.

Park had given me directions to get to the Korean residential quarter in Tokyo, on the bank of the Tama River on the outskirts of the city. Unfortunately, the living conditions were much worse there than in Park's neighborhood in Kyoto. The dwellings were mere shacks that appeared to have been built from discarded lumber and sheets of scrap tin and corrugated iron apparently collected from junk heaps. It was a dirty environment, always reeking of one stench or another. Japanese passing through the area thought Koreans were a filthy people and despised us. But we were compelled by poverty and discrimination to live in shacks without even a single proper toilet, on the banks of the Tama River, where we never knew when our homes would be swept away by flooding. How on earth were we supposed to improve such an environment as that?

In Tokyo as everywhere else, the Japanese looked down on the Koreans. Japanese elementary school children walking by our shacks on their way to school would chant loudly so that we'd be sure to hear them,

> Chosen, Chosen, paka ni su'u na,
> Nipon, Chosen, Tenno Heika, onashi. . . .
> [Don't make fun of the Koreans,
> Because we Japanese and the Koreans worship the
>   same Emperor. . . .]

They mimicked the Koreans' difficulty in pronouncing the sounds *b* and *h*, which come out sounding like *p*, and *j*, which comes out sounding like *shi* in Japanese words. *Chosen* was the standard Japanese name for Korea in those days, but it carried a derogatory connotation. Their cruel, childish mockery of our Korean accent stung like a slap in the face and made me burn with humiliation.

In Tokyo, I again stayed with a family of five, Kim Wan Seog and his wife and three children. I worked mainly on public works projects, but the work was hard, the hours long, and the pay less than half what Japanese laborers got for the same work. Sixty sen a day was the high end of the wage scale for Koreans then. Of course, as before, there was no work for me on rainy days, and in 1920 when the Depression set in, it became difficult to get work even when it wasn't raining. There were more and more Japanese unemployed, so naturally there was no work to spare for us Koreans. That's just the way things were then.

Thanks to the kindness of Kim and his family, I had a place to stay out of the wind and rain, but other Korean laborers were not so fortunate. After ten or twenty days without work, they didn't have the price of a bowl of rice, let alone the money to pay for a bath or a night's stay in a flophouse. Whenever I walked past one of them, covered with caked sweat and mud, huddled on the ground by the side of the road, it pained me to see a fellow countryman in such a pathetic condition. Yet I myself did not know from one day to the next how I was going to manage to carry on, so there was nothing I could do to help them.

Japanese tradesmen needed men to push or pull their carts loaded with goods to the market each morning, and although the pay was a mere pittance, ten or twenty sen, many out-of-work Koreans competed among themselves for the lowly work, begging the merchants, 'Please let me pull your cart! Hire me!' Scathingly, the Japanese called them *tachinbo*, that is, loitering down-and-outers. I myself had traveled all the way to Tokyo from Kyoto thinking it would be a better place. And even though I now felt that the countryside held out more hope to Koreans for a decent life than the big cities, I didn't have so much as the train fare to leave. I felt myself trapped in a dead-end life of bare subsistence along with all the other Koreans in Japan, scorned and mistreated by the Japanese as if we were just animals and not their fellow human beings.

About that time, popular resistance in Korea against the oppressive colonial policy of the Japanese and its consequent all-too-frequent cruelties came to a head. On March 1, 1919, the '3-1' independence movement was staged. But that massive demonstration, in which over a million Koreans marched in the streets demanding Korea's independence from Japan, only upset the Japanese authorities and made them more nervous. As a result, they tightened their racially discriminatory and xenophobic stranglehold on the annexed country all the more. That's how things stood when Tokyo was hit by the Great Kanto Earthquake of 1923, a terrible disaster that created even greater trouble and misfortune for us Koreans living there.

The Great Kanto Earthquake of 1923

On September 1, a torrential rain had been falling on Tokyo since before dawn. At about ten o'clock that morning, however, the fierce sun of late summer began to break through the clouds, and it looked as if the day would be hot and muggy. Nevertheless, black clouds hung low in the western sky, filling me with a vague foreboding.

As usual, I was out of work and just whiling away time at the house. One minute before noon, I felt a tremendous shock hit the house, and before I had time to think 'What the—?' the shaking became incredibly intense. I couldn't even stand up; I just crouched on the dirt floor on my hands and knees. The next moment, the situation got so bad that the word 'shake' doesn't begin to describe it. I crawled outside, and maybe it was just an illusion, but I saw or thought I saw, just for an instant, the banks of the Tama River writhe up and down, back and forth just like a snake. Huge cracks opened up in the ground here and there, and the river even appeared as if it were flowing backward!

The shaking seemed to continue for a very long time, but I think it actually lasted about ten minutes. When I turned back to look at the Korean residential district, almost all of the flimsy shacks had been at least partially destroyed, and many of them had been completely reduced to piles of rubble. Luckily, no fires started in our district, but in the direction of the city, fires were breaking out here and there and were spreading as I watched. The smoke mingled with the dust stirred up by the earthquake and hung in the air, so that the entire sky over Tokyo appeared to be smeared with black ink. Amidst those choking, sooty clouds, people terror-stricken by the sudden disaster were running about madly in all directions. People piled whatever possessions they could carry out of their houses onto carts and started to flee to safety, but because of their panic and lack of disaster preparedness, they didn't know where they should go. Most just headed off, pushing or pulling their heavily loaded carts, in whatever direction appeared to have no fires, but they were soon confronted with new tongues of flame springing up before them. Finally, realizing that no place of safety could be reached by going in that direction, they left their large carts in the middle of the street and started running for their lives. These abandoned carts and their baggage blocked the streets, adding to the confusion and danger.

As it was almost noon when the earthquake hit, most households had some kind of fire lit in a *shichirin*, a portable clay cooking stove, or their brick kitchen range, and were either preparing or already eating lunch. The wooden beams of the houses, the rice-papered sliding doors and screens, and the furniture were all brought tumbling down on top of those cooking fires by the violent tremors, so it's no wonder that the houses blazed up just like bonfires—under the circumstances, it's inconceivable that they wouldn't have. And in the midst of such a severe earthquake where a person couldn't even remain standing, nobody thought to put out the fledgling fires, and even if they had had the presence of mind to think about doing so, it would have been physically impossible to fetch the water needed for the job.

People realized immediately that this was not an ordinary earthquake, and they panicked. In the districts that bordered Tokyo Bay, some people ran shouting false reports of a giant tidal

wave coming in, 'A tsunami is coming!' Their frenzied cries
fanned the flames of terror in people's hearts, and the situation
there got completely out of hand.

Meanwhile, other wild rumors had begun to spread: 'These
fires are the work of the Koreans—it's arson!' 'The Koreans are
banding together and rising up against us. They're rioting and
looting!' 'They're using the earthquake as their chance to start a
movement for independence.' 'I saw a Korean woman throwing
poison in one of the wells!' As a result, armed soldiers were soon
standing on street corners, and policemen were running around
brandishing their sabers to no purpose. Actually—though this is
something I didn't learn until later—their disorganized behavior
stemmed largely from the fact that the Metropolitan Police Headquarters had been destroyed by fire and the chain of command in
the police department was in chaos. Far from helping to calm
public sentiment, the muddled efforts of the police ended up only
creating more confusion.

Rumors spread that there was a mountain of charred corpses
at a military clothing warehouse in Honjo and another in Asakusa,
and that the Sumida River was full of unidentified corpses. When
I looked around me at all the fires and wounded people and burned
corpses, I could easily see how such incredible reports could be
true. The fires raged on unchecked into the night; the night sky
glowed luridly from the columns of flame roiling up from the
pandemonium below, making people even more terrified and
anxious.

What was even worse, more wild rumors began to fly; people
said that we—the Koreans living next to the Tama River—were
the ones who had instigated the looting and rioting.

As night fell, the news started to spread that such-and-such
food warehouse had burned down. Dinnertime rolled around, and
people began to get hungry and thirsty and to worry about where
their next meal was coming from. About that time, the Army set
up emergency food-distribution centers and started handing out
balls of boiled rice. A little food in their stomachs went a long way

toward calming and reassuring people. But there was no rice for us Koreans—the rumors of Korean rioting had so roused public feeling among the Japanese, it was dangerous for us even to go near the food-distribution centers. We passed the night without a wink of sleep, a drop of water, or a bite of food.

At daybreak on September 2, the day after the earthquake, I was huddled on the ground with a group of other frightened Koreans, when we were suddenly surrounded by a band of soldiers, police, and civilians shouting abuse at us: 'You goddamned, lawless Koreans! Kill the sons of bitches!'

'Let's beat the shit out of the bastards, every single one of 'em!'

As they continued to shout, they frisked us to make sure one of us wouldn't pull a knife on them. Then they said they were putting us under 'police protection' and led us off, hemming us in on all sides to prevent our escape. On our way through the city streets, I saw bamboo spears and sickles leaning against the sides of houses that had escaped the flames, and vigilante groups and bands of ex-servicemen carrying Japanese swords or wooden swords; some of them even had hunting rifles. They stared at us fiercely as we passed by and looked as if they were ready to attack us at any minute. I will never forget the naked hatred in their eyes.

If one of us put up any resistance or showed even the slightest sign of opposition, our captors called him a Korean troublemaker and proceeded to beat and stab him. People say that two to five thousand Koreans—maybe even more—were killed that way, battered to death by inches and then tossed into the river.

Now and then we heard the report of a gun being fired somewhere and not-too-distant shouts of 'Banzai! Banzai!' One of the police officers barked angrily at us, 'That's another one of you filthy Koreans getting killed. And if you don't behave yourselves, you'll get the same!' Fortunately for me, the group of Koreans I was with consisted mostly of women and children; since our captors probably thought we were law-abiding citizens, they were just 'escorting' us to a police station. Other groups of

Koreans that were under arrest, however, had their hands bound
with wire that cut painfully into their wrists.

The detention ward at the police station where we were taken
was full, so we were then led to a temple in Sangenchaya, the
grounds of which were being used as a makeshift jail. They made
us sit on the ground and, saying they were doing it to prevent us
from escaping, tied us all together in a row with rope.

Frightened half out of our wits, we passed a night of horror
there. How on earth were our Japanese captors going to determine
which of us were 'lawless Korean troublemakers' and which were
'good Koreans'? And though we heard rumors that a band of two
thousand Koreans was coming to attack the temple compound,
we, of course, knew nothing definite about it and could only wait
on tenterhooks for whatever might happen next.

Our Japanese captors gave us no information at all about what
was going on or what they were planning to do with us, so it's no
wonder some of us panicked and lashed out against them or tried
to escape. Those who did, however, were peremptorily judged to
be 'lawless Korean troublemakers' and beaten senseless or killed
on the spot. Many times that night I saw Koreans brought into the
temple compound with their faces all bloody, dragged there by
Japanese who were calling them all the bad, insulting names they
could think of. Then, as if they had not already done enough, some
of the policemen and vigilantes would actually go over to the
unconscious wretch sprawled on the ground and kick his battered,
unresisting body.

Koreans kept in custody at Narashino or Meguro race track
were detained until the latter part of November, but at Sangenchaya,
we were released relatively soon, though it was still close to the
end of September and the mornings and evenings had turned
chilly. Throughout our detention, we were given only one or two
rice balls a day to eat, which made some so weak that they didn't
even have the strength to get up and go to the toilet.

Things were still quite bad for Koreans in Tokyo even after we
were released from custody. We were fortunate in that there was

now plenty of work for us clearing away the debris left by the earthquake, but in this too, Japanese discrimination against Koreans was evident. As you can imagine, conditions in Tokyo after the earthquake were pretty bad to start with, but whenever the cleanup operations turned up bodies—now weeks old, bloated and putrid-smelling, many with bones protruding grotesquely from the decaying flesh—it was always the Korean workers who were given the gruesome task of pulling the bodies out of the rubble and cremating them.

I am an uneducated man, but I had the opportunity to study Japanese at the mine in Kyushu when I was young enough to learn a foreign language easily. It may sound strange, but despite my lack of ability in other fields, I think I had a special talent for languages. Whatever the reason, the fact is my Japanese improved rapidly with each successive day. I could not help but notice my quick progress and, delighted and encouraged, consequently studied all the harder.

What I was particularly careful about and worked hardest to get right was the pronunciation of syllables beginning with *b* and of the phrases *ju-go en* and *go-jussen*, which were very difficult for Koreans to pronounce correctly and were a constant source of ridicule by the Japanese. My Korean-trained mouth naturally wanted to say *chu-ko en* and *ko-chussen*, but I strove to voice those crucial consonants correctly and practiced very, very hard. I repeated those phrases and other difficult-to-pronounce words over and over while walking down the street, eating, and even lying in my futon at night waiting for sleep to come. I practiced so much that occasionally the people around me would look at me suspiciously or steal puzzled glances at my constantly moving lips. I felt that one of the reasons the Japanese looked down on the Koreans was our strange, inaccurate pronunciation of their language; it became a point of pride with me to master their language and its difficult pronunciation, and I went at it with dogged, almost perverse, determination. In time, I could both understand and speak the language so well that I felt confident there was no telling me from a Japanese, at least as far as my speech was concerned.

For about half a year after the earthquake, I worked here and there, finally landing a live-in position as a servant and general handyman in the home of a Japanese named Tsukamoto. There, for the first time, I went by a Japanese name and concealed the fact that I was Korean. My Japanese still had a slight accent, but the people I lived and worked with merely took that as a sign that I was native to some other region of Japan; they never knew that I was Korean. Since Tokyo is a great metropolis that, like a magnet, draws people from all over Japan, I chose a distant region off the top of my head and told everybody I was from Ishikawa Prefecture.

Things were going smoothly till one day Tsukamoto turned to me and said, 'Tomorrow I've got some relatives coming from Ishikawa Prefecture, and I'd like you to meet them.' It was a foregone conclusion that if I met and talked with his relatives, my lie would be found out. I knew it was pointless to stay there any longer, so without a word to anyone I left. Tsukamoto was the first person to treat me decently, like a regular human being, since my arrival in Japan, and to this day I feel bad about running out on him like that.

Hokkaido

For several years I had wanted to visit the island of Hokkaido and see what it was like. I had heard that it was quite different from Honshu, the main island of Japan, almost like another country with its beautiful poplar-lined roads, vast plains, and magnificent forests. I longed to be in such an open-minded land among frontier-spirited people, where I might have a fair chance to improve my lot in life.

When I came upon some posted notices and standing signboards that blazoned the enticing words, 'Workers Wanted in Hokkaido,' my mind was made up in an instant, and I was soon on a train heading northeast on the main Tohoku Line.

The peaceful, rural scenery the train passed through was like a soothing balm to my spirit, which was still aching from my brutal experiences in Tokyo. Actually, the blood and sweat of many a Korean had gone into the construction of the very train track I was traveling on, but I had no way of knowing that at the time.

I transferred at Aomori to the ferryboat for Hakodate, and as we crossed the Tsugaru Straits, I was so struck by the beauty around me that I felt I had truly left the hellish scenes of the Great Kanto Earthquake far behind me and gone to Heaven.

That rapture, however, was no more than a pleasant dream that lasted just a little while. True, I had more or less mastered the Japanese language, but what sort of opportunities for work awaited me in this new land, alone as I was with no relatives or friends to introduce me or give me job references? On top of that, the entire country was still in the depths of the Depression that hit a few years after the end of World War I, and things were plenty tough for people who did have connections, let alone the likes of me.

As I might have expected if I'd given the matter any practical thought, I ended up back in the coal mines. There the door was always open to experienced miners like myself, if they were willing to put up with low wages, hard labor, and dangerous working conditions.

When I at last made my way to the hiring office of a coal mine at Mihoro in Ishikari, I stood before the Japanese supervisor and, unlike the vast majority of Koreans, spoke in relatively fluent Japanese. Far from being pleased at the idea of hiring a Korean who could communicate easily in Japanese, however, the man looked at me with suspicion.

First, I was taken to my new living quarters, the usual overcrowded, prisonlike shack, and then I went down into the pit to join the other Korean miners. We rose at four each morning, started work at five-thirty, and continued our back-breaking labor till seven at night.

It was grueling work digging coal out of the deepest pit-faces, and the constant danger we were in plagued our minds with gnawing anxiety. Just like in the mines in Kyushu, some miners got crushed under handcars, some worked till they dropped from exhaustion, and we always had fresh cuts and bruises on our faces, arms, and legs. Accidents involving small explosions often occurred; each time, the ones killed or badly injured were the Korean miners, who were always assigned to work the dangerous pit-faces. And when a Korean was hurt, he never got adequate medical attention. Sure, he would be taken to the first-aid station, but the medical treatment amounted to nothing more than a few dabs of Mercurochrome administered by a Japanese attendant who scathingly berated the injured man with insulting jibes such as 'You Koreans move too slow, you're too lazy even to get out of harm's way' or 'You probably let yourself get hurt on purpose, just to get out of work for a while.'

We had no real days off. Usually, after working like dogs through the day, we would eat the invariably plain, coarse meal provided by the company and then immediately drop our exhausted bodies onto our futons and fall asleep. The few who had the energy and desire for amusement could play such Japanese games as go, *shogi*, and *hanafuda*, often with a bit of friendly betting. Sometimes I would be invited over to the quarters of one of the married Korean workers, where I found some relief from my torment and anger by venting all my gripes about the work and how the Japanese mistreated us. But the bad thing about those visits was when we'd get to talking about our hometowns back in Korea. I would get so homesick, before I knew it I was crying out, 'Momma! Poppa!' as hot tears filled my eyes.

As the ranks of unmarried Korean laborers gradually increased, brothels—or 'comfort clubs,' as they were euphemistically called—with Korean women sprang up around the mine. Whether this was the doing of the mining company or just came about of itself, I don't know. It's hard to believe, but it appears that the Japanese government's labor policy did not just tacitly condone the establishment of such facilities, but actually promoted it as a means of keeping the Korean laborers pacified and docile.

I was twenty-five years old by this time, and not a little interested in the female sex; yet I could not think of my poor fellow countrywomen, who I knew had probably been more or less coerced to come to Japan and work in these brothels, as objects of sexual desire.

Instead, I became friendly with one of the Japanese women who worked in the kitchen at the mine and the daughter of one of the Japanese mine superintendents. When I saw that these women had a liking for me, I began to experience a pleasurable sensation of conquest over my Japanese masters. With this dark, distorted view of those Japanese women coiled deep in my heart, I led some of them into sexual relationships. Both of these Japanese women told me that they wanted to marry me and to hell with their parents' objections. 'I'll go with you to Korea, if you want—take me with you!' each of them begged. I did them a great wrong, using them so callously.

My life of anguish and hardship at the mine at Mihoro continued for fifteen years. During those years, Japan plunged into numerous military conflicts against China, starting with the Manchurian Incident in 1931, which came to be known in Japan as the Fifteen-Year War with China, lasting from 1931 to 1945. Contrary to the official propaganda disseminated by the Japanese government, Japan's involvement in these wars was steadily escalating. Domestic shortages of goods became increasingly serious; daily necessities such as clothing and foodstuffs were rationed; and people gradually came to feel the pinch in just about all areas of daily life. Of course, the ones who were hit first and hardest by these privations were us Koreans, who occupied the lowest rung of the social ladder.

Meanwhile, the Japanese government adopted a reconciliation policy toward Koreans in general, both those already in Japan and those still in Korea. Up until then, the Japanese had called us *Chosenjin*, which literally meant 'natives of the peninsula,' but now they said Korea was to be unified with Japan and we were to be called Japanese, just as if we were regular citizens of Japan.

Under the pretext of this so-called Expansion of Empire Subjects, which was actually a subtle brain-washing program, every morning we were made to recite in unison the Empire Subject Oath. In addition, at noon we had to bow in the direction of the Imperial Palace in Tokyo and offer a silent prayer for Japan's victory in the war. At the beginning of each month, we were forced to worship at a nearby Shinto shrine dedicated to the guardian god of Japan and pray for Japan's victory.

In 1938, the National Mobilization Law was enacted and the Home Islands of Japan were organized for war. Domestic conditions now became constrained to an unimaginable extent not only by the harsh restrictions on material goods but also by censorship of thought.

In Korea, the Government-General of Korea took the lead in supplying Japan with manpower and forcibly rounded up Koreans and shipped them off to Japan, where they were then dispersed to all parts of the country and used as slave labor mostly in physically demanding jobs such as mining and construction of port facilities and airfields.

More and more of these impressed Korean laborers poured into the mine at Mihoro, where I was. Our already inferior and crowded sleeping quarters could not hope to accommodate the influx of new workers, yet we were all jammed in there together, and our living conditions sank to a new level of appalling sordidness.

About that time, because of my age, work experience, and superior ability in speaking Japanese, I was elevated to the position of foreman and saddled with the role of mediator between the Japanese miners, foremen, and supervisors and the Korean laborers, especially the newcomers. This new position freed me from the hard labor of digging and shoveling coal in the deep mine-pits all day long, but now I had to contend with a new and terrible mental anguish.

The new arrivals from Korea couldn't understand Japanese, and this constantly brought the anger and hatred of the Japanese down on them. Snarling complaints such as 'They're too slow to answer' and 'These damn Koreans have got a bad attitude,' the Japanese were quick to strike the uncomprehending newcomers. Since most of these Koreans didn't even understand a shouted warning of danger, they were slow to take cover and were sometimes unnecessary victims of various accidents. Overseeing and instructing the newcomers was a demanding and painful business. It was hard to be stern with fellow Koreans, yet I knew that too much compassion and laxness on my part might backfire and put them at risk for injury. So sometimes I had to speak sharply to them just like the Japanese foremen did, but the Korean newcomers didn't understand my predicament. Some of them glared at me reproachfully and asked, 'Why do you bark at us like that? You're a Korean just like us!'

But saddest and most disturbing of all was when I was ordered to mete out corporal punishment to Koreans who, no longer able to endure the drudgery of the mine, had tried to escape and had been caught and brought back. The Japanese supervisors reasoned, 'It'll make a greater impression on them if one of their own does it instead of a Japanese.' So each time a captured runaway was brought in, I had to take up a split-bamboo whip or wooden cudgel and beat him. A few times, I held back on the force of my blows and tried to go easy on the poor wretch, but the Japanese supervisors and foremen always seemed to know immediately what I was doing; for one of them would take the split-bamboo whip from me, saying, 'Hey, that's no way to do it. You've got to hit 'im like THIS!' and then beat the hapless victim mercilessly until he lost consciousness. Faced with that alternative, I figured it was better for me to do the beating myself, so thereafter I beat the runaways hard enough to satisfy the Japanese bosses, all the while silently begging my victims, 'Forgive me!' Still, I could hardly expect my fellow Koreans to understand the anguish I suffered at having to beat them. To them, I was just a cur, a lackey of the Japanese. So there I was, caught in the middle of a no-win tug-of-war between the Japanese bosses and my own countrymen. It was hell.

Eventually, Japan staged its famous surprise attack on Pearl Harbor and rushed headlong into the Pacific War. We Koreans, along with the Japanese citizenry, were driven into still greater poverty and forced to endure one further privation after another, each of which was justified with patriotic phrases like 'For the war effort' and 'For the sake of the Nation.' From that time on, the Imperial Japanese Army involved itself directly in the production of coal, and our work became even more laborious, for the officers' orders were to increase efficiency and coal production at any cost.

Since 1939 the Koreans had been under great pressure from the Japanese government to relinquish their Korean names and go by Japanese names. Submitting to the compulsory name change, I officially changed my name to Kaneda Motoharu.

During this period, we Korean laborers were popularly referred to as 'industrial warriors,' which had a nice ring to it, but the reality of our situation was untold suffering.

The quality of the food we received—already shockingly inferior—nevertheless continued to decline. There was no longer any rice or barley in the plain meals set before us: just soybean cakes, which gave us diarrhea and watery miso soup with a bit of potato vine and occasionally a small wheat-flour dumpling floating in it.

Through my position as one of the foremen, I knew that the mining company was regularly receiving a special ration of staples that were already denied to ordinary Japanese families— rice, barley, sugar, and even rarer commodities such as sakè. The higher-ups in the company office, however, made sure that the special rations ended up in their own bellies or sold them on the black market to line their own pockets.

In 1944, the tragedy of our lot was compounded when the biggest explosion on record occurred at our mine. The blast killed more than a hundred miners, eighty of them Koreans.

During those awful years, it seemed as if I was doomed to die at the mine one way or another, whether from chronic malnutrition or some accident. Worse still, I often felt I would be better off dead, free from the unbearable misery of my life. Then, just when I felt I had reached the limits of my endurance, the Emperor of Japan accepted the Potsdam Declaration and on August 15 announced Japan's unconditional surrender to the Allies.

The Defeat of Japan and Liberation of the Korean People

Yes, that was a day we Koreans would never forget, a day that promised liberation, freedom, and independence. Yet even after the Emperor himself had announced the surrender on the radio, making it perfectly clear that Japan had lost the war, it was hard for us Korean laborers to believe and we were still doubtful; it wasn't until that night that the realization hit us that we were at last free. And when it did, many of the Korean laborers at the mine where I worked nearly went crazy with joy, waving their hands wildly in the air, dancing around their rooms, and raising shouts of gleeful gibberish. Others cried out, 'We won't be forced to work in the pits any more! We've been liberated!'

'Yes, we're free! We'll be going home soon!'

In a natural backlash to the severe privations of recent months, one group of Koreans stormed into the normally off-limits storerooms and kitchen and carried out the hidden stores of rice, barley, sugar, and sakè.

Meanwhile, the Japanese, who till that day had been so haughty and arrogant, just looked on in dazed silence, their ashen faces stony and expressionless.

Though I didn't know this till later, apparently the Japanese at some of the other mines feared that the Korean laborers there would go on a rampage once they got their freedom, so they forestalled any such uprising by forcibly rounding up the Korean miners and confining them under lock and key. But at the mine where I was, the Japanese seemed to think that there was nothing they could do to stop the joyous uproar of the Koreans. They viewed the Koreans' unruly behavior as a natural response to getting their freedom, liberation, and independence after so many years of discontent and resentment; they considered it, in a word, inevitable. Still, some of my fellow countrymen got so carried away in their celebrating, I really feel they went too far.

Before long, shouts of another kind could be heard: 'Kill the supervisor!' 'Let's get rid of the dormitory superintendent!' 'Yeah, and drag out that son of a bitch in the hiring office!' It wasn't long before the ones who were shouting for blood finally got around to remembering me: 'Let's get that Korean dog that beat his own countrymen for the Japanese!'

I was terrified. Feeling that it wasn't safe for me to stay there, I quickly slipped away from the Korean living quarters and ran to the company office. Ever since the escalation of the war and the consequent increase in Korean laborers brought forcibly to work at the mine, the mining company had instituted the policy of keeping every Korean's wages, savings, and Korean identity papers locked up in the office in order to prevent them from running away. I asked the head supervisor to hand over my papers and savings, along with my severance pay, immediately. His reply came as a crushing blow.

'That's impossible at this time,' he said matter-of-factly. 'You won't get any severance pay, anyway, since you're leaving the company of your own free will. Why don't you wait a while before leaving?' But at least he gave me my identity papers.

At this point, I truly believed I would be killed if I stayed there. Even though I had never wanted to be a foreman over my fellow Koreans in the first place, I knew it was inevitable that the Korean laborers should despise me and hold a grudge against me because of my position in the company. And above all, the fact that I had meted out corporal punishment to my own countrymen was simply . . . well . . . I can't deny that if I'd been in their shoes, I would've been crying for blood and revenge as loudly as any of them.

So there I was. I'd wasted my whole life in the service of Japan, only to end up reviled as a traitor by my own countrymen. The grief I felt at this revelation and the frustration at having no one to blame for my predicament pierced me to the very marrow of my soul. I was a broken man. Gathering together my few possessions, I left the mine feeling like a criminal on the run.

I had no particular destination in mind as I passed among the Japanese in the streets. Many of them were staggering along, weak with hunger and shaken by the shock of Japan's defeat. I retraced my steps to Hakodate and took the ferry over to the main island of Honshu. After arriving at Aomori, I continued on to Ominato, where all was chaos and confusion.

Going Home

On August 22, several thousand Korean forced laborers and their families set sail for Korea on the *Kimishima Maru*, which had previously been a naval special-duty vessel. I succeeded in slipping on board among them. Passage on the *Kimishima Maru* was actually restricted to those Koreans who had been rounded up and brought over to Japan to work at hard labor in Ominato at the naval station or in airfield and railroad construction, but when I demonstrated that I was Korean by showing my identity papers, to my surprise and relief, the Japanese officials in charge let me board without any of the usual interrogation I'd come to expect as a Korean living in Japan.

As evening fell, the *Kimishima Maru* sailed majestically out of the Ominato harbor carrying more than 3,700 Koreans drunk with the joy of going home and their newfound freedom and independence.

During the war, cargo-passenger ships had been remodeled, fitted with three cannons to increase their fighting power, and pressed into naval service as special-duty vessels. Now, as if symbolic of the fate of Japan, the gun mounts had been hastily removed, and these ships had been stripped down to their original condition in order to carry out a new duty—transporting thousands of cruelly mistreated Koreans home again—as if to atone in part for Japan's crimes against these people.

The ship's crew were former naval officers and sailors. They still wore the insignias of their rank on their collars, but it seemed to me that they didn't display the discipline or snap that had formerly been requisite in the Imperial Navy. It was obvious that they considered this voyage an unimportant yet unavoidable duty resulting from Japan's having lost the war.

The hold of the ship was filled way beyond its passenger capacity, and it was unbearably hot and stuffy, so many of us went up on deck to cool off and get a breath of fresh air. Everyone was too excited to sleep, anyway.

Gazing back toward the land we had left, I could see nothing but the ship's turbulent wake, which stood out fantastically white against the pitch-blackness of the night sea.

Memories began to flood my mind, indelible images of the days of my youth in Korea and the long years of privation and back-breaking labor in Kyushu, Kyoto, Tokyo, and Hokkaido. But I knew that soon I would be back in my beloved homeland with my mother and father. As I looked to the future, my mind drifted into a pleasant reverie about the good times to come.

During the final months of the war, I had received word from home that my two elder brothers had been brought by force to labor in Japan. If they, too, managed to return home safe and sound, how wonderful it would be to have all our family together again! With my brothers, I would help to build a new nation from the ruins left by the Japanese, and I would at last, for the first time in my life, have a life worth living. As these thoughts raced through my head, my heart swelled with excitement and anticipation.

Suddenly, however, the ground was pulled out from under me. Groups of Korean laborers had assembled on the deck here and there, and they sat in circles, talking and drinking sakè they'd gotten from God knows where. I overheard snatches of the conversation of the group nearest me, and what I heard turned the blood in my veins to ice and dashed to bits all my hopes and plans for a new life in Korea.

'Our getting dragged off by the Japanese troops and forced to work, well, there was nothing we could do about that, I reckon,' growled one of the men. 'But we can't let those bastard Koreans off the hook, the ones who rode roughshod over us—their own countrymen!—and bullied us and beat us just like the Japanese second lieutenants and sergeant majors. Nosiree! When we get back to Korea, we gotta hunt down those dogs and give 'em what they deserve—death!'

'Before I came to Ominato,' another man added, 'I was working in a coal mine where they had some Koreans who even managed to brown-nose their way into jobs as foremen. They gave us beatings and in return got their share of perks, but next time it'll be their turn to suffer. I'm gonna run down those SOBs for damn sure and let 'em have it!'

Fortunately, not a single Korean from the Mihoro mines was on board, so I was in no immediate danger. But what would become of me when the more than ten thousand Korean laborers who had worked at Mihoro returned home to Korea?

Would I never find a place to live in peace in my own homeland? For the rest of my life, would I be on the run in constant fear, skulking from place to place, hiding from my own people?

The *Kimishima Maru* was proceeding smoothly ever westward across the Sea of Japan. I stood motionless on the deck, the night breeze gently caressing my cheeks, but the anxiety in my heart grew increasingly harder to bear. If I hadn't been holding fast to the deck railing, I would have collapsed on the spot or perhaps even let myself be drawn over the side and dragged under into the ship's foaming, turbulent wake. Still another worry preyed on my mind. For about the past six months, I'd been troubled with swelling in my legs, an unhealthy pallor, and chest pains whenever I moved even a little—all, no doubt, due to years of backbreaking labor and inadequate nutrition. I feared I didn't have much longer to live.

Toward evening on August 24, the fierce heat of midsummer was just starting to abate slightly as the ship relentlessly followed the blazing sun westward. When I happened to look off the port side, I was amazed to see beautiful green mountains and a coastline. It was clear that the ship must be nearing some place on the coast of Honshu, but to my knowledge, this was not on the itinerary. The ship was supposed to sail directly from Ominato to the Korean port of Pusan.

I was extremely thirsty, so I thought I'd go below to get a drink of water and at the same time ask one of the Japanese crewmen what was going on. I went below to the galley, which was near the ship's hold. A sign was posted by the entrance to the galley, 'Crew Only,' but no one was in the galley to tell me to keep out. Figuring it would be all right if I just got some water, I slipped softly into the room. I took the nearest cup and was just about to turn on the water faucet when I heard footsteps coming down the passageway.

Instinctively, I crouched down behind one of the massive kitchen tables and held my breath. There was no longer any need for me to be blindly afraid of the Japanese as I once had been, but I had been mercilessly victimized by them for so long that I knew to the very marrow of my bones what would happen to me if I entered an off-limits place, and this knowledge manifested itself reflexively in this sort of furtive behavior.

I peeped around the edge of the table and saw that two crewmen had entered the galley. From the insignias on their collars, I could tell that one was a master chief petty officer and the other a seaman.

They didn't notice me and continued their conversation. For some reason or other, they were speaking in hushed tones; obviously they had come into the galley seeking a place where they could talk in private.

'You mean the ship's going to dock at Maizuru?'

'That's right, sir,' the seaman replied to the master chief petty officer's question. 'The duty officer said so, so there's no doubt about it.'

'This may just be a heaven-sent opportunity, and if we miss it, it may be a long time before we see Japan again,' the master chief petty officer said. 'Rumor has it that all Japanese who go to Korea will be held as prisoners of war and our ships seized. And that's not all—the Koreans'll give us a good beating or two, no doubt, to get even with us for how they were treated in Japan. God knows when we'll be able to return home!'

'Yes, the Koreans did get treated pretty badly here, didn't they? Maybe it is their turn to dish out some revenge. But the war's over now, and I can't stomach the idea of just handing ourselves over for punishment. Besides, my father and elder brother were killed in the war, and my mother is all alone, waiting for me to come home. When I think of her, sir, I can hardly stand being away from home another minute!'

'All right, then, as soon as the ship enters the harbor, we'll lower one of the cutters and get the hell out of here. The Imperial Navy is all in a shambles now, anyway, so we won't have to worry about being court-martialed.'

This was an incredible piece of information I'd overheard. What's more, it was a wonderful chance for me. From what I'd heard the Korean miners at Mihoro and the Koreans on the *Kimishima Maru* say, I knew I might very well be killed if I returned to Korea. I was desperate to get off that ship. I worked out a plan on the spot, and when the two crewmen left the galley, I stealthily followed them.

They both went into their cabins and soon came back out, each carrying a small bundle under his arm. They were really going to do it; I felt it in my bones.

The two crewmen went up on deck and acted nonchalant as they made their way past the other members of the crew, who were busy preparing to heave the ship to and drop anchor, and went to the afterdeck. Slowly the ship entered Maizuru Bay. Ahead lay an island in the center of the bay, dividing it into two parts; the ship proceeded slowly to the left of the island.

The moment the ship came to a standstill, the two crewmen shot over to the farthest aft cutter and started working to lower it.

I ran up to them and blurted out my ultimatum.

'Please take me with you! If you don't, I'll shout out that you're escaping. I know all about your plan.'

'Aren't you Korean?' asked the one nearest to me, the seaman, his tense face twisting into a grimace of surprise. 'You don't have any reason to want to leave the ship. . . .'

'I've got my reasons!'

In the face of my obvious desperation, they acquiesced and beckoned me closer, thus signaling their consent.

'Can you swim?'

'No, I've never swum,' I replied.

'Okay, then. Undo that fastening and get in the cutter.'

I untied the fastening on one side of the cutter and jumped into the boat. When the master chief petty officer untied the fastening on the other side, the cutter dropped away from the hull of the ship and onto the surface of the water. Normally, a rope would have been used to lower the boat little by little, but we were hardly in a position to take our time about it. As soon as the cutter hit the water, the seaman jumped over the side of the ship and quickly swam over to the cutter.

The other members of the crew had their hands full with the chores of anchoring the ship and didn't seem to have noticed our actions.

The Koreans, eager to return home and puzzled about why the ship was stopping at a Japanese port, merely chattered clamorously among themselves on deck. Although many of them did notice us getting away in the cutter, they didn't have a clue as to the meaning of our departure, and only pointed their fingers at us wonderingly.

The Wreck of the *Kimishima Maru*

'I got my naval training at Maizuru, so I know the lay of the land in these parts like the back of my hand,' the master chief petty officer said. 'We go straight ahead. That'll take us to Shimosahaga.'

We turned the prow of the boat toward the section of coastline he indicated, manned the oars, and made a beeline for shore. My two companions showed themselves to be true seamen and maneuvered the cutter adroitly, and in no time at all we were about three hundred meters from the *Kimishima Maru*. I think we were about halfway between the ship and the shore, when suddenly something incredible happened.

BOOM! BOOM!

Startled at the sound of explosions, I turned around to look at the ship, but it was completely shrouded in billowing clouds of black smoke.

Though we could not see the ship itself, the figures of people who had been flung from the deck into the sea bobbed in and out of sight among the waves, their screams and cries for help echoing over the surface of the water.

When the two crewmen with me saw what had happened, they instinctively and swiftly turned the cutter around in the direction we'd just come from and rowed furiously toward the scene of the explosion at a pace even faster than when we'd escaped from the ship.

'Maybe the ship struck an American mine still floating in these waters,' the master chief petty officer speculated.

As we neared the site of the wreck, the scene was simply too horrible for words. I could hardly bear to look at the countless agonies spread out like a floating hell around me—hundreds of men, women, and children, many with blood gushing from wounds on their heads or faces, thrashing about in the churning waves among the motionless bodies of others more dead than alive. Scores of survivors were fighting to keep from going under, clinging desperately to the few timbers and scraps of wood that the explosion had hurled into the sea.

The two crewmen and I pulled as many people as we could out of that watery hell and into the cutter, then again started rowing toward the shore. We had to leave many of my countrymen struggling to stay afloat and screaming for help, but the cutter was just not big enough to hold them all. There was no way we could try to save everyone. Besides, people on the shore were aware of the catastrophe, for we saw fishing boats coming out to rescue survivors. For the time being, we had done all we could, so we headed for land.

Ironically, the cutter in which we three had sought to escape from the ship was the first boat on the scene to rescue victims and the first to carry them to shore. The villagers of Shimosahaga had all turned out and were waiting anxiously on the beach for our cutter to land.

In the cutter, some of the people we'd plucked from the sea lay motionless and insensible, others were groaning from the pain of their wounds, and some had died on the way. The villagers lifted them all out of the boat and laid them on straw mats on the beach, the dead beside the living.

Once the cutter was empty, the two crewmen immediately pushed off and started rowing back to the wreck to pick up more survivors. I hadn't even had a chance to ask their names or thank them for taking me with them.

'Good luck!' they called out to me as they rowed off.

I slipped away from the crowds of villagers and started walking along the beach alone. Turning inland, I came to the Taira Elementary School; here, too, a small crowd of people had gathered on learning of the disaster in the bay. They asked me what had happened and gave me hot tea, rice balls, and some small, dried fish to eat. After resting there a while, I walked on through a place called Nakata, past Sengenji Temple, and at last arrived at Higashi-Maizuru.

By this time, it had grown quite dark.

I made my way to Higashi-Maizuru Station. I felt there was nothing I could do but go to Kyoto and appeal to Park and his family for help. Yet I was a little afraid that what with the liberation of Korea after Japan's defeat, they might have already returned to Korea or even now be preparing to leave. Unfortunately, there were no more trains to Kyoto that night, but I was able to catch the last train that went as far as Ayabe, a town a little way north of Kyoto.

My identity papers clearly stated that I was Korean, but now that Japan had been defeated in the war, being Korean was no longer the liability it had once been. My recent experiences since leaving Mihoro had taught me that now it was at times useful to make it known that I was Korean and to act a bit high-handed about it, even to the point of exaggerating my Korean accent when speaking Japanese.

When I got off the train at Ayabe, my first thought was to find a place to spend the night, but I had no money on me and I couldn't find a suitable place there.

I willed my weary feet to carry me out of the station. I went straight ahead for a bit, turned left when the street ended at a hillock, and trudged on, crossing a bridge over a big river. Beyond the bridge, the houses were sparse. After a while, I saw the blacker-than-night silhouette of a large building looming ahead in the darkness. It looked like some sort of factory. I went nearer and could dimly make out the name of the company, Ayabe Sakè Distillery, on a signboard by the front entrance.

As I'd expected, the door was locked, but I had an intuition that no one was living there. I went around the side of the building to the back and found a rear entrance secured with a small padlock, which I easily forced open without much effort. I entered the building and was immediately enveloped in a pungent smell— part-mold, part-sakè.

I was worn to a frazzle and just wanted to find some place to lie down. My trousers and shirt, which had gotten drenched in the cutter and on the beach at Shimosahaga, were almost dry now thanks to the warm, summer night breeze, but I felt cold and clammy with sweat.

The first floor of the building was filled with row upon row of sakè barrels stacked up almost as high as the ceiling. The floor was cement, and I could find no comfortable place to lay my head.

I climbed a narrow stairway almost hidden in the darkness, which led to a room apparently used for growing yeast. In a corner, I found several straw mats rolled up and tied in a bundle; I unrolled the mats and collapsed onto them like a broken puppet.

My eyes traveled up to the room's only window. Almost all the panes appeared to have been broken and, due no doubt to the wartime shortage of glass, replaced with pieces of plywood, but beams of pale moonlight shone in through the few remaining panes of glass.

Too exhausted to move, I didn't even have the energy to arrange the mats so that I could lie more comfortably. Yet, though I was so tired, sleep would not come; on the contrary, I was wide awake, and incoherent thoughts were going round and round in my head.

Scenes from the past flashed through my mind: the fields and rice paddies of Korea when I was a young boy; the back-breaking physical labor in Kyushu; my life in Kyoto and Tokyo, especially the horrible, indiscriminate slaughter of Koreans in the chaotic aftermath of the Great Kanto Earthquake; and the many hardships I endured in the black pits of the Mihoro coal mine. At last, my mind wandered through that fitful, dark night of the soul into a dream or vision in which I protected a runaway Korean laborer who was about to be beaten—I clasped him in my arms so that the cutting blows of the whip rained down on my back instead of his.

Toward daybreak, I was just starting to doze off when suddenly I was hit by a terrible, squeezing pain in my chest. My forehead was slick with a cold sweat. Just as I stretched my arms up in the extremity of my pain, as if grasping for the sky, my heart stopped beating and I breathed my last breath. With a gentle rush like a sigh, I slipped into unconsciousness, and that was my last moment of life.

A little past nine o'clock that morning, the astonished distillery employees found my body there and scurried off to report the matter to the police. I watched them do so, for my spirit had already left the flesh behind, and soon after I was lifted up into the World of the Spirits.

Later that day, having determined that I was a Korean vagrant, just some insignificant nobody who had died in the streets, as it were, and had no one to claim his body, the authorities had my body transported to the dissecting room of this medical college.

Well, that's the story of my life. It was a life of one hardship after another, with precious few truly happy, joyful times. But after I died and was lifted up into the World of the Spirits and stood in the presence of the Holy Ghost, I was comforted and blessed a thousand times over for all the pain and sorrow I had suffered during my life, so that now I am thankful for those earthly hardships.

I'm afraid I'm not very good with words. Thank you for listening to my story so patiently.

After Hearing the Second Night's Tale

After listening to the story of the wretched life of the Spirit of Kim, Yoshio and the other six spirits were so overwhelmed by the enormity of the pain and misery he had suffered that they remained silent for a while. At last, Yoshio sighed deeply and slowly began to speak.

"Thank you for telling us about your life. It must have been really terrible for you—nothing but hard labor, sorrow, prejudice, discrimination, and poverty. Speaking as a Japanese, I am deeply ashamed and sorry for the way my fellow countrymen treated you and other Koreans.

"Hearing about your experiences has made me see clearly and vividly for the first time the sins of Japan's imperialistic colonial policy.

"I have never intentionally discriminated against or looked down on Koreans. But I remember, when I was in elementary and middle school, hearing adults use those derogatory terms for Koreans, *Chosen* and *Chosenjin*, and say things like 'Is that guy *Chosen*?' and '*Chosen* always . . .' Now as I think back on those times after hearing your story, I have to admit that I heard and saw those instances of prejudice against Koreans and yet had no particular awareness that such speech and conduct were wrong, or that the very fact of my insensibility to the problem was in a way a form of that very prejudice. We human beings are so blind sometimes—we have a terrible tendency to go along about our daily business without even noticing that we ourselves are guilty of the same sins that we abhor in others.

"Your hardships as a Korean were formidable. While still an adolescent, you were separated from your family, compelled by economic hardship to leave your homeland and come to Japan, forced to do hard, physical labor in a coal mine, and worst of all, subjected to the terrible ordeal of the Great Kanto Earthquake and its violent aftermath.

"It's plain from your account of those events that that senseless massacre of thousands of Koreans cannot be explained away as simply a result of the panic of people who have been terrorized by a severe earthquake. Surely, such vicious violence grew out of deep-seated prejudice and hatred. I feel deep shame, regret, and moral indignation that such atrocities were committed by my own countrymen.

"It must have been awful for you having to work in the coal mines again after going to Hokkaido, especially since you were put in such an agonizing position between the Japanese supervisors and your fellow Koreans. It pained me more than I can say to hear that those problems continued to haunt you even after Japan was defeated and Korea at last gained its freedom.

"What a crushing blow it must have been to be bursting with joy at the prospect of being reunited with your family and full of hope for a new start in life contributing to a new, free Korea, only to have those hopes and dreams shattered by the ghost of your past deeds when you learned that you would have to hide your identity and run from your fellow Koreans for the rest of your life!

"And on top of all that, you were there when the *Kimishima Maru* exploded and sank, and saw thousands of your fellow Koreans perish in an instant. I seem to remember reading something about the incident in the newspaper, but I had no idea it was such a great catastrophe and took so many lives.

"The articles said that the ship might have struck a floating mine, but since two other ships had sailed safely through the same waters shortly before the explosions, the *Kimishima Maru* must have been exceptionally unlucky. Another theory the newspaper reported was that the former Japanese naval officers and seamen that made up her crew did not want to go to Pusan and sabotaged the ship.

"The loss of the *Kimishima Maru* was part of the price Japan had to pay for its sins of war. But how tragic that the poor, victimized Koreans sailing in that ship had to be involved in such a disaster on their way home to Korea!

"It sounds as if you had a myocardial infarction when you died at the sakè distillery in Ayabe, no doubt a direct result of your long years of physical and emotional strain and abuse.

"You said that after entering the World of the Spirits, however, you were given compensation and consolation in greater measure than all the troubles you suffered during your life. I'm so glad that you have found happiness at last.

"Thank you for telling me these things tonight."

As Yoshio finished speaking, he felt great comfort gazing at the face of the Spirit of Kim, which was so gentle and peaceful that it hardly seemed possible that he could have lived through a life of such pain and misery.

"Yes, it's true: The greater one's sufferings on earth, the greater one's consolation in the World of the Spirits and in Heaven," said the Spirit of Professor Yuhara in conclusion, walking Yoshio to the door of the dissecting room. "Yoshio, it's late. Let's say good-night now. We'll see you again tomorrow night."

Yoshio felt the smiles of the other spirits at his back as he left the room and started for home.

But thoughts of the many sorrows and unfair hardships of Kim's life stayed with him and weighed heavily on his mind.

CHAPTER FOUR

THIRD NIGHT:

The Tale of a Nisei Woman Who Was Driven to Suicide

My Father Immigrates to the United States

My name in the world of the living was Nancy Masako Ito, and I was born in Los Angeles to Japanese parents who had immigrated there from Japan.

In order for you to understand some of the things I'll be talking about later in my story, I must first tell you a little bit about my father, Ito Nobuo. He was born in Japan and went to the United States in 1906 at the age of eighteen. He was the third son of the chief priest of a small Buddhist temple in Fukushima-cho in Hiroshima Prefecture, the ownership of which had been passed down from father to son for many generations. He grew up in a peaceful country town encircled by low mountains thickly wooded with Japanese red pines.

Being the third-born son, my father did not enjoy the same privileges as the first-born son, who would someday succeed to the position of chief priest, and had to make his own way in the world. After graduating from Saijo Middle School with a distinguished academic record, my father changed his course in life. Having heard stories about life in the United States, he dreamed of making a success of himself in a new world, and instead of continuing on to the next stage of higher education in Japan, he began looking for an opportunity to go to America.

113

At that time, quite a few Japanese people from Hiroshima Prefecture were going off to the United States, people from all walks of life: they had given up on making a decent life for themselves in Japan, or had failed in business, or were spurred on by the spirit of adventure and the desire to blaze a new trail in a foreign land. Some longed to experience a new and exotic way of living, and others went seeking freedom and equality, or to evade military service.

My father had a strong love of learning, and he had high hopes for getting a good education in America, starting over at the middle school level and going on through high school to university.

When he heard that it was possible in America for anyone to go to university who had a mind to do so, if he just worked for a while and saved his money, my father could hardly wait to be on his way, and he talked his parents into letting him go.

One of my father's paternal aunts had married the priest of a Buddhist temple in the Uraderamachi area of Kyoto. Her first-born son had been sent to Los Angeles two years before by the head temple of the Nishihonganji sect of Jodo-Shinshu Buddhism, in order to complete his religious training and at the same time engage in missionary work for the temple. So my father went off to America, counting on this first cousin to help him after his arrival at Los Angeles.

Now, so that you can understand what it was like for Japanese immigrants in the United States in those days, I will tell you some of the things my father told our family around the dinner table about his early years in America.

Perhaps he talked to us so often about those days because the pain and hard times he suffered, especially the difficulties he faced living in America because he was Japanese, were so deeply etched in his heart that he could never be free of those sad and bitter memories. Or perhaps he wanted us, his children born in America and destined to live there, to know the truth about his generation's struggle and hand it down to future generations. Whatever his reasons, he told us the same stories over and over again, and to this very day, I remember every detail.

My father set sail from Yokohama on board the *Kurama Maru* and arrived in Seattle after seventeen days. The ship was one of the finest luxury liners in Japan in those days and, as such, was full of distinguished passengers such as high-ranking government officials and VIPs from the world of business and finance. When the ship set sail from Yokohama, hosts of people were on the dock to see off these eminent passengers, waving and calling out their farewells with great fanfare. In contrast, not a soul came to see my father off, so his departure was rather sad and lonely. Moreover, he was profoundly anxious about his future in America, and even as the great ship began to leave the quay, he was seized by an impulse to jump off the ship and stay in Japan after all.

'You take good care of yourself, now. For all we know, this may be the last time we'll ever see each other,' his mother and father had said when he left their home to start his long journey. Their words echoed in his mind as the ship moved slowly out into the harbor, taking him away from his family, his home, and his country. As it happened, that was their last farewell, for he and his parents were never to meet again in this world.

Traveling in steerage, my father was bothered by the incessant racket of the ship's mighty engines and the vibrations that reverberated in the walls and floors. He had brought along a textbook on English and planned to study it during the voyage, but he was so distracted by the noise around him that he wasn't able to concentrate. Worse still, he was seasick much of the time. His only pleasure on the voyage was taking hot baths, even though the bathwater had seawater mixed in.

After the ship's departure from Yokohama, from time to time my father could still see the coast of his homeland off in the distance. But when the ship passed the coast of Sendai, and had sailed past the Aleutian Islands, the waves began to roll and swell with the awesome power of the wild, open sea. It was then that my father first felt his heart tingle with excitement at the realization

that he had left his homeland far behind and was really on his way
to a foreign land.

When he finally arrived in Seattle, the city did not then have
any of the characteristic tall skyscrapers he'd heard so much about
in tales of America. But Seattle was bustling with activity. Its
streets teeming with settlers and laborers from all over the world,
the city was vibrant with life and energy.

My father traveled south to Los Angeles on the recently
completed Northern Pacific Railroad. It was all he could do to buy
his ticket; he didn't even know how to get hold of a timetable. He
had no idea what places the train he was on was passing through
or when it would arrive in Los Angeles. You would think he could
have at least picked up that sort of basic information from the
railway personnel, but he didn't have enough confidence in his
feeble command of English to ask the big-bodied, somewhat
forbidding conductor who passed up and down the aisle from time
to time. What with all the uncertainty and strange, new surroundings, he was quite nervous. All in all, it was an anxiety-ridden trip.
After arriving in Los Angeles, however, he somehow managed to
locate the Buddhist mission where his cousin, Owaki Yoshinobu,
was living and at last began to breathe easier.

But his difficulties had only just begun. My father's original
plan had been to go to school while holding down some job or
other to support himself, but things didn't work out that way. He
found that the only jobs open to people who couldn't speak
English and didn't know the local customs were menial positions
such as dishwasher. On top of that, all the jobs open to him had
work hours that interfered with his attending school, so with a
heavy heart he asked for help, and his cousin arranged for my
father to work on a farm outside Fresno, a town quite far from Los
Angeles. Many Japanese were already living in Fresno then; most
of those families had started out small, growing vegetables and
fruit or raising chickens, and by living simply and working hard,
they had managed to make their profits grow little by little.

My father's new plan was to work there for a year or so, save as much money as he could, and then start his studies in America.

He ended up working part-time on several different farms owned by Japanese. He worked hard and for as many hours as he could get, from early in the morning till late at night, intent on earning as much money as possible.

He and the Japanese farmers who employed him shared the kindred attitudes of fellow countrymen; he got along well with them and was happy in his work. They too were Japanese immigrants, who up until just a few years earlier, had worked their fingers to the bone as seasonal laborers on farms owned by white men; they had saved up their meager wages until at last they were able to buy some land of their own and start working for themselves.

As my father began, little by little, to understand the way things worked in America, he learned all too well just how difficult it was for Japanese people to live in this 'New World,' especially in the state of California.

The Anti-Japanese Movement in the Western United States

What I'm about to tell you now are some more things that my father often talked about. Please bear with me through a bit more of his history.

Before the Japanese started coming to America, there was a great influx of Chinese into California from 1850 on, which increased steadily year by year. In the beginning, white Americans found these immigrants useful, for they would work for low wages at hard labor in railroad construction, farms, orchards, and mines. But they came in ever-increasing numbers and had large families, and when the country went into a recession after the Civil War, the abundance of cheap Chinese labor started affecting the supply of jobs available to white men. Public opinion favored getting rid of the Chinese, and in 1882 the United States Legislature went so far as to pass a law prohibiting Chinese immigration. In his campaign for political office, Governor Stanford, for whom Stanford University was named, appealed to voters' concern about the problem of the growing number of Chinese in the state and said in his inaugural address that Chinese were 'undesirables.'

With the Restoration of Imperial Rule in Japan and the start of the Meiji era in 1869, the ban against Japanese citizens traveling to foreign countries was lifted, and the Japanese government officially began issuing passports. Except for the many members of the Aizu feudal clan who fled Japan for political reasons and came to the United States, the start of full-scale immigration of Japanese people to America unfortunately coincided with the birth of the social and political movement against the mass immigration into the United States by another group of Orientals, the Chinese.

The governing principle of this young, new country was that all independent-spirited people seeking freedom, equality, and justice could achieve great things according to their own abilities and efforts. America was known as a country where the door was always open to people who respected the pioneer spirit and were ready and willing to help the young country grow and develop. Yes, well, those are fine-sounding words, but what my father learned all too well and too late was that those fine-sounding words and lofty sentiments were meant to refer to free white men only and did not apply to the Japanese and other Orientals.

Appended to legislation passed in 1873 was an article stipulating that all American Negroes, both those born in Africa and those of African ancestry, could become naturalized citizens of the United States. Thus, it became increasingly clear that Orientals, people of the Mongoloid race, falling into the category of neither white nor black, were excluded from eligibility for naturalization in the United States.

It was definitely a question of race and not just of skin color, for even Japanese girls with snow-white skin could not become naturalized U.S. citizens.

One of the things that grieved my father most was an event that occurred the very year he arrived in America, 1906: the San Francisco Board of Education's decision to prohibit Orientals living in the city from attending public schools. This incident became a political problem between Japan and the United States and led to the Gentlemen's Agreement in 1908. The problem of Orientals attending public schools was resolved by the designation of all Japanese as aliens ineligible for naturalization and the passage of the Immigration Quota Law, which curbed the influx of Japanese immigrants into the United States. But this was just one example—my father saw with his own eyes and experienced firsthand many instances of prejudice and discrimination directed against the Japanese in response to what white Americans perceived as the threat of 'the yellow peril.'

After the Meiji Restoration and the abolishment of Japan's national isolation policy which prohibited foreigners from entering the country, Japan promoted a strong policy designed to enable the country to catch up with the European nations economically and technologically. In the military sphere, Japan won its war with China in 1895; and just ten years later in 1905, one year before my father's arrival in the United States, Japan won the Russo-Japanese War and, as you probably know, began to invade Korea, Manchuria, and the Kurile Islands. Japan was gradually becoming a threat to the United States, and some American military leaders and politicians looked upon Japan as a potential enemy, predicting that one day Japanese forces would land on America's Pacific coast.

Not all Japanese immigrants to the United States mainland came directly from Japan; many settled first in Hawaii and later moved on to California. Others came to the United States by way of Canada or Mexico. But whatever route they took, their numbers continued to increase rapidly.

Japanese people are by nature diligent and hard-working, so although the Japanese immigrants started out working as common laborers on farms or in mines, they launched other enterprises in a variety of areas such as tenant farming or cultivating flowers to sell. This was one factor in their ostracism by white Americans. The different physical appearance and lifestyle of the Japanese were also probably disagreeable to most Americans. Although the Japanese did not wear their hair in a queue like the Chinese, during the initial weeks or months after their arrival in the United States, they must have appeared rather outlandish in their long kimonos.

In Japan, it's quite common to see a Japanese person squatting by the side of the road to rest a bit, but to the eyes of a white person such a posture resembles that of someone defecating. In addition, many Japanese customs must have seemed crude and barbaric: men urinating publicly by the roadside or against a wall, talking in loud voices, slurping and smacking their lips noisily when eating. Furthermore, it isn't difficult to understand how white Americans, most of whom at least in principle believed in God and looked on the Japanese as heathens who neither believed in nor stood in awe of God, would have viewed the seemingly limitless influx of Japanese people into California, and their relatively high birthrate, as a threat to their American way of life. Ultimately, the underlying cause of white Americans' fear and dislike of Japanese immigrants was racial prejudice, and the social climate was such that all politicians or labor union leaders had to do to win an election was to take up the cry 'Out with the Japs!'

Finally, the California State Assembly passed a law that was in effect from 1920 to 1940, the Anti-Alien Land Act, which prohibited unnaturalized aliens from owning land in the state of California. As you probably have guessed, the target of this legislation was California's Japanese residents, who were still ineligible to become naturalized U.S. citizens. Its purpose was to make it difficult for the Japanese to engage in the business of farming and thus drive them out of the state.

In order to restrain Japan's aggressive expansion into Asia, the Washington Disarmament Conference was convened in Washington, D.C., at the request of the United States. Representatives from the United States, the United Kingdom, and Japan set the ratio of battleship tonnage at five for the United States, five for the United Kingdom, and three for Japan; furthermore, it was agreed that the Anglo-Japanese Alliance be dissolved at the end of 1922. These and other measures to undermine Japan's international standing cropped up one after another. At the same time, white residents of California and other western states were drafting and enacting new laws intended to drive Japanese immigrants out of their states if possible, or at least to prevent any new ones from arriving.

In 1924, this wave of anti-Japanese attacks culminated in the dissolution of the Gentlemen's Agreement and the establishment of the New Quota Law in its place. Since the Gentlemen's Agreement had proved ineffective in shutting out Japanese immigrants to a degree deemed sufficient by white Americans, the New Quota Law, which was essentially anti-Japanese legislation, was deemed necessary.

From 1908 to 1923, over 120,000 Japanese people were allowed to enter the United States, but because more than 110,000 left the country, the actual increase in the Japanese population in America was in fact only about 500 each year.

As I said before, my father often talked about these things in great detail over our evening meal. So now you know what things were like for the Japanese in those years in the western states of America, particularly California.

My father eventually gave up his dream of getting a college education. He got a job on a farm in Fresno, worked like a dog, and saved his pay. When he had at last saved up enough money, he opened a small grocery store in the Los Angeles district known as Little Tokyo. His store carried fresh vegetables, strawberries, oranges and other fruits, and Japanese foodstuffs such as tofu. With the establishment of this store, his life became calmer and more settled. The next step was for him to start a family of his own.

In those days, the majority of single Japanese men who had immigrated to the United States were faced with the very serious problem of finding a bride. Having come to America with nothing but the clothes on their backs, most of them lacked the money to support a wife and set up a household right away, so they tended to marry late. My father was no exception. At last, in 1919, Mr. Owaki in Kyoto helped arrange for my father to marry the second daughter of a Mr. Nakamura, who was the head priest of a temple of the Jodo-Shinshu sect of Buddhism near Otani University in the Kamigyo Ward of Kyoto. It was what was called a 'picture marriage,' in which the two parties exchanged photographs and on that basis decided to marry. So my father and mother had never met each other before agreeing to marry, but in those days, particularly the period from 1910 to 1920, picture marriages were quite common.

The custom of picture marriage ran up against the tide of American public opinion seeking to decrease the number of Japanese immigrants to the United States, and, moreover, was vehemently denounced by white Americans as a barbaric custom that blatantly ignored human rights. So in 1921, the Japanese government resolved the problem by voluntarily ceasing to issue passports to women who were intending to immigrate to the United States for the purpose of an arranged marriage. Since my father's picture marriage took place in 1919, it slipped in under the wire just two years before the cutoff.

Growing Up as a Nisei

My elder sister, Deborah Kyoko, was born one year after my parents' marriage, and I was born the following year in 1921.

From birth, my sister was physically weak, passive in all things, quiet and self-effacing. I was quite the opposite: spirited, lively, eager to be involved, and enthusiastically interested in anything and everything.

At elementary school, I was occasionally taunted and called 'Jap,' but I didn't take such teasing to heart and never thought of it as real discrimination. After all, I wasn't the only Japanese child in a school of whites, so I didn't feel particularly alone or singled out for such treatment; many other nisei, the America-born children of Japanese immigrant parents, went to my school. Besides, I generally excelled in my schoolwork, and that made me feel good about myself and helped me shrug off the childish name-calling that was occasionally indulged in by a few of my classmates.

My high-school years were also enjoyable by and large. The first week or so, some of the kids taunted me for being Japanese and looking different—some pushed the corners of their eyes into a slant with their fingers, and some threw paper balls at me—but I just ignored them and they soon got tired of it. Actually far from being discriminated against, with my naturally outgoing personality I made friends easily and had very few unpleasant experiences in high school. Once in a while on the city streets I encountered some white person who muttered 'Jap!' in a hateful tone of voice at me as we walked passed each other, but not once was I confronted with any sort of aggressive prejudice or violent behavior, perhaps because I was a girl.

Like most other nisei children, I had a strong desire to do well at school, and though it's not very modest of me to say so, I was always the top student in my class.

In school I learned the importance of freedom. The study of American history instilled in me a strong sense of pride in America and love for my native land.

The vast majority of Japanese immigrants came to the United States without much schooling, and they wanted their children to get at least a high-school education. They believed that a good education was the best gift they could give their children and future generations as a means of self-preservation against the racial prejudice and discrimination they would have to face. To that end, many parents sacrificed their own luxuries and pleasures and, despite severe economic hardship, sent their children on to university after high school.

These Japanese immigrants, who had grown up under the influence of Japanese history and culture back in Japan, were reluctant to break their ties with their former homeland across the seas. Moreover, because of the somewhat precarious position of the Japanese in the United States at that time, they were worried that their children would be handicapped by not knowing the Japanese language if at some future time they and their families were compelled to return to Japan to live. Consequently, the parents organized and set up private Japanese-language schools for their children. These classes were usually held on Saturday afternoon.

Most Buddhist temples and Christian churches in the Japanese communities in the United States, and also the individual chapters of the Japan Association, had their own Japanese-language schools. Despite my strong family ties to Buddhism, I attended a Japanese-language school affiliated with a Christian church simply because it was near our house.

As I have said several times, the issei—my parents' generation of Japanese immigrants to America—had to endure incredibly severe and cruel anti-Japanese prejudice and discrimination in the western part of the United States, especially in California. With the enactment of the Anti-Alien Land Act, the issei had been designated as aliens ineligible for naturalization and were prohibited from owning land in the United States. They managed, however, to establish some measure of economic security by purchasing land in the names of their nisei children, who were automatically granted American citizenship by virtue of having been born on American soil. In this way, our issei parents entrusted their dreams for a brighter future to us, their nisei children.

In the face of the anti-Japanese movement, which did everything in its power to drive the Japanese immigrants out of the United States, many issei gave up all hope of having any decent life in America and returned to Japan. But others were determined to reside permanently in their adopted homeland, and they worked hard to put down roots in their American communities. After they had lived in the United States for ten, twenty, or thirty years, the land of their birth gradually began to fade from their minds and recede farther and farther into the shadows of memory, until in time it was no more real to them than an image in a painting. In short, they began to feel alienated from Japan and ultimately came to embrace America as their true homeland; for it was, after all, the country dearest to their hearts, the land where they had lived and worked most of their lives, and had raised their children.

Naturally, the vast majority of us nisei regarded the United States as our one, true homeland. Nevertheless, a few nisei—really, only a handful—could not take the atmosphere of contempt and disdain generated by some prejudiced white Americans. Some nisei were unable to get a good job even though they had a college education—solely because of racial discrimination—and this frustrated them greatly. In time, some nisei came to feel ashamed of their racial ancestry and curse their Japanese blood.

In the period when my father left Japan, the middle schools in Japan were organized on a five-year system and the academic content of the classes was quite intellectually demanding. Having graduated from middle school with an excellent academic record, my father was among the intelligentsia of the issei. He had clear, well-developed ideas about how Japanese immigrants and their children should conduct their lives in America and a vision of what sort of future they should strive to create for themselves.

My father wanted us nisei to grow up regarding America as our homeland, but at the same time, he also believed that we would inevitably have to cope with various social problems in America because of our Japanese lineage. He felt strongly that it was necessary for the children of issei to have a 'nisei identity' and to acknowledge and appreciate their Japanese culture and heritage. He wanted me to spend some time in Japan in order to see the country of my ancestors with my own eyes, to experience the traditional Japanese lifestyle, and to get some Japanese education.

He believed that the experience I would get in Japan would strengthen my appreciation of my racial and cultural identity and enable me to lead a better life as an American citizen in the future.

If possible, I really wanted to enter UCLA right after gradu-ating from high school. But I also wanted to go along with my father's wish for me to spend some time in Japan, for I respected him and his views; and I myself felt that seeing the homeland of my parents would be a meaningful experience for me and serve to clarify my spiritual roots as a nisei. But I guess the deciding factor was really my outgoing personality; I was curious by nature and interested in all things, some would say perhaps even a bit flighty and impulsive. I decided to go, thinking a stay in Japan wasn't such a bad idea as long as it was just for two or three years.

In the spring of 1939 my father applied to the State Depart-ment to obtain a passport for me. At that time there was already a sky-high stack of serious political problems between Japan and the United States, and some people even spoke of the possibility of war. As a result, it was not easy for me to get a passport; it took two months, twice the usual time, but at last I got one.

There were other nisei wanting to visit Japan at that time too, but some of them were unable to obtain a passport in time before their departure and had to set out on their journey with only a certificate issued by the Bureau of Immigration.

Although nisei children were automatically American citi-zens, issei parents usually registered their children's names at the Japanese Consulate to obtain Japanese citizenship for them as well. This, of course, gave the children dual citizenship. Appar-ently, this course of action was recommended by the consulate.

When you consider the precarious, politically unstable posi-tion of the Japanese living in America at that time—not knowing if or when they might be driven out of the country, unable to plan for the future with any certainty or security—you can't really blame the issei for preparing for the worst and obtaining Japanese citizenship for their children.

To white society in America, dual citizenship was tantamount to straddling the fence of nationality, as it were, and this simply gave them another excuse to criticize the Japanese who obtained it. In response, many nisei who wanted to integrate themselves into American society as much as possible had their names removed from the consulate registry and thus officially relinquished their Japanese citizenship in order to turn aside such criticism. And I was one of them. It happened that I departed for Japan after I had given up my Japanese citizenship, so it was as an American citizen that I set out for Japan.

My parents bought so many American hams, canned foods, and clothing for me to take with me, both for my own use and as gifts for the Owaki family, with whom I would be staying, that I ended up taking more than ten pieces of luggage when I set sail for Japan on board the *Arabiya Maru.*

Even now, I remember vividly how I felt as the ship left the San Pedro Harbor in Los Angeles one week after the July 4 Independence Day holiday.

Japan, My Parents' Native Land

As I stood on the deck of the *Arabiya Maru*, the great ship slowly started to pull away from the quay. The colorful paper streamers, which stretched from our hands to the hands of our loved ones on shore, seemed to symbolize the bonds of love that linked our hearts and theirs. As I watched, the fragile streamers broke and fell gently down onto the surface of the water, and I felt a pang of sadness at seeing the last physical link between me and my family give way so easily. Through tear-filled eyes I saw the blurry forms of my mother and father and my big sister, Deborah Kyoko, get smaller and smaller and at last vanish from sight.

The ship sailed north along the California coastline, and then turned west. For a while, the lively music of a radio broadcast of American jazz filled the corridors of the ship, but as we progressed westward the music got fainter, and it was then that I felt, with a twinge of mingled excitement and anxiety, 'Now I'm really leaving America.'

The ship sailed along the Aleutian Islands, trailing its white-foam wake behind, and we arrived at Yokohama on the seventeenth day of the voyage.

My first impressions of Japan, the native land of my parents, were threefold: First, it was unbearably hot and humid; second, the air was stagnant; and third, the disgusting stench of raw sewage was everywhere. Flush toilets had not yet come into widespread use, so the pervasive stench was unavoidable. But I had a terrible time getting used to using the Japanese-style toilets, which instead of sitting on, you have to squat down over. Those toilets were awfully awkward and uncomfortable for me at first.

Mr. Owaki had come all the way from Kyoto to meet me when the ship arrived. After collecting my luggage, we went to Tokyo Station. I was amazed at the technologically advanced electric trains operated by national and private lines, and the tall buildings that lined the streets around the station. We boarded a special express train on the Tokaido Line and arrived at Kyoto in about eight hours, right on schedule. I had been led to expect the trains in Japan to be punctual, but the degree of punctuality was simply amazing: Our train slid smoothly up to the platform at Kyoto Station not a minute or even a second off schedule.

The train station in Kyoto was also quite large. In front of it stood the Central Post Office, and to the north, a Western-style department store named Bussankan. A bit farther off stood the magnificent grounds of Higashihonganji Temple, and beyond that low, matchboxlike houses with gray-tiled roofs. Compared with the bright, light-colored appearance of American cities, what struck me most about the Japanese cities was their drab grayness.

There is a world of difference between just hearing about something and seeing it for yourself. The Japan I encountered was radically different from the image of it that I had carried in my mind since childhood, and I was rather confused and bewildered at first.

Taking off one's shoes in the entryway and then stepping up into the house proper; sitting on the tatami-mat floors; and, since I was a woman, having to sit in the correct manner with my legs tucked demurely under me, not out to the side—in almost every conceivable way, the customs of Japan were different from those I was used to in America, and in some cases the exact opposite. I had a lot of difficulty getting used to the daily customs of Japan. And on top of all that, everything—even the eggs!—seemed to smell of fish.

My Japanese was far from adequate, but luckily Mr. Owaki arranged for me to take a crash language course with the wife of Professor Arito of the Department of Japanese Literature at Doshin University. Because the professor and his family had spent some time in New York in a study-abroad program at Columbia University, they were quite familiar with the American lifestyle. They understood the culture shock I was experiencing and did all they could to help me adjust to my new environment.

Partly because of my relationship with the Arito family, I enrolled at Doshin Women's College in the Department of English Literature the following April, in 1940.

The college had been founded by a Christian mission; it had a long history and an atmosphere of freedom, quite unlike regular Japanese colleges. At that time, Japan was already at war with China and had signed the Tripartite Pact with Germany and Italy, by which the three countries were bound to support each other in the event that the United States entered the war in Europe. As a result of these developments, other college campuses became rather constrained and militaristic; in contrast, the tone of our university seemed all the more open and relaxed.

Student life there was very pleasant for me. The broad campus lawns were dotted with New England-style school buildings of brick, and externally the school looked just like an American college campus.

American nisei visitors to Japan in those days tended to be looked at somewhat askance by many of the Japanese, as if they were outsiders of some sort, but not once did I feel myself the object of that sort of discrimination at Doshin. On the contrary, the students were friendly and considerate to me; their hearts and minds must have been influenced by the Bible verses they heard at the chapel service each morning, teaching them to be kind and hospitable to travelers and to love their neighbors as themselves.

The world outside the campus gates was quite different, steeped in the somber, joyless hues of wartime sacrifice and privation. Everyday necessities such as clothing and even matches were already being rationed; and clothes were no longer made of wool or cotton, which were no longer available, but of *sufu,* a coarse, low-quality, man-made fiber.

'Extravagance is an enemy' was the phrase on everyone's lips. People were encouraged to wear the national uniform for civilians. Women wearing shoulder sashes printed with kanji that read 'Women's National Defense Association' stood on street corners, appealing to passersby to join the war effort by sewing a few stitches in one of the many 'thousand-stitch waistbands' they were making to send to Japanese soldiers at the battlefronts in northern China. People believed these densely stitched waistbands acted like a good-luck charm to protect the soldiers from enemy bullets.

Boys in middle school usually went to school wearing khaki uniforms and gaiters. If any music was heard in the streets, it was invariably a rousing war song such as 'Going Off to the Front,' 'Barley and Soldiers,' 'Patriotic March,' 'Greater East Asia March,' or 'Battleship March.'

Middle school students and female students were strictly forbidden to walk in the shopping and amusement quarters or to enter movie theaters or coffee shops, and were policed by teacher patrols to make sure that they did not do so. University and college students, on the other hand, still had some degree of freedom.

I enjoyed stopping at one of the coffee shops on Sanjo or Shijo Street with some friends on the way home after classes and listening to the classical music on records played there. Cream soda and ice cream were still being served then, and American and European movies were still playing at the movie theaters in the Kyogoku district.

So even as Japan was in a state of war, I was able to have some nice times with my college friends—for a little while, that is.

The fighting in Europe which had begun in 1939 was becoming increasingly intense and widespread thanks to the relentless aggression of the German Army under the command of Hitler. On the pretext of establishing the Greater East Asia Co-Prosperity Sphere, Japan was also widening the scope of its invasion of other Asian countries and had already begun its occupation of French Indochina.

In the summer of 1941, relations between the United States and Japan went from strained to critical. Japan felt itself hemmed in and menaced by the ABCD powers: the Japanese news media popularized this abbreviation, which stood for America, Britain, China, and the Dutch East Indies. In August, the United States banned the export of petroleum to Japan. Apparently, it was mainly the Japanese military that then propagated the public opinion that Japan was ready to go to war in order to defend itself.

I kept abreast of the situation, avidly reading the newspaper and listening to radio news reports about Special Envoy Kurusu being sent to the United States to join Ambassador Nomura in initiating talks to circumvent war. I clung desperately to the hope that, ultimately, war between the United States and Japan could somehow be avoided.

Nevertheless, I knew that if America and Japan did go to war, as of that moment I would be unable to return home to my parents any time soon. The thought of that filled me with such anxiety and eagerness to leave Japan that I sent a letter to my parents in Los Angeles telling them I wanted to return to America. Since I had heard rumors of mail between the United States and Japan being opened and inspected, I didn't write about my fear that war seemed imminent, but simply buried the mention of my desire to return to America among other bits of general, everyday news. My parents nevertheless evidently read between the lines, for they replied with a letter in mid-November requesting me to return home as soon as possible. I already had the money for my return trip, so without delay I contacted a steamship company and booked passage on the *Tatsuta Maru*, which was scheduled to set sail from Yokohama on December 2.

Since my departure for America was so hurried and sudden, I had no time for a proper farewell to my classmates at college. Besides, war had not actually broken out at that point, and I looked forward to the voyage with a light heart. Thinking that my return to the United States would be only temporary, I merely notified the college's business office that I would be absent from classes for a while. In what little time I had to prepare for the trip, I hastily packed only what I could manage to carry by myself. I thanked the Owaki family for their many kindnesses to me during the year I had stayed with them and, feeling very sad at having to leave them, went by train to Yokohama, where I boarded the *Tatsuta Maru*.

On board the ship, I realized for the first time that tensions between Japan and the United States had reached a desperate pitch. I also learned that the American government had responded to Japan's final proposal with what the Japanese news media termed the 'Hull Note,' an ultimatum from Secretary of State Cordell Hull.

The ship was packed with as many passengers as it could accommodate, many of them agitated and fearful. Some of the Americans on board expressed doubts as to whether the ship would ever reach the United States safely, and some predicted that this would probably be the last ship to depart from Japan bound for America.

Unfortunately, their fears and predictions proved correct. The slender thread that held Japanese-American relations together was indeed nearing its breaking point. Or rather had already broken, for though we on the ship had no way of knowing it, a Japanese naval task force had already set sail from Hitokappu Bay in the southern Kurile Islands and was, even then, on its way to attack Pearl Harbor.

War Breaks Out Between Japan and the United States

On December 8 in Japan, when the announcement of war came over the ship's public address system, a pall of anxiety and grim uncertainty fell over the ship's passengers and crew. It was the historic announcement from Imperial Headquarters: 'In the early dawn this morning, December 8, Japan entered a state of war against American and British troops as a result of a hostile engagement in the western Pacific Ocean.'

The faces of the Japanese passengers, most of whom were sailing to the United States on urgent business or some special mission, became drawn and white with fear. And those of us passengers who were nisei struggled under the even greater shock of being torn between our two homelands.

Some white American passengers panicked and tried to persuade the captain to keep the ship on its course for the United States, but he had orders from the Japanese government to turn the *Tatsuta Maru* back to Yokohama.

After we arrived back in Japan, the immigration procedures, which had been so simple when we left Yokohama less than a week before, were now quite complicated and difficult. Still, nisei with Japanese citizenship had a relatively easier time of it than those like me with only American passports. As far as the Japanese immigration officials were concerned, we had become enemies of Japan the minute war had been declared. It may have been my imagination, but even the immigration officials' way of looking at me seemed different from how it had been before. The regular police and even the Military Police were on hand to keep a close eye on us as, one by one, we went ashore.

I was permitted to reenter Japan on the condition that I return to the address I had been staying at before leaving the country, so I went back to the Owaki family in Kyoto. They had read in the newspaper that the *Tatsuta Maru* had returned to Japan; but having no idea when or if I might be returning to their house, they had been rather worried about me.

My life in Kyoto began anew. But now that Japan was embroiled in the Greater East Asia War and fighting the United States as well, the country was in a state of full-scale war, and I was living there as the holder of an American passport—in other words, as one of the enemy.

The next day, two plainclothes officers from the Foreign Affairs Section of the Kyoto Police Department lost no time in coming to the temple where the Owaki family and I lived. They asked me in great detail about my life in America, my purpose in coming to Japan, and my nationality; they took copious notes and then left.

This disturbing interrogation brought home to me and the Owaki family the seriousness of my position as a citizen of an enemy nation during wartime.

I started attending classes at Doshin Women's College again, and my classmates treated me the same as before, with no sign of animosity or aloofness. Actually, they seemed quite interested to hear about my experiences on board the *Tatsuta Maru*..

No matter how proficient I became in Japanese, and accustomed to the Japanese lifestyle, my sole pleasure was going to see the American and European movies shown at two or three movie theaters in the Kyogoku district near the Uraderamachi area. To this day it seems strange to me that American movies continued to be shown for a few months after the start of the war between Japan and the United States.

I remember one movie I saw in Japan featured Fred Astaire and Ginger Rogers tap-dancing; and I saw my first color film there, in which Marlene Dietrich starred. Surprisingly enough, one theater even showed a movie about the American superbomber called the 'Superfortress,' which flaunted America's military strength. Even amidst the strict discipline and control that the government maintained over every aspect of life in Japan during wartime, you would occasionally come across this sort of ludicrous oversight. Perhaps it was a sign of the self-assurance of Japan and the leeway it felt it could afford, having already achieved great military victories early in the war.

After a few months, however, a new order of wartime constraint and an extreme surge of hostility took hold of the country. The use of English was forbidden, and insulting terms for the enemy, such as *kichiku-beiei*, meaning 'American and British fiends and savages,' came into popular use.

As the fighting became more intense, the mood in Japan became increasingly rigid and constrained, and this eventually affected the instruction at my college. We had been assigned to labor-service groups and were often sent to help out at neighboring farms or to work at some factory or other, so regular classes were no longer held. Naturally, such frivolous personal adornments as permanent-wave hairstyles were forbidden, and we went to school wearing the typical women's attire in those times, baggy work-pants and shirt, with a heavily padded, cotton air-raid hood tied over the head.

Coffee shops and restaurants, where people went before the war to relax and momentarily get away from the stress of everyday life, were either forced to close due to lack of business or continued to remain open with almost no customers. The war made itself felt everywhere. For example, in order to keep his permit to do business, the owner of a restaurant on Kawaramachi Boulevard that had been called Delikessen before the war had to change the way of writing its name from simple katakana letters to kanji that had the same pronunciation but conjured up an appropriately heroic-sounding military image and literally meant 'leaving one's hometown to fight the decisive battle.' That's the sort of oppressive and all-pervading militarism the Japanese people had to live under during the war years.

Since I was an American citizen, detectives from the *Tokko*, the special secret service section of the police department, often came to question me at the Owakis' temple; and on occasion they even called me out of class at college and took me to the police station, ostensibly to question me, but actually to harass me. Each time, the demand was the same; they wanted me to give up my American citizenship and become a Japanese citizen.

One time, a *Tokko* detective came to the temple while I was at the college, went up to my room, and searched all the drawers of my desk and bureau. Mr. Owaki and his family were shocked at this breach of privacy. As he left, the detective warned Mr. Owaki, 'Get rid of all those English books.' When Mr. Owaki tried to reason with him, explaining that I was a college student majoring in English literature, he told Mr. Owaki that even the reading of textbooks that were written in English might lead to acts that served the interests of the enemy.

A few days later, when I spoke of this incident to a neighborhood boy who was attending Yoshidayama High School, he tried to make me feel better by telling me an absurd but true experience of his own. He had been lying on the grass in the park grounds of the Kyoto Imperial Palace, reading a book of philosophy that happened to have a red cover, when a *Tokko* officer came over to him, called him a Red, and confiscated the book.

Many dual-nationality nisei who had been compelled to remain in Japan decided to give up their American nationality and keep only their Japanese citizenship. All male nisei who did this and were old enough for military service were then drafted into the Japanese armed forces.

Despite continual harassment of various sorts and repeated demands by the Japanese authorities, who were maddeningly persistent, I had no intention of relinquishing my American citizenship. Whether I liked or disliked Japan had nothing to do with this decision. I had given the matter a lot of thought and looked at the problem from every conceivable angle, and no matter how I looked at it, my heart recognized only one true homeland—the United States of America.

My classmates at Doshin Women's College, the Owaki family, and the neighbors were all kind, big-hearted, well-meaning people. It was heartbreaking to see them forced to make one sacrifice after another—in the midst of dire privation and without hope of reward—all for the sake of the war effort.

As the war entered its second year, Imperial Headquarters continued to announce victory after victory, even though Japan was no longer actually winning every battle as it had in the early stages of the war. Yet despite the optimistic wording of the official news reports about such incidents as Japan's loss of several aircraft carriers in the Pacific Ocean during the Battle of Midway in June of 1942 and the War Ministry's abrupt reversal of its position on the importance of holding Guadalcanal on December 31, something did not ring true. There were certain, if subtle, signs that led people to suspect that the war situation was not all that the announcements from Imperial Headquarters claimed it was.

About that time, I became close friends with one of my classmates, Takenaka Mari, the daughter of a physician. Circumstance had brought us together: Since her father's internal medicine clinic was on Teramachi Street just south of Shijo Street, we walked home the same way from college, and we were also in the same labor-service group. In his youth, Mari's father had studied abroad in Germany and had been at one time an assistant professor of internal medicine at Seito University, so he was particularly understanding and sympathetic of my situation. He often invited me to their home, and each time I was treated to a small serving of cake or candy, though sweets were scarce and very hard to come by in those days.

Mari's big brother, Yutaka, was a medical student at Seito University. I occasionally ran into him at their house and talked with him a bit. Mari was beautiful, and her brother was kind-hearted and handsome in a refined way. Since I was alone and feeling pretty vulnerable at being so far away from my family, even though I was living with relatives, it was only natural that I should fall for such a fine young man as Yutaka.

I felt as if the bud of some beautiful, crimson flower had sprung up in my heart, grown and swelled to maturity in the twinkling of an eye, and then all at once burst into glorious bloom.

Yet my contact with Yutaka always involved Mari, and our communication was limited to pleasantries and small talk. We had no opportunity to talk together intimately, let alone do anything romantic like holding hands, because the country was at war and people turned an accusing eye on young couples who so much as dared to walk together in the streets, making them feel guilty of selfishness and a lack of patriotism.

Yes, I must have been in love, for now during classes at college, I could think of nothing but Yutaka. Occasionally, I would suddenly feel that my classmates around me must surely be able to see in my face the great joy that had taken over my heart, and I would blush a deep red.

Even now I cherish the memory of a certain night. An evening concert of string quartets by some top-class musicians from the Kansai Symphony Orchestra was to be held at the Japanese-German Cultural Center, where Yutaka often went since he was very good at German. The program included selections from the works of Mozart and Beethoven. As I look back on those few hours now, I marvel that we were granted the opportunity to spend such a rich, fulfilling time together in the midst of that savage, bloody war.

It was Mari who had invited me to the concert, but when we took our seats, there in the seat next to me was her big brother, Yutaka.

I sat through the concert as if in a dream, enveloped by beautiful music and exquisitely aware of Yutaka's presence close beside me.

My soaring spirit was brought back to the cold reality of the war, however, each time my gaze fell on the black curtains that covered every single door and window in case of an air-raid alert, or the huge portrait of Hitler glaring down fiercely at the audience from its place on the wall.

After the concert, we walked out of the Japanese-German Cultural Center, located near the intersection of Higashiyama Boulevard and Konoe Street, and made our way home through the darkness of blacked-out Kyoto, savoring the lingering echoes of that wonderful music in our hearts.

'Tonight, Mozart's "The Hunt" and Beethoven's Third String Quartet were exceptionally good. The performances by Iwamoto and Date were wonderful,' Yutaka said fervently, his voice full of admiration.

The concert that night helped us forget, for a few hours, the horror and sorrow of the war that had engulfed our lives, but the harsh realities of life in wartime Japan were upon us again the very next day.

Particularly hard for me to bear was the constant pressure to accept Japanese citizenship; the *Tokko* detectives came to talk to me once every two weeks, just like clockwork. It wouldn't have been so bad if I had been the only person involved, but I knew that these visits disturbed the Owaki family and that they, in turn, were concerned about them disturbing the neighbors. I felt very unhappy about that.

There was an American woman in her mid-seventies, a Miss Davis, who had been teaching English as a missionary at Doshin Women's College since before the war. Although she too had become one of the enemy with the outbreak of war with the United States, there was ample evidence of her long-held pro-Japanese views. Moreover, the authorities probably thought that one old foreign woman posed little threat on the home front. Consequently, she was allowed to continue living in her residence on campus behind Gloria Hall. One day, she offered a few kind words of support and advice to me regarding my situation and, in particular, the question of my American citizenship.

'If you wish to retain your American citizenship, there's no need to change it for Japanese citizenship against your will,' she said, encouraging me to stand my ground.

For me there was only one homeland: America, where I was born and raised, the country of freedom and democracy, the country that extolled equality and human dignity. Although prejudice and discrimination did exist in America to some degree—Americans were, after all, only human, and humans are far from perfect—nevertheless, I believed those problems would be overcome someday. Most of all, I knew that America was my true homeland because my heart used to nearly burst with pride when gazing up at the Stars and Stripes in my elementary and high-school days, whereas the Flag of the Rising Sun stirred no emotion in me whatsoever. In short, it was not a question of doing what was most practical and making things easy for myself; it was a matter of the heart, and as such, completely beyond my control.

The more often officers from the *Tokko* and, later on, the Military Police came to pressure me to accept Japanese citizen-ship, the more adamantly I cried out in my heart, 'I am an American!' and continued to refuse.

As a last resort, they threatened to discontinue my ration tickets. At that time food was in extremely short supply, and cutting off my rations would have amounted to condemning me to starve to death. But for all their fearful blustering and intimida-tion, they never carried out their threat.

In March of 1944, I graduated from Doshin Women's Col-lege. Not only was my dear family unable to be with me to share that moment of pride and joy with me, but I had no way of even telling them the good news.

Unmarried, unemployed women under twenty-five years of age were mobilized into the labor service corps and stationed at munitions plants or some similar workplace. In order to avoid labor service, most of my fellow graduates sought and found employment on their own where they could choose the type of work they would do.

Boys old enough to be employed were drafted into military service. In the spring of 1944, it was not difficult for women to find jobs, since the draft deferments previously accorded to university students of the liberal arts universities had been rescinded in October 1943, and the majority of these students had been sent into combat in December that same year.

But things were different in my case. I had no connections in Japan, I was a citizen of an enemy nation, and even though I had graduated with a major in English literature, there were no jobs where I could put my expertise in English to practical use. I had almost no hope of finding employment.

My friend Mari's big brother, Yutaka, was on good terms with two men from the Japanese-German Cultural Center, Mr. Eckardt and Mr. Eversmeyer. He introduced Mari to them, and she went to work there as a secretary and was not called up for labor service.

Fortunately, Yutaka was thinking about potential places of employment not just for his sister, but for me as well. He introduced me to Yagi Kunihide, whom he had met at Seito University. After graduating from the Department of Law, he had been drafted into the Imperial Army; he had recently finished his officer's training and received a commission as second lieutenant, and was now assigned to Central Defense Headquarters located in Osaka Castle in downtown Osaka.

Working at Central Defense Headquarters

In mid-April, about one month after my graduation from college, Yutaka escorted me on the train down to Osaka Castle, despite his being terribly busy with his medical studies at the university. The short time we spent together on the train from the Keihan Line's Sanjo Station to the terminal Osaka station at Temmabashi was one of the happiest times of my life.

The strict military discipline and elaborate formalities for gaining entrance to the Central Defense Headquarters in Osaka Castle were formidable. Arriving at the broad gateway in the towering stone wall around the castle, where guards stood with their rifles at the ready, we announced the purpose of our visit and were allowed to enter. Inside the gate, we found a group of some ten or fifteen soldiers; we were again asked to state our business and to sign in at the guardhouse. Then we waited for Second Lieutenant Yagi.

When he appeared, the order 'Ten-hut!' rang out sharply, and all the soldiers stood at attention. I found it all rather intimidating.

Second Lieutenant Yagi led us into the interior of the castle, to a room that resembled a small movie theater. The room was rather dark, and one wall was covered with an enormous map of the area designated by the Japanese government as the Greater East Asia Co-Prosperity Sphere, with the Japanese Islands in the center, flanked by the continent of Asia to the west and the Pacific Ocean to the east. Red and green lights were blinking on the map here and there.

In front of the huge map, just where the audience would be seated if the room had been a movie theater, sat some of the top military commanders of Japan, intermittently scanning the vast map of Japan's domain, dispatching orders.

I was really quite surprised to find such an elaborate military planning facility in Japan, but more than that, I was amazed that Second Lieutenant Yagi had the authority to bring a civilian like me there. Since he evidently did, I gathered that despite his low rank as an officer, he was nevertheless a person of some importance at Central Defense Headquarters.

He was, after all, a graduate of the prestigious Seito University, so perhaps the career military officers thought highly of him for that reason.

I was told to report for work the next day and given an employee identification card. Since they had the card already made up for me, Second Lieutenant Yagi must have decided to hire me when Yutaka had first contacted him about giving me a job.

So, despite my being a holder of an American passport and a citizen of an enemy nation, I ended up working in what was at that time one of Japan's most important centers of military intelligence.

Yutaka and I went back to Kyoto on the train together, and at his invitation, I joined him for a cup of coffee—what passed for coffee in those days—in a coffee shop called Window of Night near the intersection of Kawaramachi Boulevard and Rokkaku Street. I remember exactly what music was playing on the record player: Beethoven's Fifth Symphony conducted by Furtwängler followed by a Mendelssohn violin concerto played by Yehudi Menuhin.

As we said good-bye a short time later outside the coffee shop, Yutaka said, 'Since you're starting work tomorrow, I guess you'll be pretty busy from now on, won't you? Take good care of yourself and be careful. The American air raids will probably come fast and hard from now on, so watch out for yourself on the trains down to Osaka and back.'

I thanked him for his help in getting the job and for coming down to Osaka with me, and he replied, 'It was my pleasure. I really enjoyed our time together today.'

On hearing those few words, my heart sang with joy, and I felt as if all my past and present troubles and all my anxiety about the future had been swept away.

But as my fellow spirits have already said, we never know what's going to happen from one minute to the next, do we? Happy as I was that day, that was the last time I ever laid eyes on Yutaka.

Starting the next day, I commuted daily to Central Defense Headquarters in Osaka Castle. Yutaka was always terribly busy, overburdened as he was with extra courses at the university; because of the war, his class's graduation had been accelerated, and he was now in his final year of study. In addition to attending classes, he also had to work a certain number of hours each week at a factory he had been assigned to, for by that stage of the war, even medical students were being called up for labor service. Neither of us really had any free time to get together.

My work at Central Defense Headquarters was to translate into Japanese all sorts of English documents that had been captured from American troops and passed along to our headquarters from Imperial Headquarters. I also monitored radio messages transmitted by American troops at the front, who were working their way ever closer to Japan's Home Islands.

In a way it was a terrifying job, for I was privy to up-to-the-minute reports on the progress of the war, information to which other Japanese civilians had no access.

The government kept telling the people, 'We won this battle, and that one, and that one . . .' But I knew the truth. In the naval battle for Midway Island, Japan's main task force had been completely wiped out, and this major defeat had been followed by a string of losses—the defeat at Guadalcanal, the annihilation of the garrisons on the islands of Makin and Tarawa, and the surrender of Saipan. It was a hopeless situation, and these defeats cast a steadily growing, dark shadow over Japan's future and prospects for victory.

In spare moments during the day, I could listen to the propaganda radio broadcasts from Tokyo, which included news and music programs, directed at American troops in the Pacific islands. The radio announcers' command of American English was so far beyond what most native Japanese would be capable of, I figured they were probably nisei. The organization and content of the programs, too, were stylish and professional, so they must have been using captured American soldiers with radio broadcasting experience. Several female announcers took turns being in charge of the broadcast, but the programs were always designed to make the American soldiers listening at the battlefront feel homesick.

As a nisei who had grown up in America, I wondered if instead of making them sick of war, that sort of programming wouldn't make them want to win the war just that much more quickly so they could hurry back home.

Life during wartime became increasingly tough. First high school and then even middle school students were mobilized to work in munitions plants. In the summer of 1944, the evacuation of school children began; they were sent away from their homes in the cities to live with families in the neighboring countryside, where their parents hoped they would be safe from the terrible bombing raids.

Everyone expected that sooner or later the decisive battle of the war would be fought on the Home Islands, so even the women were drilling and preparing to fight the invading enemy with bamboo spears.

In spite of the apparent hopelessness of the war situation, the average Japanese genuinely believed in the eventual victory of Japan, known throughout Japanese history as the 'Land of the Gods.' Knowing as I did the true extent of how badly Japan was faring in the war, it filled my heart with pity and sorrow to see civilians who, on the basis of the dire conditions on the home front—bombed-out cities, people slowly starving, the depletion of all commodities and resources—surely must have had some doubts about the outcome of the war. Nevertheless, they betrayed not a sign of their doubt and instead readied themselves to fight to the death—every last man, woman, and child—rather than surrender their beloved homeland to the enemy.

Although to the Japanese I was technically one of the enemy, when it came right down to it, the same Japanese blood that flowed through their veins flowed through mine, and I was stuck in the same war-blighted environment as they were. Consequently, my feelings about the war and its eventual outcome were all mixed up.

On the morning of July 14, 1944, I put on my baggy work-pants and blouse, which Mr. Owaki's aunt had been kind enough to sew for me, since of course I had no mother in Japan to do such things, in readiness to set out for Osaka. I was just going out the door when my friend Mari telephoned. She told me that Yutaka's graduation had been moved up even earlier; he was to enter the naval medical training school in Kanagawa Prefecture as an officer-in-training to become a naval surgeon, and would be leaving for Tokyo that very night.

'So,' I thought to myself, 'now even medical students, who were the last group of university students allowed to retain their draft deferments in order to finish their education, are being forced to graduate without being able to complete their studies.' I took this turn of events as an unmistakable sign of Japan's descent into the final, desperate stage of the war.

Yutaka's train was scheduled to depart from Kyoto Station at nine o'clock that night, and I thought I would have plenty of time to make it back from Osaka after work and see him off, so I went to work at Central Defense Headquarters in Osaka Castle as usual. But as I rode on the train, and all through the day as I translated enemy documents, hot tears filled my eyes every time I thought of my dear Yutaka going off to war.

For the first time, I realized with a pang of anticipated loss that he was the person in Japan I most trusted most and the person I held dearest.

At five o'clock, the usual quitting time at Central Defense Headquarters, I hurried out of Osaka Castle and, breaking into a trot, made for the Keihan Train Line's Temmabashi Station. I felt sure I would have no trouble reaching Kyoto Station in time to see Yutaka off at nine o'clock.

But wouldn't you know it? Two military policemen came up from behind and called to me to halt. At first, I thought they were just going to hassle me again about my American citizenship, but it turned out that today of all days they wanted me to go with them to Military Police Headquarters for questioning.

I explained to them that I was on my way to see someone off at Kyoto Station and was pressed for time, but they proceeded to escort me forcibly to Military Police Headquarters. There was just no reasoning with them; they didn't care if I had something very important to do or not. During the interrogation, they took no notice of my employee identification card. They asked me what sort of work I was doing; what I, a citizen of an enemy country, was doing going in and out of a center of military intelligence; and how I had come to have such a job. In addition, they made me give the names of everyone I had contact with. Over and over again, they asked the same tiresome questions, the answers to which they no doubt already knew from checking with Central Defense Headquarters.

Finally, they ordered me forcefully not to breathe a word to anybody about the top-secret matters I was privy to and warned that if I did, I would be punished more severely than a Japanese citizen would be—as an enemy spy!

Then they came back to that same old question: 'Why don't you change your nationality and become a Japanese citizen, and thus demonstrate your loyalty to Japan?'

It was after seven o'clock when they finally released me and I walked out of Military Police Headquarters. I prayed that somehow I would be in time for Yutaka's departure, but when I arrived at the entrance to Kyoto Station, it was already nine o'clock. I ran like mad into the station, but when I reached the platform, the Tokyo-bound train was disappearing into the engulfing darkness.

'Too late!' I cried in bitter frustration, 'Goodbye, Yutaka, good luck!'

I stood there alone for a while. Then a group of people who had come to see their friends and loved ones off came walking back from the far end of the platform, and Mari was among them. She rushed over and hugged me tightly.

'My brother seemed to be waiting for you to come, right up to the last second,' she said, knowing that Yutaka and I had grown fond of each other.

Heartbroken, I went to work at Osaka Castle as usual the next morning.

The Last Days of the War

At last, we intercepted an enemy news report that American troops had landed on Guam. Then we learned in early October that an American task force had attacked Okinawa, and American troops had landed on Leyte Island and won a crucial naval battle in Leyte Gulf.

The war situation was getting worse and worse; as if to prove it, American B-29 bombers made an air strike against Tokyo on October 24, the first of many more to come.

The following March 9, in 1945, B-29s descended on Tokyo in a massive attack. The first major air raid on Osaka occurred during the night of March 13 and continued into the early hours; since the Spirit of Shiono Yoshiko has already described that terrible holocaust in detail, I will skip over it. I will, however, tell about the horrors I witnessed during the later air raids on Osaka. I have much to tell you, Yoshio, that may seem tedious and repetitious, but it's necessary so that you will be able hand down the terrible truth about the tragic reality of war to future generations.

The first air raid on Osaka occurred at night. I was in Kyoto then, but of course the air-raid sirens blared all through the night. The next morning as I left for work, I looked in the direction of Osaka, and the western sky was black with smoke.

On the train, I was tense with terror at what sights I imagined awaited me in Osaka and, at the same time, possessed by a morbid curiosity to see the gruesome aftermath of the bombing. When I got off the Keihan train at Temmabashi Station, I was shocked to find the entire area reduced to a vast expanse of burned, blackened ruins, among which fires were still blazing fiercely here and there. I could see as far as the Namba district—all of the buildings and houses that had stood there the day before were just gone, obliterated! Luckily, Osaka Castle was untouched, but the soldiers on duty were totally exhausted and near collapse.

After that first major air strike on Osaka, Japan's military strength went into an abrupt decline, just like a stone rolling downhill. Despite a continuing onslaught of enemy air raids, there were no Japanese fighter planes to give chase, and we no longer heard the sound of anti-aircraft artillery. Japan's retaliatory resources were depleted and nearing exhaustion; we were defenseless and at the mercy of the enemy.

The air strikes on Japanese cities grew more intense and more frequent; huge B-29s heavy with bombs and incendiaries loosed a torrent of fire and destruction on the helpless civilian population.

The Keihan Line trains often ran behind schedule, due to power outages or delays during air-raid alerts. Consequently, my commute to and from Osaka was not as punctual as it had been before. From time to time, the train stopped between stations because of an air raid, and the other passengers and I had to jump down onto the track and take cover in the nearest air-raid shelter.

The military arsenal boasted by Japan to be the largest in the Orient was located quite near Osaka Castle, and although it had survived previous air raids unscathed, its proximity made the area where I worked quite dangerous, for there was no telling when the Americans would bomb the area again in an attempt to destroy the arsenal.

Air-raid warnings came frequently and I often had to scurry into an air-raid shelter at the first blare of the sirens even while I was walking the relatively short distance between Osaka Castle and the Keihan Temmabashi Station.

In early April, American troops landed on Okinawa. From intercepted American military radio news broadcasts, I gathered that the superdreadnoughts *Yamato* and *Musashi*, two great symbols of Japan's war power, had been sunk. The situation was starting to look very black for Japan.

Anxious thoughts spun through my mind over and over again: If America won the war, I would be one of the victors since I was still a U.S. citizen; but how would it look to the Allies, my working for Central Defense Headquarters, a Japanese military intelligence center, during the war? These thoughts and a dreadful uncertainty about what would happen to me when the war ended preyed on my mind and depressed me no end.

One day when I was feeling particularly low and downhearted, the air-raid sirens went off while I was walking to Temmabashi Station after work, so I rushed into an air-raid shelter next to Naniwa Dental College not far from the station. Many dental students and patients and personnel from the hospital across the street had already taken shelter there. The shelter was packed, and from inside came angry shouts,

'Don't come in! There's no more room!'

But I ignored them and forced my way in, squeezing myself between the closely packed bodies—or rather, I was pushed in by the people behind me, who were also desperate to get inside.

Once safely inside, I caught a glimpse of a military uniform directly behind me, and when I turned around to look at the man, I saw he was one of the military policemen that had taken me to Military Police Headquarters for questioning the day Yutaka had left for Tokyo. I noticed he was wearing the insignia of a sergeant major on his collar. Evidently, he, too, had been caught by the air-raid siren on his way somewhere and had chanced to take refuge in the same shelter as I.

The rumbling thunder of bombs exploding in the distance and the deafening boom of nearby blasts filled my ears, and earthshaking tremors jolted the shelter. Whenever a bomb exploded close to the shelter, the single light hanging from the ceiling swung wildly, so that the narrow cone of light from its specially shaped bulb reeled back and forth, casting weird shadows over the cowering figures of the people below.

The people around me put their hands over their ears or their heads and tried to lie facedown on the ground, but that was impossible. There were just too many people crammed into the shelter, so we all sat huddled together waiting for the ordeal to end. Some of those near the entrance remained standing and peered out at the sky overhead to see what was happening.

Since Central Defense Headquarters had not spotted a large formation of planes flying north that day, I knew it couldn't be a full-scale air raid. It was probably just a sporadic attack by a handful of carrier-based planes from an enemy task force far out at sea. Still, it wouldn't do to leave the shelter until the all-clear was sounded. By and by, the sound of the enemy planes seemed to be receding into the distance; everybody in the shelter began to breathe easier, but nobody made a move to leave.

It was then that I first noticed that the MP sergeant major right next to me had snuggled up against me protectively to shield me from any falling debris. Thinking that it must have been his intention to reduce the danger to me as much as possible in the event of a direct hit, I smiled shyly at him to thank him for his kind gesture. He smiled back and, without a word, drew me close to him. I was shocked and started to cry out in protest, but the words caught in my throat, partly because of shame.

I had never been in such close physical contact with a man before. Especially in Japan, physical demonstrations of affection between men and women in public were not condoned in those days; and except in special cases, young women never held hands with or kissed a man and were, of course, virgins.

In that overcrowded air-raid shelter, however, when I had first felt my breasts pressing against his hard, muscular chest and now all the more so when he put his arms around me, a heat I had never before experienced coursed through my body and an indescribably pleasurable sensation filled me from head to toe.

My face flushed hotly, my hands became damp with sweat, and my breathing became quick and hard. It was simply beyond the power of my will to suppress my body's physical response to him.

Meanwhile, the all-clear sounded, and people began to leave the shelter. No one said a word, but surely they must all have been thinking, 'This is terrible, having to hole up in some air-raid shelter every time you turn around. What the hell is this country coming to?'

Yet they didn't dare breathe a word of such unpatriotic grumblings in public, so they kept their true feelings bottled up inside and said nothing at all.

My body still hot with arousal, I too got up and left the shelter. The air outside was cool and fresh; after a few deep breaths, what I had felt momentarily in the shelter suddenly seemed shameful and disgusting. I set off hurriedly toward the station without looking back to see what had become of the man who had elicited such disturbing feelings in me.

By this time, it was completely dark. Although the air-raid warning had been lifted, the preliminary-alert siren continued to blare. There was not a light on anywhere; the area was sunk in total darkness. I eventually found my way into Keihan Temmabashi Station thanks to a dim, low-wattage light that faintly illuminated the entrance, and boarded a train for Kyoto.

For some reason, I felt relieved when the train started to move, and by the time it reached Kyoto, I had at last recovered my composure and felt released from the sordidness of the incident in the air-raid shelter.

Though I tried to behave normally, I was nervous and uncomfortable around the members of the Owaki household that night, for I felt that they must be able to see that something had happened.

The next day, I went to work as usual and, as was my habit, lost myself in my radio-monitoring and translation work. At quitting time, I left Osaka castle and started for home.

You won't believe it, but the air-raid warning sirens started blaring just as I was walking along the same street and at the same time as the night before.

As if drawn there by some force outside my control, I rushed headlong into the same air-raid shelter as the night before. And by some incredible coincidence, the same MP sergeant major was there once again, right beside me.

I said nothing as he pulled my tense, taut body to him without any hesitation, as if it were the most natural thing in the world.

I'm ashamed to admit it, but for some reason, some part of me that must have been the animal side of my nature had been hoping that he would do just that. And although he didn't actually do anything to me beyond just holding me in his arms, the mere sensation of my breasts pressing against the hard muscles of his chest sent a burning wave of desire surging through my body and made my mouth dry with excitement.

When the all-clear sounded, I left the shelter and headed toward Temmabashi Station, and this time the sergeant major escorted me. Without glancing at his face or offering a word of thanks to him for walking me to the station, I hurried aboard a Kyoto-bound train that, luckily, was waiting on the track ready to depart.

As the bombing raids intensified and became more frequent, my work at Central Defense Headquarters increased. The American troops, which by now had advanced as far as the Mariana Islands, had increased the number of B-29s sent to bomb Japan to two hundred, then three hundred, then even more, and were also sending in P-51 fighter planes. My main duties were now to intercept their radio communications and figure out the movements of the American troops.

Even now I clearly remember the names of certain squadrons that came up repeatedly in the course of my work: the 73rd Squadron stationed at Aslito Airfield on Saipan, the 312th at Tinian's northern airfield, and the 314th at Guam's northern airfield.

After the first major air raid on Osaka, although B-29s flew over Osaka in April and May dropping bombs and incendiaries and the preliminary-alert and air-raid-warning sirens were often heard, the hits were scattered and these were not full-scale attacks. Those months were a relatively calm period for Osaka, but not for other cities; nearby Ashiya and Nishinomiya were bombed heavily; and Tokyo, Yokohama, and Nagoya were virtually destroyed. In addition, U.S. fighter planes often dropped floating mines into the waters of the Inland Sea and Osaka Bay.

Berlin fell on May 2, and six days later Germany surrendered unconditionally. From then on, friendless and alone, Japan doggedly continued its hopeless war against the rest of the world on its own.

The civilian population knew that the day when the final, decisive battle would be fought on Japan's Home Islands was close at hand.

The second major air strike on Osaka occurred on June 1, from 9:30 a.m. till just before noon. Since this was a daytime attack, the bombs could be aimed with much greater accuracy than during the previous major air raid, which had been at night. A total of more than five hundred B-29 bombers and P-51 fighters, most flying out of Iwo Jima, descended on defenseless Osaka; as you can imagine, the destruction was overwhelming. The targets of this attack were areas that had escaped destruction in previous raids.

The third major Osaka air strike came on June 7. Again, the attack force of B-29s consisted of almost five hundred planes. Their target was the arsenal, located in the northwest corner of the Osaka Castle compound.

This all-important arsenal, however, was not seriously damaged this time, either. The enemy's imprecise bombing instead inflicted terrible suffering on the hapless residents of the neighboring areas. I heard that Johoku Park had been a veritable hell on earth. The bombs of the B-29s and the machine-gun fire of the cavorting P-51s hit hundreds of people who had taken refuge there. The next day, Central Defense Headquarters got word that in Johoku Park alone, 230 people had died outright and several times as many had been injured. Similar casualties and devastation were reported to have occurred along the banks of the Yodo River as far as Higashi-Yodogawa Ward beyond the Nagara Bridge.

In the fourth and fifth major Osaka air raids on June 15 and 26, respectively, most of the remaining factories were reduced to blackened ruins, including the Sumitomo Metals foundry. The arsenal alone sustained only slight damage.

Whenever an air raid occurred while I was at work, I of course went down into the underground bomb shelter at Central Defense Headquarters in Osaka Castle. But when the air-raid sirens started blaring while I was walking the short distance between Osaka Castle and Keihan Temmabashi Station, as often happened, I invariably ran to the shelter where I had happened to meet the MP sergeant major.

By all rights, I should have loathed this man, who was one of the MPs who had for so long regarded me as one of the enemy and treated me as such, had done their best to coerce me into changing my nationality to Japanese, and had kept close watch over my comings and goings at Central Defense Headquarters as if I were a spy. Nevertheless, in the midst of that terrible war, feeling myself at the mercy of forces beyond my control, and with the defeat of Japan seemingly just around the corner, I wanted, in some deep, dark corner of my heart, to feel his body touching mine there in the air-raid shelter. I wanted it, and yet my desire made me feel dirty and disgusted with myself.

Especially when I recalled the sight of the mutilated bodies of innocent, young schoolgirls killed in the bombings, their pitiful corpses scattered here and there among the ruins just after an attack, my guilt was almost more than I could bear.

Ah, why are human beings so susceptible to sin? One night when the preliminary-alert sirens were blaring, I left Osaka Castle and started on my way home. The MP sergeant major approached me in the street and motioned to me to come with him. Despite my shame and misgivings, I went with him. He led me into the deserted air-raid shelter, the site of our previous encounters. Of course, I should have refused to go with him, should have run away from him. But I was beyond the call of right or reason! Some diabolical force put me at his mercy.

In those terrible last days of the war, seeing people killed by bombs right and left, not knowing from one minute to the next if I would live to see the morrow, I fell into a black state of mind. My bleak outlook was further compounded by my personal dilemma of being torn between the two warring sides. On the one hand, I was an American citizen, and if the United States won the war, I would be one of the victors; but at the same time, while still hoping for the victory of my true homeland, America, there I was living in Japan among people of the same blood and ancestry, all of us suffering the privations and horrors of war together. It was a time of despair, and caught between these intense, conflicting emotions, I became nihilistic and reckless. Feeling myself powerless in the face of the madness and destruction around me, I threw caution to the wind and went with the MP sergeant major. I really didn't care any longer what happened to me.

As I lay under him on the cold, dirt floor of the dark air-raid shelter, a scene from my childhood suddenly flashed before my mind's eye. It seemed like something that had happened ages ago, in another lifetime. When I was a young girl, my parents took me to the Olympic Games the year they were held in Los Angeles. They waved little Japanese flags and cheered for the athletes from Japan, but I, though no more than a child, felt confused and wondered which side to cheer for—the Americans or the Japanese?

When we finished having sex, he told me his name was Matsui Izumi. I know it must sound incredible, but until that moment I hadn't even known his name. And even then, I hadn't asked him to tell me; I really didn't care. Afterward, I left the shelter and walked to the train station in a daze.

I felt no personal attraction to or interest in this man whatsoever, let alone any sort of emotion like romantic love. I didn't even feel favorably disposed toward him. Quite the contrary, solely on the basis of his being an MP, I considered him a contemptible cur, a militaristic fanatic with a dangerously narrow, lop-sided view of things.

Having had that sort of loveless, sexual relation, I felt more and more keenly the existence of lust and carnal appetite within me, and I was tormented by intense self-loathing. I tried to ease the burden of my conscience a little by telling myself that he had raped me, but in the innermost depths of my soul, I knew that my utter absence of resistance to his advances amounted to consent.

On my way home that night, I sat motionless in the Keihan train, my unfocused eyes trained vacantly on the darkness beyond the windowpane. The image of my dear Yutaka flashed before my mind's eye again and again, though I tried not to think of him. I came to the grievous conclusion that, having sullied myself that night by sleeping with a man whose name I didn't even know, I no longer had the right to love him. Wretched with remorse, I resolved never to see Yutaka again.

From mid-June on, the food situation of the civilian population became increasingly dire. The transport system was in a state of paralysis due to daily bombing raids; there was a drastic shortage of manpower, since all able-bodied males had been drafted into the armed forces; and most of what little food and supplies still remained were set aside for military use. People made dumplings by mixing their meager ration of wheat flour with such things as sawdust, tea dregs, acorns, and persimmon rinds. Even the leaves and tough stems of potato and sweet potato vines were consumed. The government distributed directions on how to cook silkworm pupae, grasshoppers, rats, and snakes; and these were eaten as a source of protein.

Having conserved the supply of powdered eggs and honey that my father had sent with me when I came to Japan, I was able to supplement my diet a little with what remained of these provisions. In addition, since I was a civilian employee at Central Defense Headquarters at Osaka Castle, I received extra rations of hardtack, just like the military personnel stationed there. Although I was still always hungry, I did get a few necessary nutrients and was still in good physical condition compared with the majority of people, whose malnourished faces were pale and drawn and had puffy, dark rings around the eyes.

But the human spirit is easily laid low, isn't it? I became terribly despondent after my sexual encounter with Sergeant Major Matsui. As my depression deepened, I even lost my appetite. Obviously, I was psychologically devastated by the experience.

Reports of the annihilation of the Japanese troops on Okinawa Island and the extent of the catastrophic civilian casualties were received at Central Defense Headquarters hourly.

In the fifth major air strike on Osaka on June 26, mainly key industrial targets were bombed, and the Konohana district was the focus of the attack. Once again the military arsenal next to Osaka Castle escaped damage. In similar air strikes around that time, however, many military targets in Nagoya and elsewhere were blasted off the face of the earth.

On July 10 there was a major air raid on nearby Sakai City, just south of Osaka; and in the seventh major Osaka air raid, on July

24, the attack formation was reported to have consisted of no less than two thousand enemy aircraft.

Around that time, small fighter planes such as the Vought Corsair and Grumman Hellcat from U.S. task forces cruising in the waters off Tosa and Kishu could be seen almost daily, cavorting in the sky over Osaka as if they owned it, coming and going as they pleased.

Finally, with the dropping of the atomic bomb on Hiroshima on August 6, Russia's entry into the war on the side of the Allies on August 8, and the dropping of a second atomic bomb on Nagasaki on August 9, the fall of Imperial Japan was imminent.

During this period, Central Defense Headquarters was collecting information from all parts of Japan on the damage status of small-to-medium-sized cities and towns and had a pretty accurate grasp of the situation. And from intercepted wireless communications between enemy fighters and enemy ships cruising in coastal waters, we gathered that landing operations would begin before long.

After the destruction of Hiroshima, the public was informed only that the city had been leveled by a new type of bomb, but officials at Central Defense Headquarters had a strong suspicion that the bomb had utilized atomic energy. They were not surprised, however, for they had known that the atomic bomb was in development and had expected it to be used sooner or later. The civilian population, on the other hand, who were by then more or less inured to the almost daily bombing raids and usually ignored the single B-29s that occasionally flew over their cities, went into a sort of panic at the idea of a single plane dropping a new type of bomb on them.

Ultimately, there was nothing anyone could do about it. This and other events soon to follow triggered the beginnings of unrest and confusion at military headquarters across the country, and in some parts of the military the situation got out of hand.

From the various bits of radio-intercepted information I had access to, I gathered that it was evidently the dropping of the atomic bomb on Hiroshima on August 6 and Russia's entry into the war on August 8 that made the Japanese Supreme War Council decide to accede to the demands of the Potsdam Declaration.

On August 10, a memorandum was secretly sent to all Osaka police chiefs, informing them that surrender was a possibility and advising them to prepare to cope with the public turmoil that might follow such an announcement.

On August 12, I intercepted an American radio news broadcast from U.S. Secretary of State Byrnes to the rest of the world, announcing that Japan was willing to accept the Potsdam Declaration if certain conditions were met.

Along with the relief I, as an American citizen, felt at this news, I also had cause for serious thought precisely because of my status as an American citizen, since I had, in a sense, collaborated with the enemy by working at a Japanese military intelligence center. I knew full well that Yutaka had introduced me to Second Lieutenant Yagi with nothing but my best interests at heart, but the fact remained that my working at Central Defense Headquarters was open to a damning interpretation from the U.S. Army's point of view.

On August 14, the Supreme War Council, in the presence of the Emperor, formally resolved to accept the Potsdam Declaration. Ironically, that same afternoon the seemingly indestructible Osaka military arsenal was destroyed in the final major air raid of the war.

This arsenal, widely acclaimed as the largest in the Orient, had come through all the previous bombing raids with little or no damage, only to be blasted to smithereens on the last day of the war. Although the fate of the arsenal was not a significant factor in the outcome of the war, how regrettable it is that the countless employees working there—particularly the young students mobilized for factory work—had to lose their lives when the dawning of a new age of peace and democracy was just one day away! For me, this tragedy epitomized the cruelty and senselessness of war.

On my way home that day, I saw that the Joto Train Line's Kyobashi Station had also been hit in that final air raid. The mangled bodies of scores of schoolgirls lay half-buried amid the debris of blasted train cars and tracks. The summer sun was still dazzlingly bright in the evening sky and illuminated all too clearly a sight I will never forget: Previously hidden from view behind its imposing stone walls, now leveled, the famous arsenal was nothing more than a pile of smoldering debris and worthless rubble.

Japan's Defeat and Occupation by the Allies

The next day, August 15, was that momentous day when the Emperor's voice was broadcast on the radio and heard by millions of Japanese people for the first time. The Pacific War, which had lasted three years and eight months, had ended in defeat.

The Japanese had fought with an unshakable faith in the indestructibility of their sacred homeland; and toward the end, they had steeled themselves to the inevitability of enemy troops landing on Japan's shores and, taking up bamboo spears, had been ready to fight to the last man, woman, and child. But they were totally unprepared for the Emperor's announcement that Japan had lost the war and surrendered, and the shock left many stunned and bewildered.

Some military die-hards clamored for people to put up do-or-die resistance to the surrender. From time to time flyers were dropped from some of Japan's few remaining fighter planes, urging all Japanese to rise up as one and continue the fight. We hadn't seen a Japanese plane in so long, we wondered where they could have come from. I'm sure all of us here remember the events of those days quite well.

When the initial shock had passed, the next problem the Japanese faced was devising a policy for coping with the Occupation Army troops that were to be stationed in Japan. In particular, serious discussion was held as to how to keep Japanese women from being raped.

Even though the war was now over, I had not been relieved of my duties at work. Despite my mixed feelings, I continued to report for work each day at Central Defense Headquarters to clear up unfinished business, the main part of which was burning documents. One after another, papers and reports stamped 'Top Secret' went up in flames. I noticed a striking contrast between the expressions of relief on the faces of the civilian population—who were undoubtedly glad that the war was over, even in the midst of their misery—and the pale, tense faces of the high-ranking military officers.

About one week after the end of the war, Second Lieutenant Yagi informed me that as of the next day, I need no longer report for work since I was a U.S. citizen. He also advised me that in the future, for my own sake, I'd better not say anything about having worked at Central Defense Headquarters if I could help it, and asked me not to divulge to outsiders anything I had heard or seen there. His manner that day betrayed a curious mix of genuine affection for me as a person with whom he had worked side by side for a long time and deference to me as an American, one of his country's conquerors.

Like the all the Japanese civilian employees there, I received my pay, a blanket, and a ration of hardtack. Then I returned to Kyoto.

The mental and physical exhaustion of wartime seemed to catch up with me all at once. I was terribly anxious about the future. Daily attacks of severe nausea and vomiting left me so weak I could hardly stand up, and I spent the better part of each day at home in the Owakis' house.

The American Army's Occupation of Japan began in late September. Its Kyoto headquarters were set up in the Daiken Building on the corner of Shijo Street and Karasuma Boulevard. The art museum and industrial exhibition hall in Okazaki Park, the Miyako Hotel, the Kyoto Hotel, the luxurious Western-style residence of the owner of Daimaru Department Store, and all the better houses of Kyoto were requisitioned as residences for Occupation Army officers. Rows of houses and even a school, rumor had it, had been built on the grounds of the Kyoto Botanical Gardens for married U.S. servicemen and their families.

One day in early October, a jeep suddenly pulled up and stopped outside the gate of the Owakis' temple, and two Occupation Army servicemen with Japanese faces—apparently nisei— got out and came toward the house. The entire Owaki family was stunned at their arrival, and no one made a move to go outside. Far from it, they ran back into the main hall of the temple and locked the door behind them.

'You, of all people, shouldn't go out there. It's dangerous for a young girl like you,' Mr. Owaki said, trying to get me to join them, but I cautiously went out to meet the two servicemen. I felt sure that everything would be all right once they learned I was a U.S. citizen.

The two Occupation Army servicemen came through the front gate, and on seeing my face, one of them cried, 'Nancy!'

For an instant I didn't recognize him. He looked very grown-up, with a determined look on his face and a military uniform. But then I realized that he was Robert Takagi, an old high-school classmate of mine from Los Angeles. You can't imagine what joy and happy memories filled my heart on seeing a familiar face from my former life in America!

'I've got a letter for you from your father, and I've also brought some army rations for you to eat,' Bob said. 'Being here during the war must have been awfully hard on you, Nancy.'

Bob spoke in English, of course, and I did, too. It felt wonderful to use my native language once again. Despite my long stay in Japan, I still thought in English, and English was my natural mode of expression.

'I'm sorry to have to tell you this, Nancy, but your mother is dead. Ever since the Japanese attack on Pearl Harbor, Japanese people living in the United States have had to endure one hardship after another. All their assets were frozen, and they were forced to live in internment camps out in the desert, far from the Pacific Coast. These camps were awful places; for example, they hastily remodeled a horse stable in Arizona to house some internees. Your mother wasn't very healthy to start with, so it's no wonder she got sick living in those substandard conditions. In the end, her heart and kidneys just gave out and she died. Your father told me that right up until she breathed her last, she was worried about you being stuck in Japan during the war and regretted having sent you here.

'But that's enough sad talk for today. From now on, you have nothing to worry about. First, I'll get to work on finding a way to get you home to America real soon. And if you have any problems in the meantime, you just come to me and I'll take care of them. I'm assigned to the Intelligence Section at GHQ.'

Bob said all of that in practically one breath. When he told me what I was most concerned about, how my mother and father were, the shock of her death was so great it was all I could do to keep from crumpling to the ground.

By this time, the Owaki family had finally ventured out to see what was going on, and I introduced Bob and his friend, whose name was Paul Fukada, to them. The Owakis were shocked and saddened to learn of my mother's death. I must have been white with shock. Seeing my distress, Bob and Paul said that they had come that day primarily to ascertain my whereabouts, and then excused themselves and left.

Returning to my room, I opened the letter from my father and read.

'My Dear Nancy, I fear I have caused you to suffer many hardships by sending you to Japan. I am so sorry,' the letter began, and then went on to give the details of my mother's death. My father wrote that he thought it would be difficult to make a comeback in California, where he had lost everything because of the war, so he had gone to Chicago for the time being and was living in an apartment on Clark Street, planning to open a grocery store again sometime in the future.

The next day and the day after that, Bob came by after he finished work at GHQ in the Daiken Building. He brought me chocolate bars, chewing gum, and other goodies that I had not tasted in a long, long time, along with some daily necessities, soap and the like.

I think it was about his fifth or sixth visit when, all of a sudden, he turned to me with a grave expression on his face and said, 'You didn't give up your U.S. citizenship during the war, did you? You lived here in Japan as an American. That must have been very hard on you. I know I told you I'd do my best to get you back to America soon, but I've run into a bit of a snag. The Intelligence Section says there's a problem with your case, and your name is on a special list. If you had become a Japanese citizen during the war like most of the other nisei in Japan, the problem could be resolved one way or another in time, even if you'd collaborated in the war effort as a Japanese citizen, for example, by being in the Imperial Army. But working in a place like that—a regional military headquarters!—while you still were a U.S. citizen . . . well, it just looks bad. I don't think they'll go so far as to charge you with treason, but it looks as if it's not going to be easy to get you permission to return to the States.'

I was rather taken aback to learn that the Occupation Army already knew that I had been employed at Central Defense Headquarters, but I proceeded to explain to Bob what had happened. I told him I had taken the job out of absolute necessity because it was the only one I could get during the war, that I hadn't been involved in any overtly anti-American activities, and that my main duties had been translating English documents and intercepted radio messages into Japanese and typing.

I also told him how I had clung to my U.S. citizenship in spite of the intense pressure and threats brought to bear against me by the *Tokko* and the Military Police simply because I refused to abandon my pride in being an American, and described how

difficult it had been for me to do that while living in Japanese
society during the war. Even as I spoke, I knew that no one who
had not been there in Japan during those terrible years could
understand the full extent of the hardships and harassment I had
faced.

'I know,' Bob replied, 'I know you've been through a terrible
ordeal. And I admire you for having held on to your U.S.
citizenship. I'm sure it took courage and determination to do so.
But now that the war's over, your actions are being scrutinized in
a different light, and I'm just telling you that as far as the
Occupation Army is concerned, what you did looks sort of . . .
well, questionable.

'According to the Constitution, there are four ways in which
a person might forfeit his right to U.S. citizenship: enlisting in a
foreign country's armed forces, voting in a foreign country's
election, working in a foreign country in a job that only citizens of
that country are permitted to do, and becoming a naturalized
citizen of a foreign country. The commission of any one of these
is sufficient to strip a U.S. citizen of his right to citizenship, and
apparently you are suspected of having committed the first and the
third.

'When General MacArthur came to Atsugi, a group of news
reporters came with him, and the first thing they set about doing
was tracking down a character called "Tokyo Rose." The State
Department is taking a hard line on this; they intend to focus all the
attention on some one specific individual and hold her accountable. They don't care if they catch someone who merely read
propagandistic scripts written by some other person or persons
unknown; they don't care if the role of Tokyo Rose was played,
in fact, by several announcers; and they don't care that her
programs may even have been broadcast from somewhere in the
Philippines. They're out to pin the rap on one person. Tokyo Rose
had a big effect on American troops at the front lines, and now
somebody's got to pay.

'That's why this woman named Iva Toguri is currently being held in custody pending investigation. They're probably going to make her the scapegoat. Like you, she came to Japan before the war broke out and resolutely refused to give up her American citizenship. And because of that, now she's going to be brought to trial on suspicion of treason.

'Nancy, I'm worried about you because your case has some points in common with hers. I don't think we need to be concerned about the fact that you translated English documents into Japanese, but whereas Iva Toguri was employed by Radio Tokyo, you worked at a regional military headquarters, so Occupation authorities see you as having stronger ties to the military.'

I knew quite well that Bob was not passing judgment on me. I could see that he was telling me all this because he was genuinely concerned for me. Nevertheless, for a few moments as he talked, everything went black before my eyes and my weary, troubled mind teetered on the brink of panic.

Like most other young women in Japan during the war, I had taken a job in order to escape being mobilized into the labor service and sent to work in a factory. Yet even though it was only by chance that I had ended up working at Central Defense Headquarters in Osaka Castle, and though I had meant no harm to the United States by working there, I was now faced with the incredible but all too real possibility of being tried as a traitor to my beloved homeland. Of course, I believed in the justice system of the U.S. government and didn't question its position on the matter, but it was a terrible shock to me that things had come to such a pass.

After the day of our talk, every time Bob came to see me, he brought a copy of the U.S. armed forces newspaper, the *Stars and Stripes*, which carried articles almost daily about the Tokyo Rose affair: 'Who is Tokyo Rose, the radio vamp whose alluring voice made soldiers homesick in the jungles and at sea?' 'Iva Toguri, a nisei born in California and a graduate of UCLA, has been arrested and will be brought to trial!'

I felt that since my name was on a special list somewhere, it was only a matter of time before the Occupation Army came after me, too.

Though my mother, whom I had wanted to see once more if possible, had died in the internment camp, I still longed to see my dear father, my sister Deborah Kyoko, and close friends in America—but now, would I ever be able to return?

Since the end of the war, I had been in poor health and tended to stay indoors. In order to cheer me up, Bob came by in his jeep every chance he got and took me out for drives around Kyoto.

Wire fences surrounded the art museum, the industrial exhibition hall, and the civic auditorium in Okazaki Park, and the Occupation Army had even built a small, white church within the enclosure. Seeing the American-style houses among the trees in the Botanical Gardens, I felt just as if we were driving through an American residential district.

Oddly enough, till then I had seen almost nothing of Kyoto. When I first came to live with the Owakis, I did little more than commute to and from the college; and later, what with my work in Osaka and the war going on, I hardly had time for sightseeing. In Bob's jeep, however, we were able to make a cursory tour of the city's principal sights in just half a day, and he drove me all over.

The city's two finest Western-style hotels, the Miyako and the Kyoto, had been requisitioned for exclusive use by the Occupation Army. Bob took me to eat in the restaurants of these hotels, which ordinary Japanese people could not even go near; I knew he was trying to give me a little pleasure in life before the Occupation Army got around to arresting me.

The kinder Bob was to me, the sadder and more despondent I felt. Sometimes over a cup of tea or during a meal with him, I would suddenly catch myself staring off into space, lost in a private hell of anguish about what I had done and what was to become of me.

Then came the final blow that sealed my fate. My menstrual periods had always been regular, both before and during the war, perhaps because of my relatively large build or because I had been fortunate enough to obtain somewhat more nutritious food than most Japanese people during the war. Recently they had suddenly stopped. At first, I didn't worry about it very much, partly because I knew that many other Japanese girls and women had had their periods stop or become irregular during the war years due to malnutrition and overwork. But when my breasts became swollen and my nipples darkened somewhat and, more than anything else, when I started getting morning sickness, it suddenly dawned on me that I must be pregnant.

'But surely that's impossible,' I tried to convince myself, 'I couldn't have gotten pregnant from just that one sexual encounter with the MP!'

At that time, I knew very little about sexual matters or childbirth, and my lack of knowledge made me all the more anxious about the possibility of my being pregnant. I had to find out for sure, so I summoned up all my courage and went to an obstetrics-gynecology clinic near the intersection of Shinmachi Street and Imadegawa Boulevard.

After examining me, the doctor told me I was four months pregnant. When I heard that, the world reeled before me and I felt I was falling headlong into a black pit from which there was no escape. I'm sure you can imagine my distress.

Although I knew, of course, who my baby's father was, the only information I had about him was his name, Sergeant Major Matsui Izumi. I didn't have a clue what had become of him since the war had ended, but because he had been in the Military Police, I thought it likely he had concealed his identity and gone into hiding somewhere. Besides, even if I had been able to find him, I could never have brought myself to go to him and tell him that our loveless sexual encounter amidst the confusion just before Japan's downfall had resulted in the start of a new life, the baby inside me.

In my heart dwelled two homelands. One had suffered a devastating defeat, and the other . . . ! My dear mother had already died during my absence, and now not only was it possible I might not be able to return to my one, true home, but in return for all my perseverance and efforts to hold fast to my American citizenship, I might even be arrested for treason any day now!

On top of that, I was faced with the shameful fact of being four months pregnant with the baby of a man I didn't even really know. No one would congratulate me on such a birth. Nor could I expect anyone to understand my situation.

It seemed the only course left to me was to take my own life.

I agonized over the decision, racked my brains for some way out of these difficulties, but in the end, there just wasn't any other way for me.

Who was there to see me safely through my time of need and show me the right course to take? Yutaka, who had gone off to be a surgeon in the Imperial Navy, was the person I looked up to most. I felt he was the only person in the world who could help me find a better solution; but I couldn't go to him with this problem because, for the life of me, I could never have told him I was pregnant. Besides, after receiving his commission shortly before the end of the war, Yutaka had gone to sea on some important mission on board one of the few remaining large, I-class submarines and had not been heard from since. As the days continued to pass with no word of him, I knew in my heart that he would never return, and this snuffed out my last spark of hope.

I think the crucial factor in my decision to end my life was that psychologically I was simply at the end of my rope. What had become of the cheerful, bright-spirited, full-of-life Nancy I had been in America only a few years before—it felt more like a lifetime before! My anguished soul reached out for guidance, some solution to this grievous mess I had gotten myself into, but whichever way I turned, there was only darkness. In short, I had lost the capacity to think clearly.

Toward the end of October, I swallowed a grain of potassium cyanide, which Central Defense Headquarters had distributed to its civilian employees, especially the women, just before the war ended in case American troops landed near Osaka.

I was tormented by guilt at taking the tiny life inside my body with me into death, thus denying my baby a chance to live. I wrote a letter to my father in America begging his forgiveness, a letter to the Owaki family thanking them for all their kindness and apologizing for the trouble I had caused them, and a brief note saying that I wanted to donate my body to be used for the training of medical students, to help them follow in the footsteps of my dear Yutaka, the only person I had loved and respected with all my heart.

After Hearing the Third Night's Tale

When the Spirit of Nancy Masako Ito had finished speaking, Yoshio sighed heavily. Not, of course, as one sighs after a boring speech has come to its long-awaited end; far from it, for Yoshio was genuinely and deeply moved by the spirit's tale of a life buffeted about by the winds of adverse fortune.

Yoshio had listened to her tale with anticipation bordering on fear as she related the whirlwind of events and totally unforeseen developments, wondering what might happen next, and an almost prayerlike longing for her to have a little peace and happiness to soothe the sting of the adversity that plagued her life.

The other spirits also sighed as one, under the weight of emotion evoked in them by her pitiful story. Yoshio was somewhat surprised that these spirits from another sphere of existence still retained the capacity to respond as a living human being would. Some of them were so deeply moved that they were shedding tears of sympathy.

When he could bring himself to speak, Yoshio turned to the spirits and said, "The story just told us by the Spirit of Nancy Ito has deeply touched me. It's incredible, isn't it, what cruel foolishness human beings are capable of! The problem of Japanese discrimination against Koreans came up in Kim's story last night, and now we've heard about what it was like when the tables were turned and Japanese immigrants and their children had to endure terrible racial discrimination and injustice at the hands of white Americans."

Then, addressing the Spirit of Nancy Ito, he continued, "Thank you for telling me things I never knew and reminding me of what I studied once in history class but had forgotten. I've really learned something important from your story tonight.

"The war having ended just less than a year ago, I remember very well just how cold-hearted and ruthless war is. I too was in Kyoto during the time of the air raids in nearby Osaka, so I know all too well what terrible tragedies were inflicted on the people there.

"The hardships and suffering engendered by this war are not over yet. Look at the food situation: There's been not a single sign of improvement since the war ended; if anything, the food supply is worse now than it was during the war.

"Christianity teaches us that it is a sin to take one's own life, to destroy this body, which was created by God, and the life within, which was given by Him. But there are instances where one is driven by circumstances to the utmost limits of endurance; and while it's quite a simple matter for others to sit back from the situation and say, 'Suicide is a sin against God,' or, 'Killing oneself is a breach of faith against Buddha,' I can understand how to that person in extremity with his back against the wall, death may appear to be the only choice.

"The Spirit of Nancy Ito said there was no one to show her what path to take and guide her safely and wisely through her terrible predicament. Unfortunately, that's correct; there was no one she could turn to. And as she also mentioned, people do lose their ability to think things through clearly when they are driven into a psychological corner. She was probably in a state of profound depression."

At this point, the Spirit of Professor Yuhara said, "Nancy Ito's life was indeed full of heartbreak and suffering. The death of her beloved mother, the prospect of being charged with treason because of the problem of her citizenship, her guilt at having had sex with a virtual stranger compounded by her shame at finding herself pregnant, and the near-certain death of the only man she truly loved—all these problems converged on Nancy at the same time. As a result, she was driven beyond the boundary of what human beings can bear.

"Of course, I do not intend to defend suicide, but no one can look at the tragic events of Nancy Ito's troubled life and honestly say, 'If I'd been in her shoes, I would've somehow been able to overcome those problems and continue living.'

"What we hope you will learn from her experiences is the lesson contained in what Jesus Christ said in Matthew 11:28-30: 'Come to me, all you who are weary and burdened, and I will give you rest. Take my yoke upon you and learn from me, for I am gentle and humble in heart, and you will find rest for your souls; for my yoke is easy and my burden is light.' The words of Christ are true, Yoshio—believe what He says. Nancy had no chance to come in contact with Christ's teachings during her life on earth. Neither did Shiono Yoshiko or Kim Han Sik.

"But now in the World of the Spirits, enveloped in the love of Jesus Christ, who is Himself God, all of us spirits who stand here before you have found true peace and true joy.

"Death, Yoshio, will set you free from all the pain and suffering of this ephemeral world.

"Death is not the end of everything. It is the beginning, for when people are lifted up into the World of the Spirits after death, they begin a new existence. Blessed are those who are granted the faith to believe this during their life on earth.

"In the world of the living, some people hear the Gospel about mankind's salvation through Jesus Christ and yet choose to close their ears to it, and some even actively oppose it. God the Creator gave mankind free will, including the capacity to choose between good and evil. Accordingly, it is important that a person accept the Gospel readily and without question, for as Jesus Christ said, 'He who has ears, let him hear.'

"Some people will naturally ask, 'But what of the people who never have the chance to hear the Gospel?'

"In order that all people should hear the Good News of mankind's salvation, God commanded the Apostles and all believers down through the generations to work towards that end by preaching the Gospel.

"Into the dangerous, benighted wilds of Africa and the innermost depths of Asia, into the midst of those stricken with leprosy and among the poor and the oppressed—these evangelists and missionaries renounced all worldly desire and ambition and went out into all corners of the world to spread the Gospel."

Then Yoshio asked, somewhat hesitantly, "What happens to the fetus in a case like this? I mean, since Nancy Ito died with the fetus in her womb, is the fetus, too, permitted to enter into eternal life and the love and peace of God?"

Yoshio was picturing in his mind the formative process of a fetus in the womb from fertilization to the fourth month of development, which just recently had been the subject of some embryology lectures he'd attended. Knowing that Nancy Ito's fetus would have taken human form by the fourth month, Yoshio wondered what would happen if that fetus died, particularly if it died as a result of its mother's suicide.

Yoshio also knew that there was a high incidence of miscarriage during the first trimester of pregnancy, and that many abortions were performed during the first trimester. What became of those fetuses when their brief lives were ended?

"I would imagine," Yoshio added, "such fetuses continue to develop in the World of the Spirits or in Heaven and become the people they would have grown up to be if they had been allowed to live out their lives on earth."

"Since there is nothing Almighty God cannot do," the Spirit of Professor Yuhara replied, "what you have just said is possible, but as a general rule the fetus enters the World of the Spirits in its mother's womb. As you no doubt have learned, since the fetus's brain is not fully developed, there is almost no mental activity in the first few months of development.

"In the case of Nancy Ito, for example, you probably imagine her bringing the fetus to full term and bearing her baby in the World of the Spirits and then holding the spirit of her baby to her breast, but all that is nothing more than your limited, worldly conception of what happens. Being human and unable to conceive of things in any terms other than those of your worldly existence, you hope it will be so and thus you imagine it will be so. First and foremost, you must realize that the eternal realms of the World of the Spirits and Heaven exist on a plane that transcends your worldly time—terms such as 'four months' or 'nine months' have no meaning there.

"Thanks to the compassion and mercy of God, the spirits of fetuses that die before they can be born are admitted into eternal peace and joy. So I say to you, the living, pray for the sake of these tiny souls. Of course, God already knows your prayers before you speak them, but the act of prayer is an important part of faith, and God hears and approves of the prayers offered up to Him.

"My, my, we've ended up in another catechism session, haven't we? You must go home now, Yoshio. You look very tired; I'm afraid these late meetings with us three nights in a row have exhausted you. The time spent with us is probably interfering with your studying, too. Let's call it a night."

"Thank you for listening so patiently to my rather long story," the Spirit of Nancy Ito said to Yoshio. "Go get some rest now, and be careful on your way home."

Yoshio quietly left the dissecting room.

The dark branches of the tall pines bordering the Kyoto Imperial Palace along Teramachi Street stood out blackly against the dark night sky, but through the tips of the branches Yoshio could see a multitude of stars scattered thickly across the entire firmament, twinkling, eternal, far removed from the trivial events—the joys and sorrows, even war and peace—of the earth below them.

CHAPTER FIVE

FOURTH NIGHT:

The Tale of a Child Prodigy Whose Great Promise Was Ruined by Carnal Desire and Alcoholism

My Childhood

My name when I was alive was Sumita Shogo, and I was born in the town of Fukuchiyama in Amada County, Kyoto Prefecture.

Compared with the stormy lives of the three spirits who preceded me, I've led a rather unremarkable life. In accordance with last night's request by the Spirit of Professor Yuhara, I shall tell the story of my life as concisely as possible.

I was born in 1907. Fukuchiyama, the town where I was raised, is a castle town that grew up around Fukuchiyama Castle, where in feudal times Akechi Mitsuhide once lived. It didn't have any industry to speak of, but, as you probably know, was an important center of agricultural industry for the many farming villages in the region engaged in silkworm-raising, equal in importance in Kyoto Prefecture to Maizuru and Ayabe. The 20th Army Regiment had been stationed there for several decades, and though, of course, it could not compare with the large marine corps at Maizuru, it gave the town a strong militaristic character. Fukuchiyama was also known for its traditional folk-dance song. When I was a young boy, the Yura River, which flows east of town, would overflow its banks whenever there was a heavy rain.

175

The house where I was born was a small house on a narrow, back street in the Nagamachi district in the center of Fukuchiyama.

My father died before I was old enough to attend elementary school, so I remember him only vaguely, at best. He was a carpenter, apparently a pretty skillful one. One image of him remains clearly before my mind's eye: him sitting on the porch in summer with the sliding doors open, wearing only long underpants and drinking sakè.

According to my mother, he was good at his trade and made enough money to support his family, but he was a drunk and spent a great deal of money on sakè, so our family always had to live frugally. After the death of my father, my mother had a hard time of it, since she had to support single-handedly a family of four: herself, me, and my two younger sisters. During the day, my mother worked at a store in Gofukumachi owned by a Mr. Tokuda, who was a wholesaler dealing in sugar and sweets. The store carried on an extensive trade supplying shops throughout Fukuchiyama and also some as far away as Ayabe. My mother received a small amount of money for cleaning, preparing meals for the other employees, and any other chores that needed doing; she was sort of a maid-of-all-work. In addition, she worked at home nights sewing kimonos, and thus managed to make ends meet.

When I reached school age, I started going to Fukuchiyama Elementary School, which was near the train station. Though I feel a bit awkward saying so myself, the fact is my academic performance was excellent, conspicuously superior to that of my classmates. I was particularly good at arithmetic—so brilliant, in fact, that my teacher was amazed at my ability. I was also better than the other children at sports and was first in my class in running, jumping, and throwing a ball.

Consequently, word of my extraordinary abilities spread through the neighborhood, and I was considered a child prodigy. Perhaps I was conscious of all this attention around me, for I came to be somewhat conceited; I remember thinking my classmates were pretty stupid and marveling to myself, 'Don't they know even as simple a thing as that?'

In those days, after graduating from elementary school, a boy would usually follow one of two courses. He would help out at home and learn his father's trade, then take over the family business sometime in the future; or he would be sent to live with and work for another family while learning a trade and later go into business for himself. In the middle-to-upper-class families, however, any child who exhibited some degree of ability for study was sent on to middle school, but such children made up less than one-third of the average graduating class.

In January of the year in which I was to graduate from elementary school, the principal and the teacher in charge of my class called my mother in for a meeting and advised her that she must contrive somehow or other to continue my formal education. My mother was more than willing for me to continue my schooling, but refused their arguments repeatedly on the ground that she simply didn't have the money to pay for it. They even went so far as to say that it was a terrible waste for such a gifted student as myself to remain buried in obscurity and that it was a loss to society, but that I was to be pitied most of all. It happened that the proprietor of the store where my mother worked, Tokuda Jyuzaemon, was known for being a big taxpayer in the town, so the principal himself went and entreated him to pay my school expenses for at least the five years it would take to graduate from middle school.

This Mr. Tokuda was the second-born son of an old family in the village of Tonoichi, and because all his family's resources had naturally been allotted to the first-born son, he had started out with next to nothing. He endured much hardship and eventually made a success of his business and become a wealthy man. But as far as he was concerned, making money was the only thing worth living for. For a self-educated, self-made man, he had precious little interest in any sort of charity or service to the community, such as paying for the education and betterment of a person of ability unrelated to him by blood or marriage. People said he was a miser. Some said it was hard to get him to listen to any proposal that didn't promise quick results and a tidy profit.

The principal was quite aware of all this and persuaded the town councilor to act as the go-between for his request to Mr. Tokuda. Perhaps because the humble and earnest request came from the principal himself, who was a prominent figure in the town, it was successful; and Mr. Tokuda agreed with unexpected readiness to pay my school expenses.

The principal also convinced Mr. Tokuda that I should not be under any obligation to repay the money in the future and should be free to choose my future path in life without any influence on his part.

Thus, the great expectations of my teachers for my academic future were realized. After finishing elementary school, I was able to enroll at the prestigious Amada MiddleSchool in Tanba.

I got high marks in middle school as well, and was always at the head of the class. Still, that didn't mean I spent all my time studying.

On the contrary, I spent my afternoons with my classmates happily playing baseball, a sport that had at last become widely known in Japan, even in the countryside.

We didn't have all sorts of fancy baseball equipment like catcher's mitts, fielder's gloves, bats, and such, but we managed to play conventional baseball on the school grounds. I was always pitcher; I couldn't throw a regular curve ball or one that dropped just before it reached the plate, but batters had a lot of trouble trying to hit my well-controlled fast ball. The balls I pitched were difficult for the average middle school student to hit; many a time I chuckled with delight as I struck out three batters in a row.

Perhaps because I was a natural athlete, I was also a powerful batter; I could hit a home run whenever the ball was pitched by one of my classmates, and so had a batting average better than most. Since my performance was outstanding in both studies and sports, the teachers at the middle school also acknowledged the singularity of my intellect and native ability, saying that such an exceptional student as myself came along only once in ten years, if then.

Well, when my five years of middle school were done, the elementary school principal and Mr. Tokuda came to my aid once again. With the recommendation of the principal of the middle school, they arranged for me to enroll in the Biological Sciences Department to do premedical study at Kanto High School and live as a *shosei*, working for room and board in the home of Fujiyama Katsumi, an alumnus of Amada Junior High School and practicing attorney in Tokyo.

Studying in Tokyo

In those days, you could find many *shosei* living in the homes of attorneys. During the day, they assisted their benefactor and learned the law by observing him at work, and at night, they attended evening classes at a private university, all the while dreaming of one day sitting for the bar examination and becoming an attorney. But in my case, since I was taking the regular course in the Biological Sciences Department of a government high school and attending classes during the day, I did hardly any of the work normally expected of *shosei*. In fact, I did little more than sleep in the 4.5-tatami-mat room allotted to me and attend classes at school. This arrangement, so convenient for me, was possible solely due to the benevolence of Mr. Fujiyama.

Mr. Fujiyama was an outstanding attorney of wide repute, and he had many clients, so that the additional financial burden on the household budget of supporting one or two dependent *shosei* was a mere drop in the bucket, as it were, and mattered not a bit to him.

Physically, he was a large man, with a refined, august appearance and a serene manner reminiscent of the great Chinese thinkers of ages past.

Despite Mr. Fujiyama's benevolence, I chafed under the psychological burden of my dependence on him. After returning from high school, I never failed to spend some time sweeping out the entryway and cleaning or straightening up his office, in an effort to lighten my feeling of obligation to him as much as I could.

Attending high school in those days usually meant living away from home in a school dormitory, and that was considered a privilege. The students often had parties there and could engage freely in roughhousing, which gave them a chance to revel in their youth and also strengthened the bonds of friendship. Most high-school students generally wore a shabby school uniform, a shapeless cap, and geta, with a short cape thrown around the shoulders in the winter; this attire was designed solely to cultivate in them a spirit of austerity and unaffected manliness, and they took pride in it. The school I was attending, Kanto High School, however, was located in the middle of the great city of Tokyo and had a unique character. Namely, a considerable number of the students commuted to school each day from their homes or student boarding houses, so few lived in the school dormitory; furthermore, the students' attentiveness to their personal appearance was impeccable—in their head-to-toe urban finery, they had quite a gentlemanly air about them, and of course, they wore shoes, not geta. In contrast to the average high-school student's indifference to personal appearance, the students at my school prided themselves on their sharp appearance.

Mr. Fujiyama was in his early fifties then and extraordinarily energetic. He would take on and finish one new case after another, so he must have had a large income. But true to the saying, 'Great men are susceptible to feminine charms,' he had a reputation for carrying on with women, and although I didn't notice anything unusual when I first began to live in his house, in time I realized that something rather shocking was going on.

With him lived his legal wife, Suzuyo, and her younger sister, Chiyo, and Mr. Fujiyama was having sexual relations with both of them. At first, I could hardly believe it—two sisters sleeping with the same man under the same roof—but there it was, right before my eyes. I was still a mere babe in the ways of the world, really quite naïve, and yet in time I naturally became aware of this unusual situation in the Fujiyama household.

What puzzled me most, however, was that there seemed to be no particular feelings of jealousy or hatred between the elder sister, Suzuyo, and the younger sister, Chiyo, at least not outwardly, though, of course, I couldn't speculate as to their private thoughts and feelings. They both appeared to live with the attorney in perfect harmony.

Neither Mr. Fujiyama nor either of the two women made any particular effort to conceal their unusual relationship. True, they probably couldn't have concealed it from us *shosei* and the kitchen help even if they'd wanted to, but they were always frank and open about it in front of the household servants. We were all instructed to address both the wife and her younger sister as Mrs. Fujiyama.

When Mr. Fujiyama made one of his frequent trips to Kyoto, his hometown, or a business trip to some other part of the country, the two women took turns accompanying him.

While he and the one woman were away, it may have been just our imagination, but we fancied we could detect a bit of irritableness in the one who had been left behind. But then, it would have been unnatural for her to feel no jealousy at all.

At the time, Suzuyo was forty-five years old and Chiyo was thirty-eight. Both were beautiful in different ways, but age will tell; the beauty of the elder sister was tinged ever so slightly with the shadow of age, while the younger sister's face and form gave the impression of still being in the prime of womanhood. Suzuyo was a graduate of Yamato Women's Higher Normal School, and Chiyo a graduate of Iidabashi Women's Higher Normal School;

each of them had done some teaching at one time. Both sisters were highly educated and cultured for women of that period. Their distinguished background and accomplishments made it all the more incomprehensible to me why such obviously intelligent women would continue living in such an unusual, presumably frustrating situation. I guess it was just one of those things, one of the mysteries of relations between the sexes. I couldn't help thinking it was unnatural that neither of the two women had borne any children, but purposely not bearing children might have been a cunning way to continue their three-way relationship with Mr. Fujiyama.

It was during the summer vacation of my third year of high school that the event that was to change my destiny took place. I had been a *shosei* in the Fujiyama household for about two and a half years at the time.

Even during the school breaks, I did not return home, but used that time to repay Mr. Fujiyama's kindness by diligently cleaning places that were too time-consuming to do during the school year, straightening up the office documents, and occasionally making copies of judicial precedents for him. Naturally, I also greeted clients, showed them into Mr. Fujiyama's office, and served them tea during their consultations.

It was quite a change of pace for me, and I enjoyed those summer days. A few days before the Bon Holidays, August 10, I think, Mr. Fujiyama went to Kyoto for about one week to examine a witness in an upcoming case. His wife, Suzuyo, went along as his secretary and personal factotum.

The Temptation of Sex

That night, I had finished my routine household duties for the day and had just settled down at the desk in my room to read a Reclam edition of a German novel, when suddenly Chiyo entered my room.

'Sumita, I've made you a cup of tea. And I brought along some bean-paste sweets we received from one of the clients.'

In Mr. Fujiyama's house there had always been a clear-cut line of demarcation between the family members and the hired help, and the house was run in such as way as to keep each person in his proper place. Till that moment I had been nothing but a poor student from the country working around the house for my keep, a lowly *shosei* not worthy to be treated as an equal by the family of the illustrious Tokyo lawyer. To say that Chiyo's unprecedented entrance into my room astonished me doesn't tell the half of it.

To be sure, Chiyo had never displayed any particular coldness or condescension toward me, but the same could be said of her elder sister, Suzuyo. Their attitude toward me, the other two *shosei*, and the household help had always been, for lack of a better term, businesslike, and they treated all of us the same.

'Why . . . uh . . . thank you . . . ,' I stammered.

I completely lost my composure and proceeded to make a fool of myself: In my nervousness, I knocked my fountain pen off the desk with my elbow, and when I bent down to pick it up, cracked my head hard on the corner of the desk. I was mortified. I felt my face flush beet-red, which vexed me all the more and, in turn, caused my cheeks to burn even redder. It must have been quite a sight.

'My, my, I seem to have startled you. What are you reading?'

Chiyo reached from behind me to pick up the book on top of the desk, and just as she did, her breast brushed against my face for a moment. Through the thin cotton of her loosely wrapped, after-bath kimono, I could smell her womanly scent, so intoxicating.

'It's . . . it's *The Sorrows of Young Werther*, by Goethe,' my tongue-tied mouth at last managed to answer. What with my astonishment at her presence in my room and the effect her scent was having on me, my heart was pounding like a hammer.

You won't believe what she did next.

Without any warning, she took my face in her hands and put her lips to mine.

Of course, I was a virgin with no sexual experience whatsoever.

Her fingertips moved delicately down my body. . . .

She reached over with one hand and switched off the lamp on the desk, and we tumbled down onto the tatami floor in each other's arms.

From first to last, she took charge of everything.

I never dreamed that losing my virginity would be so simply and quickly accomplished.

'What a sweet boy,' she murmured, not to me but to herself, as she opened her big eyes wide and gazed at me intently. Her slightly plump lips parted in a sweet, alluring smile, revealing beautiful, snow-white teeth. Then she mischievously put her right forefinger to her lips, gesturing silently, 'Shhhh . . . ,' and got up, slid the door open, and left more quietly than when she had entered.

Till that night, she had been nothing to me but one of the ladies of the house, someone on a different social plane from me; not for a moment had I ever thought of her as a woman, as an object of my desire. But now, by virtue of those few moments of passion, she had become my darling, and my mind was filled with the image of her face and figure as she left my room. Seductive visions of her seared my brain, and my excitement would not subside. I lay there staring up at the ceiling, unable to rein in my turbulent thoughts, and didn't get a wink of sleep that night. Over and over, I asked myself, 'Why did Chiyo choose me to give herself to? Why did she come to my room and not the room of one of the other two *shosei*?'

Inexperienced as I was in the intricacies of male-female relations, it nevertheless seemed to me that she must have been jealous, after all, of Mr. Fujiyama's having taken her elder sister Suzuyo with him on the trip and had only come to me to get back at him.

And from the perspective of her needs as a woman, it was certainly possible that she had been driven to me out of sexual frustration. She couldn't have been getting more than half of Mr. Fujiyama's physical affection, at the most. She was a mature woman in her late thirties with a normal, healthy appetite for sex.

Even though Suzuyo and Chiyo put on a show of calm and contentment and appeared to live together on good terms under the same roof in this ménage à trois revolving around Mr. Fujiyama, wasn't there some jealousy between them, after all, which they merely kept hidden from view?

At that point in my night-long ruminations, I was reminded of a particular scene in a famous Kabuki play, in which serpents— incarnations of jealousy itself—lay coiled atop the heads of two women who were rivals for one man's affection.

Well, after that first encounter, both Chiyo and I became consumed with lust for each other, our passion as wild and uncontrollable as the waters surging through a burst dam.

We gave ourselves up to the pleasures of the flesh and enjoyed each other every chance we got. At the time, I had just turned twenty and was full of vigor, decidedly well suited to satisfy her carnal desires. After all, no matter how robust and virile Mr. Fujiyama was for his age, there are limits to the sexual performance that can be expected of a man who has passed the middle milestone of life. Certainly, there could be no comparison between his sexual performance and that of a young man like myself.

Chiyo was a hot-blooded woman in her sexual prime, and she sneaked into my room almost every night seeking physical gratification.

Even after Mr. Fujiyama and Suzuyo returned from their trip to Kyoto, the door to my room continued to open softly in the middle of the night, though I'll never know how Chiyo managed so skillfully to slip away from her sleeping place beside them. And each night I lay awake expectantly, waiting for that gentle sound at the door that told me my fevered wait was over. The awakening of my sensuality seemed to have paralyzed my reason, my conscience, and even my fear of discovery.

The summer vacation ended. With the coming of fall a new school term began, and my former school-life awaited me. This term's studies, the last six months of my third and final year of high school, were very important. I was majoring in biological sciences, the equivalent then of premedical study, and from the day I entered high school I had set my sights on studying medicine at Tokyo University. And in keeping with that goal, I had maintained an excellent academic record.

However, after that summer break when my relationship with Chiyo had begun, my zeal for study declined radically. To tell the truth, even I could scarcely believe the extent to which my powers of concentration, memory, and analytical thought had been blunted.

Naturally, my academic performance suffered. My grades, which before had been near the top of my class, dropped to middle ranking and then even lower. My faculty adviser didn't know what to make of it. When the time neared for the university entrance examinations to be held, he told me flat out that I had no chance of passing the examination for entrance to the School of Medicine at Tokyo University. But since his decision was not the final word in the matter, I was free to attempt the examination if I wanted to. Some students who failed in their first attempt to pass the examination after high school would then study for another year and try again the next year, but that path was not open to me. Since I was being supported in my studies by benefactors who believed me to be of superior intelligence and worthy of a higher education, I would never be allowed such indulgence.

I might have had a chance to pass the entrance examination to the School of Medicine at some university other than Tokyo University, but that too was out of the question; since I depended on Mr. Fujiyama for my room and board, I could not leave the Tokyo area.

I had originally become motivated to study medicine not because of any medical tradition in my family or because I liked it, but merely out of acceptance of the general opinion of the day that a gifted student should become a doctor. On top of that, it took four years to graduate from a School of Medicine, one year longer than the usual departments of study at university; and after graduation, one had to work for several years without pay. When I started thinking over all these things, slowly but surely I began to doubt the advisability of continuing my education through the study of medicine.

Equine Science

Having given up the idea of taking the entrance examination to the School of Medicine, I decided to take the examination for entrance to another department in the Natural Sciences Division of Tokyo University, one that required a similar background in science, namely, the Department of Agricultural Science's School of Animal Science, where I intended to major in equine science.

Japan was riding on the wave of a political policy of national prosperity and strength, and the improvement of horses, specifically, maximizing a breed's potential, became a link in a chain of projects intended to increase the nation's strength; it was a much-talked-about subject because of the urgency and gravity with which it was regarded as an undertaking of national importance.

Besides the direct significance of equine science as it relates to the improvement of horses used by the Imperial Army, this field of study was also attracting a lot of attention because of its potential contributions to the transport industry in an era when automobiles had not yet come into widespread use and to farming, which was not yet mechanized. One could even say the work of breeding horses better suited to serving mankind had come to be regarded as a national mission.

I found the lectures and practical training classes in equine science that I attended really quite interesting. Yet if you mentioned you were a student of equine science to the average man in the street, he had no idea what you were studying. Admittedly, it was an offbeat field of study, so much so that at the mention of it even a quite well-educated person would tilt his head to the side as if wondering if there really was such a field of learning as the science of horses.

Nevertheless, the horse has played a role in mankind's history from its earliest days, so equine science was a firmly established and systematized branch of academic specialization. Compared with other nations around the world, Japan was running far behind the pack and had made but slow progress in equine science, as well as in the other sciences.

The horse made its first appearance in man's history as the prey of primitive hunters in the Diluvial epoch. From the ruins and artifacts of the cities of ancient Mesopotamian civilization, we know that by 3,000 B.C. men were raising and breeding horses.

The human race devoted great energy to creating new horse breeds suited to a specific purpose or type of work by selectively mating horses with different abilities and characteristics—for example, fast horses; horses with strong pulling capacity; horses with an aggressive disposition; gentle-natured horses—in order to achieve a new breed that had the desired combination of abilities. To give an example of which you have all probably heard, I could mention the Anglo-Arabian horse, which originated from breeding an Arabian horse with a Thoroughbred, or the Anglo-Norman horse, which originated from crossing a Thoroughbred with a Hackney.

The Imperial Army was conducting research to create horses better suited to highly specific applications for use in the cavalry, artillery corps, military transport corps, and so on.

Of course, it goes without saying that the range of my studies was exhaustive—everything from the evolution, physiology, and anatomy of the horse to its diseases and their treatment.

Especially since I had come from the small country village of Fukuchiyama and had once dreamed of being of service to mankind by becoming a doctor of medicine and thus making a name for myself, I could not completely free myself from that long-cherished aspiration and throw myself wholeheartedly into this new area of study, equine science. But I was, after all, the only person from Fukuchiyama ever to attend the great Tokyo University, and I was proud of that accomplishment, at least. For me, at any rate, the study of equine science was truly interesting and rewarding.

During my first year at university, everything in my life went on as before. Mr. Fujiyama allowed me to continue living in his house, I attended classes during the day, and Chiyo came to my room almost every night.

About the time I started my second year of studies, thanks to introductions and requests from fellow students and laboratory researchers at the university, I began to get jobs tutoring upper-grade middle school students who were hoping to attend high school, college, or a university preparatory course. I felt that if it was at all possible, I wanted to be independent of Mr. Fujiyama, so I resolutely took the plunge and told him that I would no longer need his financial assistance.

Naturally, I did this after talking the matter over thoroughly with Chiyo. We both took great pains to ensure that the secret of our illicit affair did not come to light or be noticed by the other members of the household. We felt that for the time being we were safe, but the psychological strain of it all had just about pushed us to the breaking point.

First of all, Chiyo agreed that my moving out of the house was a good idea. Then she busied herself looking for a place for me to live and decided on the Uchikoshi Apartments right next to the tracks of the National Railway electric train line, near Nakano Station. When we agreed that I should take an apartment there, she insisted on paying the rent and informed me that she would visit me at the apartment whenever she got the chance.

I could understand Chiyo's position. Even though our trysts would necessarily be fewer now than before, she probably wanted us to have a place where we could spend time together, just the two of us, without worrying about getting caught, instead of running what was surely a great risk in continuing our love affair in Mr. Fujiyama's house, under his very nose, as it were.

Maybe that's why, when she came to the apartment about once a week, she was much more uninhibited than I had ever seen her before, almost bestial in her sexual abandon. I guess since she was far from the prying eyes of her brother-in-law's household, she felt free to express the full depth of her passion. But I was young and had no experience of other women, and found her unbridled behavior embarrassing and even, at times, repellent.

During my three years at the university, I learned to like the taste of sakè. I started drinking on special occasions at school, parties, and the like, but soon I took to stopping off for a few drinks and a bite to eat at one of the many sushi stalls or cheap drinking joints on my way back to my apartment from the neighborhood public bath.

After all, in those days street-stall sushi cost only five or six sen for the cheaper varieties such as squid, squilla, or red tuna, so even a person like me earning his living working part-time as a tutor could afford to eat there.

Not far from Nakano Station was a whole street lined with cheap drinking joints, as a result of which my alcohol consumption increased steadily. Who knows, perhaps I succumbed so readily to the lure of alcohol because the blood of my long-dead drunkard father flowed in my veins.

But more than that, I think it was the desire to escape that drove me to drink. You see, having been labeled as a child prodigy, in my heart I had come to believe it and was conceited about my intellectual superiority. But ever since I had started sleeping with

Chiyo, my academic performance had dropped and I had given myself over to lust to such an overwhelming degree that even my career plans had been wrecked. I'm sure you are all familiar with the popular saying, 'At ten, a child prodigy; at fifteen, a clever youth; over twenty, just an ordinary man.' Well, I who had once been a child prodigy was now not even just an ordinary man, but had been reduced by my carnal appetite to a state of wretchedness that was far worse than that of a boy who simply could not live up to his potential. Tortured by regret over the abysmal state of my life of shattered dreams, I think the real reason I turned to drink was to dull my consciousness and thus escape—if only temporarily—the pain that gnawed at my heart.

Meanwhile, I finished university, graduated, and found a place of employment.

A Civil Servant in the Ministry of Agriculture and Forestry

As I mentioned earlier, my grades were no longer exceptionally good; I may once have been highly lauded as a child prodigy, but now I was an ordinary person. My faculty adviser did not recommend my staying on at the university for graduate study, so I took a civil service job at the Ministry of Agriculture and Forestry.

Once I began working at the Ministry, my free time became limited. There was also the possibility that I might be sent out of the city on business trips or even transferred to another locale. When Chiyo realized that we might be separated, her sexual passion became even wilder than before, almost crazed. She still came to see me regularly once a week at the Uchikoshi Apartments, which she had found for me when I was still at university.

I don't know what pretext she used when she left Mr. Fujiyama's house each week to come to my apartment. Whenever I asked her, she merely turned away my question with a playful 'That's my business!'

For the first two years or so at the Ministry of Agriculture and Forestry, I spent most of my time at my desk and was sent out of the office only on local business to the government-operated horse park in a Tokyo suburb. In time, I was transferred to the Ministry's stud farm at Hichinohe in Aomori Prefecture.

I had my hands full calming Chiyo when I told her the news, but since there was really nothing either of us could do about it, she eventually became resigned to my leaving.

I arrived at my new post on the appointed day. The stud farm was a vast expanse of pastures and grazing land. It was so big that the farm hands and ministry employees used a small, covered railroad car drawn by a single horse along a track that ran through the farm to travel back and forth between the small town of Hichinohe and the area where the farm office and living quarters were located. I was amazed to see such wide-open spaces in Japan.

Here, the great enterprise of improving Japan's horses was conducted. The vast expanse of grazing land was partitioned by fences into large paddocks, five or six of which made up each farm division with its own stable. There were different divisions for the different classifications of horses: breeding stallions, pregnant mares, yearlings, and two-year-olds.

I was provided with a house that stood next to a road lined with cedars and had lots of open space around it. The exterior of the house was done in the Western style, but the interior was Japanese style. The residence was much too big for a bachelor like myself.

The other employees' similar residences dotted the road here and there, and beyond them farther down the road stood a clubhouse for the use of the higher-ranking ministry employees. There I could take my meals and at night have a few drinks and socialize with my co-workers. It was really quite a comfortable, relaxing place for us single men posted there.

We called the club the Gallon Club, after a renowned breeding stallion at the stud farm that had made a big contribution to the improvement of Japan's horses. Gallon was such a fine piece of horseflesh that almost all the best race horses in Japan at that time were descended from him.

Life at the farm brought me a relief of sorts at being free from the dark shadow of my furtive entanglement with Chiyo, and the time I spent there was quite pleasant. It was a lighthearted, carefree existence that I had not experienced for the past several years. More than anything, I was glad to be out from under Chiyo's watchful eyes, which burned with jealousy at the mention of anything to do with my life at the office in Tokyo, particularly my dealings with other women, even if they were really nothing special and just ordinary office acquaintances. To while away my free time at night, I started drinking whiskey in addition to my usual sakè at the club, and my alcohol consumption skyrocketed. Night after night, I would weave my way back to my lodgings just a few hundred steps from the club, shouting and raving like the drunkard I was, having got in the habit of talking loudly and yelling every time I had a few drinks.

On Saturdays, I would go for a ride in one of the horse-drawn carts or on one of the horses kept in the stable for horseback riding, eventually heading over to the town of Hichinohe for a bit of fun.

Having majored in equine science at university, naturally it had been necessary for me to learn to ride horseback. Whenever the Tokyo office had sent me out to the government-operated horse park on business, I had spent the better part of my time there on the back of a horse. Consequently, I was quite at home in the saddle and loved to ride. I would ride my horse at a gallop or even at a run to Hichinohe and back, and along the way make him jump many of the fences that separated the farms—yes, that was irresistible fun to a horse-lover such as I.

Hichinohe was a small town, and there was nothing to do there. There was only one bar, where I would go to drink whiskey and flirt with the waitresses. I became quite friendly with one of the waitresses there named Natsu. I relished my release from Chiyo; but once a week without fail, a letter from her would arrive, each one an uninterrupted profession of her love for me. In an attempt to banish those monotonous, irksome letters from my mind, I downed glass after glass of whiskey with Natsu. At one end of the counter was an old hand-crank phonograph that played the same record over and over again, songs like 'Red Wings' and others whose titles I can't remember. I think the singer was Mari Kita.

My work at the farm cleansed and purified me in both body and spirit, and filled me with the pleasure of freedom: the vast wide-open grassland and the boundless sky stretching out overhead; the sensation of walking on grass wet with the morning dew; leaning against a rough-hewn fence and gazing serenely at the setting sun and the landscape bathed in a brilliant scarlet by its fiery beams; the foals nursing; the growing male camaraderie among the farm employees; and mingling with the simple, straightforward farm hands.

But with Japan's increasing militarization and invasion of China, which had begun with the Manchurian Incident, the growing shadow of war came surging steadily onward across Japan even to this remote, peaceful farm.

One by one, my fellow employees and farm hands were called up for military service. At my draft physical, the army doctor had given me a Class C draft classification because of my extreme nearsightedness, so I figured I didn't have to worry about getting a draft notice except in the most extreme circumstances. Nevertheless, it was painful for me to watch the men I had become close to leave the farm for military duty a few at a time.

At the end of my third year of duty at the stud farm, in March, I was ordered back to the main office in Tokyo.

Back in Tokyo

Since living along the National Railway Chuo Line was convenient for commuting to the Ministry, I took up residence in the same place as before, the Uchikoshi Apartments, though in a different set of rooms, once again on the instructions of Chiyo.

During this second tour of duty at the Ministry of Agriculture and Forestry's main office, I didn't stay glued to my desk, but was sent out on frequent business trips to Hokkaido, Aso and Kagoshima in Kyushu, and my old haunt, Hichinohe, in Aomori Prefecture. Since it almost always took a full day's train ride to reach my destination, these trips were hard on me. But although there was Ministry work to be done at the prefectural office, the trips gave me many opportunities to visit stud farms, which was always a pleasure.

As my fellow spirits have already related, conditions in Japan had been growing more oppressive year by year. During a terrible blizzard in the winter of the year after my return to the Ministry offices in Tokyo, the 2-26 Incident took place—a botched coup d'état—as a result of which the militarization of the country was sped up even more.

One day about a year after returning to Tokyo, I got a telephone call from Mr. Fujiyama's secretary asking me to stop by his office after work. As ever, my dissolute relationship with Chiyo was continuing, and what immediately occurred to me, probably because of my guilty conscience, was that Mr. Fujiyama had found out about our illicit affair, a thought that chilled me with anxiety.

For the rest of the day, I kept my eyes trained on the papers on my desk, but my mind was elsewhere. Now and then, a feeling of mortal dread came over me, closing around my chest like a fist and making it difficult for me to breathe. When the Ministry offices closed at five o'clock, I left the building and headed for Mr. Fujiyama's house.

As I sat in the train, I even started thinking that it would have been strange for him not to have become aware of an affair such as ours, which had been going on for so many years. A multitude of fears, questions, and dreadful scenarios swirled through my apprehensive brain: What steps would he take and, in turn, how should I respond? When cross-examined by him, how much of the truth should I reveal? More to the point, how much had Chiyo already told him?—for what I said would depend on how much I thought he already knew. Why, oh, why hadn't she and I foreseen this possibility and arranged previously what our stories would be? Over and over, I agonized over these questions.

But deep down I knew that when push came to shove, I was no match for the investigative skills and keen, analytical mind of as talented a lawyer as Mr. Fujiyama. Moreover, neither Chiyo nor I had any excuse for our immoral conduct; the wrongdoing was entirely on our part. Under the circumstances, even if I tried to throw the question of morality back at him by pointing out that he himself was guilty of having, in effect, two wives, I knew that in the end such a ploy would serve no purpose. His immorality was one thing, mine and Chiyo's was quite another; there was no point trying to equate the two in order to exonerate myself and her.

So it was with no little trepidation that I opened the door to Mr. Fujiyama's office and entered. Yet the moment I stepped into the room, 'Ah! Sumita, my boy! It's been such a long time; you mustn't make such a stranger of yourself. But I'm glad to see you're looking well,' Mr. Fujiyama said, all smiles, coming over to me with open arms and patting me on the shoulders. His manner was open, warm-hearted, free and relaxed. I was greatly relieved, for in that moment I knew intuitively that he knew nothing of Chiyo's and my affair.

'You must forgive me,' he continued, 'for summoning you here and taking up your valuable time, now that you are a busy government official. But you're at an age now where you need to start thinking about finding a wife and settling down, and I think I've got just the girl for you—a nice young teacher of Japanese at Musashi Girls' Academy. Why don't you let me arrange a meeting for you, and you can see what you think of her. Actually, I haven't met the girl; this is Chiyo's idea. She's been looking for a wife for you and recommends this young woman highly.'

Mr. Fujiyama said all this in the most casual, straightforward manner, as if he had nothing but my interest at heart, and on the surface the suggestion sounded casual. Yet a compelling undertone lurked beneath his lighthearted manner, one that made it clear to me that he wouldn't take no for an answer.

My heart missed a beat when he mentioned Chiyo, but what baffled me more than anything was why Chiyo had spoken to him about finding a wife for me and why she had not said anything about it to me beforehand. Her suggesting a prospective bride for me was incomprehensible, for I had long known her to be an intensely jealous woman.

I agreed to a formal introductory meeting with the young woman. That being settled, Mr. Fujiyama and I sat down to a fine dinner of sushi, after which I left.

The next time Chiyo came to my apartment, I got a surprising glimpse into the hitherto unimagined inner workings of a woman's heart and mind.

Evidently, Chiyo did not want to break off her relationship with me, nor did she have the inclination, courage, or confidence to give up everything she had with Mr. Fujiyama and start a new life with me, which would indeed have been impossible from the standpoint of common sense. Yet I was now of an age when men usually got married and couldn't very well remain single for the rest of my life. Sooner or later, she knew, through an introduction by some family member or business connection or my meeting a suitable woman on my own, I would marry.

That being the case, Chiyo preferred to have a hand in the tying of my marriage knot and select my bride herself. I was sure she would choose a woman less attractive than herself if possible. Furthermore, as it turned out, she intended to continue seeing me as before.

This may sound strange coming from me, but despite her interference in my life, I didn't think Chiyo was a bad person. She was a kind, intelligent, beautiful woman. Her sexual frustration

resulting from the unusual circumstances of her living arrangement with Mr. Fujiyama and Suzuyo, his wife and her own sister,
however, had driven her to develop a burning physical desire for
me, which then led her to act contrary to good sense and enter into
an immoral relationship with me. And I, being young, had let her
drag me along with her down the sordid path of carnal desire, and
for that I too was to blame. True, I was young when we started our
affair, but that was no excuse. If I had had any sense of justice at
all and considered the practical and moral consequences of having
an affair with my benefactor's mistress and let my reason rather
than my lust control the situation, I would never have found
myself in the ridiculous position of having my lover choose a wife
for me.

The woman Chiyo had selected as a prospective bride for me
was Arita Sumiko, the eldest daughter of Professor Emeritus Arita
Gen'ichi, who had just retired from the faculty of a private
university in Tokyo. Our first meeting took place in the lobby of
the Imperial Hotel, and who do you think was her escort? None
other than Chiyo herself, sitting in as Mr. Fujiyama's representative, with a look of utter innocence on her beautiful face.

At twenty-seven, Sumiko was a few years past the usual
marrying age for women, but she was unpretentious and had an
intelligent face, though not a beautiful one. All in all, she made a
favorable impression on me. With her face free of make-up and
her hair pulled back in a simple bun, Sumiko had quite a scholarly
air about her.

In that respect, she was quite a contrast to Chiyo, who always
created around herself an elaborate, almost ostentatious air of
glamour. Somehow, as I sat there looking at these two women
utterly opposite in style, I felt I understood all too clearly Chiyo's
real motive in choosing Sumiko to be my wife.

Marriage and its Ruin

The wedding took place in November of the following year. My mother's advanced age and failing health precluded her attempting the long journey from Fukuchiyama to Tokyo, but my two younger sisters attended. Hideko, the elder of the two, was married to a dentist by the name of Mizuno and lived in Yoka; and Sadako, the younger, lived in Nagoya with her husband, an Imperial Army lieutenant named Otsuji.

I found a nice, new home for us in the Matsubara district in the Shibuya Ward. By then I had risen to the position of assistant section chief at the Ministry of Agriculture and Forestry and was a mainstay there. My reputation was such that everybody in the office referred all questions concerning horses to my unequaled and readily acknowledged expertise—'If it's anything to do with horses, ask Sumita.' My success at the Ministry enabled me to buy a small but freestanding house for my bride and I to live in.

To my utter surprise and consternation, the very day after the wedding Chiyo telephoned me from the Tokyo Dai-Ni Hotel to tell me she had taken a room there. She asked me to go to her there. Although the war had prevented Sumiko and me from going on a honeymoon trip, I did get about one week off from work. On the spur of the moment, I couldn't come up with any particular reason to refuse Chiyo's summons, so I acquiesced to the urgency in her voice and went to the hotel she had named. I found her room, and the instant I opened the door she ran to embrace me, crying and sobbing bitterly.

It was only after I had made love to her—out of sheer force of habit rather than any sort of tender feeling for her—that she calmed down.

Afterward, I returned to Sumiko's and my new home in Matsubara, my conscience tormented by guilt at having been unfaithful to my new wife the very day after marrying her. She believed the story I had told her about being called in to the office on some urgent business and, without questioning me about it, was waiting patiently for my return. In my heart, I told her I was sorry and begged her forgiveness a hundred times over, but of course, I never actually said anything to her.

After marrying me, Sumiko continued her teaching job at Musashi Girls' Academy as before, and since I naturally was still employed at the Ministry, our dual-income lifestyle prevented us from seeing much of each other except late at night.

Even after my marriage, my alcohol consumption kept on increasing. I took advantage of every legitimate opportunity to drink, such as farewell parties for co-workers going off to war or being transferred out of the main office. On days when there was no such event, I would stop off someplace after work and get loaded before going home, for when I was sober, I couldn't bear to look my wife in the eye because of my guilt at continuing to have sexual relations another woman.

After coming home from her job, my wife would fix dinner for the two of us and await my return. Invariably, I came home drunk and disheveled, yelling and carrying on loudly enough to disturb all the neighbors. Usually, I hardly touched the meal she had prepared and set out for me; instead I would pour some green tea over a bowl of rice and slurp this down, and eat a few pickles; then I would lumber off straight to bed and sleep like a rock. Deep down inside, however, I knew my loutish behavior was hard on my wife and I felt sorry for her.

Not long after, the Sino-Japanese War broke out, and Japan got mired increasingly deeper in the quicksand of war. In my section of the Ministry, our orders came down unequivocally: Maximize the potential of the breeds of horses used in the Imperial Army and implement an increase in the number of superior horses available for military use.

Of course, the actual business of procuring horses for military use was performed directly by the Imperial Army, but my section's task was to devise the breeding projects that were fundamental to the entire operation. The job before us was not as simple and straightforward as the manufacture of a weapon. Our work had to be performed within the fixed period of the horse's gestation and with only a limited number of animals, since usually only one foal was born at a time.

With each additional co-worker drafted and sent off to war, the volume of work increased for those of us who remained at our jobs in the Ministry. I was sent out on more and more business trips all over Japan, to stud farms and associations of farms that bred horses as a sideline; my job was to maintain direct supervision and communication between the horse breeders and the Ministry.

About that time, however, I began to notice a slight shaking in my fingers. Unless I took a furtive sip now and then during the day from the bottle I kept in a drawer of my desk at the Ministry, I found myself irritable and unable to think straight. I didn't need to be a medical doctor to realize that these were symptoms of alcoholism.

As the war dragged on with no end in sight, alcoholic beverages had become generally hard to get in most cities, but fortunately or unfortunately for me, because of my frequent opportunities to get out of Tokyo on business, I had little trouble procuring locally brewed sakè or a type of rotgut called *shochu*. That's really the main reason I never minded being sent off on business trips so often. Sure, I liked the atmosphere of the stud farms well enough, but it was coming home laden with a good supply of liquor—whether bottles presented to me as gifts or those I'd made arrangements to buy on my own—that I really looked forward to.

Japan became ever more deeply embroiled in the war with China, until at last our country made its fatal plunge into the Pacific War against the United States.

Sumiko's and my marriage was a dreary, pathetic farce. I felt no affection for her and merely acted out my role as husband to keep up appearances, which made our relationship wearisome and insipid. Nevertheless, in the second year of marriage, our miser-

able union was blessed with the birth of a son, whom Sumiko's
father named Kunio.

Sumiko had taken piano lessons from an early age and played
quite well; she was also interested in vocal music and had a lovely
soprano voice. She would often sing arias from Mozart's *Don
Giovanni* or Verdi's *La Traviata*, accompanying herself on the
piano. I was practically tone-deaf and was altogether unable to
participate in or generate any enthusiasm for her love of music. I
remember the titles of the operas I just mentioned only because I
asked her now and then what she was singing and she told me.

As one would expect, her being a teacher of Japanese, Sumiko
had a good knowledge of Japanese literature and often read and
studied the classics. I certainly did not consider myself unintelli-
gent, yet I had no special pastime or interest. Literature left me
cold, and I had not the least interest in ideology or philosophy. In
short, with regard to our personalities and interests, Sumiko and
I didn't have a single thing in common.

Sumiko was by nature a quiet, retiring person, but she became
progressively taciturn, and that was probably my fault. She must
have thought of me not as her husband at all but just some loud-
mouthed, stinking drunk she had mistakenly pledged to share her
life with. Sitting in our cold, cheerless home night after night
waiting for her husband to come home, Sumiko came to harbor
feelings akin to a sort of resignation that drove her to withdraw
further and further into her shell with each passing year.

I continued to see Chiyo regularly. The pattern was always the
same: Every time we met, she would work herself into a state of
mingled jealousy, guilt, and joy at seeing me again. When she
started crying, I would make love to her to placate her. Then she'd
be calm and smiling and doggedly pester me to set the date of our
next tryst. As far as I was concerned, our relationship was purely
physical.

In time, Sumiko set up a wall between herself and me, so even
though she pretended to be unaware of the existence of the 'other

woman,' I think she must have sensed with her woman's intuition that I was having an affair.

The symptoms of my alcoholism worsened steadily, despite the difficulty in procuring liquor of any sort due to the increasingly stringent conditions in wartime Japan.

Even now, I remember how on April 18, 1942, just a little over four months after the outbreak of hostilities on December 8, 1941, the Tokyo air-raid sirens suddenly started blaring as B-25s zoomed over the heads of the citizens, who were still elated over Japan's initial series of victories. That was the first Tokyo air raid, carried out by the audacious Lieutenant Colonel Doolittle's bombing squadron.

Immediately after the attack, Sumiko's father, who had moved his household out of Tokyo to the city of Kawagoe some time before, came to the house announcing his intention to take Sumiko and Kunio back with him, both for their safety and to get them away from me. My wife's parents had known for some time that their daughter's marriage was not working out and was not a happy one, and they were disgusted at my uninterrupted descent into alcoholism.

'Try living apart for a while. It'll give you a chance to reflect on how you've been living your life.'

With that, the former professor proceeded to rake me over the coals, telling me in no uncertain terms what a disappointing son-in-law I had turned out to be. He said he had put up with one thing after another time after time, but had finally reached the limits of his patience.

I, for my part, said nothing. What could I say? I knew better than anyone that I had no right to say anything. I was painfully cognizant of the truth of his scathing tirade, and my conscience was not so dulled that I had the audacity to refute what I knew to be the simple truth and oppose his taking his daughter back.

As a wife and as a woman, Sumiko had so few shortcomings as to be almost perfect. I thought she was an exemplary person, and I admired her.

As her father ranted and lectured me on the error of my ways, his face contorted and his hands trembling with anger, I kept expecting Sumiko to interrupt his diatribe with the brief but conclusive declaration, 'I'm not leaving my husband.' This, however, was merely wishful thinking on my part, for she did no such thing. Evidently, she had had her fill of me as well.

The next morning, everything belonging to Sumiko and Kunio, including the piano, was bundled up and carted off to Kawagoe.

Kunio, who would soon celebrate his second birthday, did not even answer me when I called out my last good-bye to him. Instead, he clung to his mother, regarding me fearfully.

I could hardly blame him for acting like this, since I had never behaved like a father toward him. Although I had never hit or used physical violence on the boy, he had seen me raving and heard me bellowing whenever I was drunk—which was by then almost a daily occurrence. How could anyone, even I, expect a child to love such a father?

I was devastated by the departure of my wife and child; I felt an overwhelming sense of personal loss and failure. Nevertheless, the exigencies of wartime made my work to improve Japan's horses a vital mission.

In those days, there was a saying: 'You can get a soldier with a single piece of red paper, that is, a draft notice, and round up an army for next to nothing; but that won't work with horses—you have to buy them.' The social climate was so forcibly imbued by the government with the spirit of sacrifice of personal interest for the sake of the common good that the Imperial Army could obtain horses for military use at a cheap price. Consequently, as the war escalated, the demand for more and better horses increased, and my business trips out to the countryside continued as usual, despite my problems at home.

It was no time for me or anyone else to be preoccupied with their own personal affairs; the country was at war, and everyone was expected to do their part to assure Japan's victory. Besides, if it hadn't been for my bad eyesight, at my age I'd have been drafted and sent to the front long before, so I tried to ignore the shambles of my personal life and continued to put in long hours at work.

Facing Defeat

Day by day the war intensified. The tides of war had turned, and now the Imperial Navy was inferior in strength in the Pacific area. Despite the desperate measures of the military authorities, false news reports and propaganda to the contrary, the civilian population somehow sensed the truth. Under the strong influence of years of political indoctrination both before and during the war, however, their belief that Japan would yet win the war was upheld by their conviction that the Emperor's troops and their sacred land could not be defeated.

In reality, Japan's string of defeats in the Pacific had enabled U.S. troops to fortify their base of operations in the Mariana Islands, and the enemy was now in a position to start direct bombing attacks on the Home Islands. On November 30, 1944, B-29 long-range bombers flew over the cloudy skies of Tokyo and sent down a rain of bombs. On the afternoon of January 27 of the following year, the downtown area of Tokyo was bombed for three hours from about two to five o'clock, most of the bombs falling around the stretch of Ginza Boulevard between Shinbashi and Kyobashi. That day I saw flames pouring out of Kyukyodo, the famous shop for calligraphy supplies, and Kyobunkan, one of the city's largest bookstores.

From then on, formations of one or two hundred B-29s bombed Tokyo on a regular basis, destroying military installations and factory districts, of course, but also ordinary residential areas.

Now the home front had been turned into a battleground. Each bombing produced countless victims and incalculable suffering; the numbers of dead and wounded reached staggering levels.

Looking back now, it was just after the total annihilation of the
Japanese troops stationed at Manila in the Philippines—though,
of course, at the time neither I nor any other ordinary civilians
knew the true state of the war—that the Americans launched a
massive night air raid on Tokyo, which began the night of March
9 and continued till just before daybreak the following day,
turning the city into a veritable inferno. It was later reported that
there were about one million victims, over 83,000 of whom were
killed. In the gray dawn after the attack, I saw countless bodies
strewn along the roadsides, amid smoldering piles of ash and
rubble. Power, gas, and water lines were broken, and none of the
city streetcars or other public conveyances were running. The
situation was terrible beyond words; I felt helpless in the face of
such overwhelming carnage and destruction. The most horrific,
heart-wrenching sight I came across was when I looked down into
the Sumida River and saw the surface of the water covered with
the corpses of people who had run into the river to escape the
flames and either died of the unbearable heat or drowned.

I remember thinking at the time, 'It is wrong to continue this
war any longer.' I felt that the energy and hard work I had
dedicated to the improvement of military horses for the sake of my
country had all been a dreadful mistake.

Yet the people of Tokyo rallied, and encouraging cries once
again rose ever stronger calling for all Japanese citizens to stand
firm and resist defeat to the last breath, to prepare to fight the
decisive battle on home soil, and to defend the national polity at
all costs. Soon after, however, another air raid on April 14
destroyed not only residential districts but parts of the Imperial
Palace and the famous Meiji Shrine, both important popular
symbols of the country's Imperial regime.

Even though the better part of Tokyo was already nothing but
burned-out areas of ash and rubble, a few days later carrier-borne
enemy aircraft came in the wake of the B-29s and relentlessly
targeted the buildings and houses that had somehow survived the

previous bombings and fires; they combed the blackened ruins from high above and doggedly continued the systematic destruction of Tokyo, while the civilians below looked on in an anguish of utter helplessness. I need hardly say that by this late stage of the war, Japan's military resources were so severely depleted that there were no Japanese aircraft in the sky to intercept the enemy bombers.

In the midst of all this, I was sent to Iwate on Ministry business. When I returned to Tokyo, I was shocked to find that my house in Matsubara, which had till then somehow been lucky enough to escape destruction, had been burned to the ground in the so-called Last Great Air Raid on May 24—25. I was struck dumb with unspeakable sadness at the pathetic sight of my books—which I had collected through the years ever since my days at university and which were very dear to me—reduced completely to ash along with the bookcase, but standing in the same position as when I had last seen them, having retained their shape and turned into books of ash.

Mr. Fujiyama had already evacuated his household to Kameoka north of Kyoto in September of 1944. This put an end to Chiyo's and my affair, but at our last meeting she made me promise to see her again after the war was over. It was irresponsible of me to make such a promise with the future of Japan so uncertain—or rather, with life itself so uncertain, for as you will soon learn, my life took an unexpected turn and I never saw her again.

The situation now was such that with each passing day I felt more and more certain that the whole country was rushing headlong into annihilation—you could almost feel it in the air. One of my co-workers at the office was letting me stay temporarily at his house at Koganei in the suburbs, and I was commuting each day to the Ministry offices on the Chuo Train Line.

The National Railway electric trains were in bad shape; the blast-damaged, ramshackle cars looked pathetic, their glassless windows boarded up with cheap plywood. A great many of the railway employees had been drafted for military service, and women mobilized into the labor service were making up the consequent shortage of manpower. Perhaps thanks to what one might call the never-say-die spirit and tradition of the National Railway, the railway workers' heroic sense of mission to keep at least the electric trains running at all costs, serving the city and its suburbs, did indeed enable them to manage somehow to continue train service, even under such trying conditions.

As June passed into July, people still spoke of the war as a holy war that we must fight to the bitter end, although most of them could see that the situation was hopeless. Yet no one dared breathe a word of such negative, unpatriotic thinking.

Most people no longer felt afraid of dying, perhaps because they'd become used to seeing so many people around them blown to bits by enemy bombs or burned to death in the subsequent fires, or perhaps because they'd come to the egotistical conclusion that they alone would be spared. Maybe they were simply so sunk in utter despair that they were resigned to whatever fate befell them and prepared for the worst.

Throughout the city, the corpses of the dead lay neglected and rotting amid the blackened, smoldering ruins, for no one had the time or energy to pull them out of the rubble and give them a proper burial. There was nothing to eat; you couldn't find a water tap that was in working order. In the streets I chanced to see a half-mad mother hurrying off to some imagined sanctuary, carrying her headless baby on her back, and another mother just standing staring vacantly with her dead baby on her back as if she knew there was no place to run. I saw people shuffling lifelessly through the streets, their hair filthy, unkempt, and charred to a reddish-brown by the searing heat of the flames they had narrowly escaped. I could hardly bear to look at their faces, smeared with sweat and dirt, and caked with dried blood from their own wounds or those of their dead loved ones. Their civilian uniforms or baggy work-pants and shirts were covered with dust and ripped open in places, but the people were too shattered in spirit to notice and try to cover themselves. In times of such helplessness and despair, perhaps it's natural for people to no longer care what happens to them. Actually, it might be that very lack of concern for one's own safety that makes it possible for a person to survive the ruthless calamities of war.

The air raids continued relentlessly. Now, in addition to the B-29s, small P-52 Grumman fighter planes joined in the attacks, cavorting in the skies above Japan and bombing targets with unrestrained swagger and audacity, as if to say, 'Haven't you had enough yet? Take this! and this! and this!'

The various events leading up to Japan's defeat—the surrender of Germany, the loss of Okinawa despite tremendous casualties, the dropping of atomic bombs on Hiroshima and Nagasaki, the invasion of Japanese-held Manchuria by Russian troops in wanton disregard of Russia's nonaggression treaty with Japan, the final days of the Empire, and Japan's acceptance of the terms of unconditional surrender stipulated in the Potsdam Declaration—all occurred as described previously by my fellow spirits.

In the months following the end of the war, Japan's government and economy were turned upside down by the changes enacted by the Occupation Army under the direction of General MacArthur. Exhausted by the long years of wartime privation and hardship and shocked at Japan's defeat, the Japanese entered a period of bewilderment and lethargy. At the Ministry of Agriculture and Forestry, however, we were very busy destroying documents and preparing for the changes we expected the Occupation to bring. In November, I was sent on business to a Ministry-run stud farm at Aso in Kyushu.

Very few steam locomotives were still in service, and even fewer were completely undamaged; most of them seemed to pant and gasp along the track. The passenger cars, dirty and without window panes, were crammed to bursting with repatriated colonists and demobilized or discharged soldiers returning to their homes, along with civilians traveling out into the countryside to forage for food. Many of them were hanging half outside the doors, clinging desperately to the handrails, or riding on the roofs of the train cars. More often than not, people had to get in and out through the windows, and yet you were still better off riding in one of these overcrowded passenger cars than in the freight cars that were also in service then, some of which were merely open cars that gave passengers no protection from the elements.

The National Railway service was in utter chaos. The few remaining undamaged train cars had been requisitioned by the Occupation Army, and these trains were given top priority in scheduling and track availability. Trains carrying Japanese passengers or freight were permitted to run only in between the periods when Occupation Army trains were using the tracks. This situation was a daily, poignant reminder of Japan's utter defeat and the difference in status and privileges between the conquerors and the conquered.

Anyway, those were the conditions under which I traveled by train to Kyushu, and the journey was a nightmare. The rice rations provided by the government had dwindled to practically nothing, so I had very little food to take with me to eat during the trip, and this was a serious hardship. In those chaotic months just after the war ended, even if a traveler took along some ration tickets for rice, he probably wouldn't be able to find a restaurant open for business; and if he did find one, about all the meal he could expect would be a thin, watery rice porridge.

When I finally reached my destination, not only was I able to satisfy my hunger, though the food was plain, but my hosts presented me with a bag full of rice to take back with me, owing to my status as a bigwig from the Tokyo office of the Ministry.

By this time, there was an extreme shortage of all types of liquor, including sakè. There were reports that not a few people had actually gone blind from drinking crude methyl alcohol. Though I put my hosts to rather a lot of trouble, I managed to obtain some of the local sakè and *shochu*.

I had been unusually tired and listless before setting out on this trip to Kyushu, but because in those days no one had enough to eat, I thought nothing of it. From the moment I found myself a seat and settled down in the train back to Tokyo, however, I became feverish. Sometime after we passed through Himeji, my temperature rose sharply, and I began to shiver uncontrollably; I had to use the toilet often, and I noticed that a pinkish rash had broken out on my arms, legs, chest, and abdomen. By the time the train passed through Osaka, I was slipping in and out of consciousness. Worst of all was the grueling ordeal of having to make my way again and again through the jam-packed train, squeezing between people crushed together shoulder to shoulder, to get to the toilet because of my diarrhea. When the train reached Kyoto Station, I knew I could not continue my journey in that condition, and I jumped out of the train.

I have no recollection at all of walking along the platform or up and down stairs, but somehow I made my way to the ticket gate, where my strength at last failed me and I fell senseless to the floor.

Anyone could tell just from looking at me that I was seriously ill, so some of the station employees carried me to the Kyoto Prefectural Isolation Hospital.

I had typhus, which was believed to be transmitted by clothing lice, and my case was complicated by malnutrition and liver damage caused by years of alcohol abuse. Since my resistance was extremely low and, moreover, there was no specific medicine to treat typhus at the time, the disease progressed quickly. Soon I was passing blood in my stool, and I contracted peritonitis due to an intestinal perforation. I died three days after being admitted to the hospital.

The hospital sent word to Sumiko, who was still legally my wife, but the message took some time in reaching her; and anyway, in the postwar confusion she could hardly drop everything and come at once to Kyoto, much less find a way to transport my remains back to Tokyo. In the end, it was decided that my body should be donated to a medical school for medical research. My corpse was moved to Rakuhoku Medical College, where it was kept overnight and a token funeral service was held for me in the school morgue. Then my body was treated with a preservative so that it could be used for dissection later.

Though old and feeble, my mother was still living in Fukuchiyama, and I did have two younger sisters, but my body was turned over to the medical school before word was received from any of them in reply to the notification of my death. Quite some time later, my mother and sisters gave their consent to the donation of my corpse for medical research.

Given that my death occurred right at the height of the postwar confusion, this handling of the situation was unavoidable, and I blame no one.

The instant I died, my soul left my body and ascended into the World of the Spirits. The transition from my earthly existence to the World of the Spirits was a very gentle experience. I felt as if I were slipping out of the garment of worldly life to begin an utterly new, eternal existence on the spiritual plane.

In the World of the Spirits my many sins, which I never thought about very seriously during my lifetime, have been pointed out to me with painful clarity, and I deeply regret the wrongs I committed. This time spent in the World of the Spirits is preparing me for the moment when I shall be lifted into Heaven by God.

That is my story, dull and trivial as it may be. Thank you for listening so patiently.

After Hearing the Fourth Night's Tale

"They say that life is stranger than fiction, but the various twists and turns of the lives of the Spirit of Sumita and the other three spirits I've heard from are truly beyond all imagining—these were indeed stormy, far from happy lives," Yoshio said in a rush of emotion. "I've had very little experience of life so far; compared with all of you, I've passed my days in uneventful peace and quiet.

"Furthermore, while it's true that all of us here in this room experienced this tragic war, each in a different way according to his or her particular circumstances, I have been indeed fortunate—more fortunate than most—in that my family's house in Kyoto was not burned down, and the only hardship I suffered during the war was having my studies disrupted and being compelled instead to spend that time working at a munitions factory. Standing here before all of you now, I feel somewhat guilty for having come through the war years without any serious misfortune. And yet, the war did not leave me completely un-scathed: Many of the students at my former middle school who were mobilized into the labor service and sent to work at Handa in Aichi Prefecture were killed by flooding or enemy bombs, and I still grieve for them.

"I'm studying hard now in order to become as good a doctor as I can to help the sick. Moreover, I am determined to devote myself in some way to seeing that Japan never again makes the terrible mistake of engaging in warfare, for the sake of all the young men my age who laid down their lives in foreign countries in the name of the Emperor, and for the sake of the countless people who lost their families, their homes, and everything they owned because of the war . . . For all their sakes . . ."

"Well, Yoshio," the Spirit of Professor Yuhara said, "it's time for you to return home now and attend to your studies so that you may achieve your goal. Thank you for coming here tonight.

"The story of Sumita's life was indeed moving. People are truly weak and susceptible to temptation. By meeting Chiyo, the course of Sumita's life was changed utterly. As a result of their affair, this once-admired child prodigy was reduced not just to an ordinary person but to a drunken, miserable wretch who wasted his abilities. Truly, people never know what life holds in store for them.

"If Sumita had exercised more control over his physical desire and not allowed his illicit affair with Chiyo to drag on, but had resolutely broken off his ties with her, his sin would not have been so great.

"God points out to each spirit all the sins he or she committed while alive—even those committed unwittingly—and doesn't overlook a single one, so that the anguish the spirit suffers under what we might call His scourge of love may lead him or her to repentance.

"God's way is not as some spiritualists and religions teach, where, for example, a person who has led a life of lust and sexual passion is cast into a sea of blood after death. In the World of the Spirits, the more greatly one has sinned on earth, the more that person's spirit is able to partake of Christ's redemption in the compassionate hands of God.

"While in the World of the Spirits, the Spirit of Sumita has already been made keenly aware of the sins of his life, has sincerely repented his wrongdoing, and has acknowledged Christ as his Savior, so in due course he will be lifted into Heaven. Of course, the passage of time in the World of the Spirits cannot be compared with that on earth, for the one is eternal and the other temporal.

"But if we get into a discussion about that, we'll be talking all night. So go home now, Yoshio. I had intended for you to hear two tales tonight, but the hours have slipped away too fast once again, and the story of one life has taken up all of tonight's allotted time."

CHAPTER SIX

FIFTH NIGHT :

The Tale of a Man Who Experienced the Horrors of War as an Artilleryman in the Mountain Jungle of Luzon

My Childhood

Even when I try to recall my childhood, I can't remember much about it; everything that happened then is long gone beyond the veil of oblivion. Only vague, dim images come to mind, which could be actual events or just remembered scenes from some black-and-white movie. Still, I'll try to rouse my sleeping memory and retrace the story of my early years—but don't expect it to be very entertaining. After all, I was just an average, run-of-the-mill guy.

My name in the temporal world was Yoneda Isamu. I was born near Nishihonganji Temple in the Sakyo Ward of Kyoto.

My father was the first-born son in a family of Kyoto dyers who had been in the business for generations. If he had been strong and healthy, he would have taken over the family business and continued to expand it, as was naturally expected of him, but partly because he was born with a weak constitution, he wasn't much interested in the family business. Besides, he had a weakness for women; by the time I was ready to start elementary school, he had already squandered his entire inheritance on geisha in the Miyagawa-cho entertainment quarter, which was relatively nearby, and for lack of money had moved my mother, my little brother, and I out of our ancestral home to a small house in Fushimi.

On top of having to deal with his new poverty, my father contracted tuberculosis after the move to Fushimi. I remember seeing his eyes bulging in his gaunt, disease-ravaged face late one afternoon; the rays of the setting sun streamed in through a tear in the paper of one of the shoji sliding screens and bathed his stubbly beard in a weird light that turned it a ghastly red. That's my earliest memory of him: those great, staring eyes and that frightful, red beard.

My mother was called Kosan. My little brother was about three years old then, and our mother had a hard time of it, looking after our sick father and trying to raise two young boys. I don't clearly remember the details of our family life, but looking back, I would have to say that my mother was a good wife to my father, who had squandered his inheritance on other women. She was dutiful and long-suffering—to all appearances, at least, though I have no idea how she really felt inside.

Though he was a less-than-perfect husband, he was still the father of her two children. Tuberculosis was generally thought to be a fatal disease in those days and he looked terribly ill even to an untrained eye, so perhaps she wanted to be nice to him and make him as comfortable as she could before he died.

It really must have been terrible on her trying to run a household burdened by debts on loans that my father had taken out, no income, and the care and feeding of an invalid husband and two small children. I remember she would sit in the living room sometimes staring vacantly out at the small patch of weeds growing by the house next door. She probably didn't know where to turn to for help and was at her wits' end.

They say in Japan that when one god abandons you, another god takes you under his wing. Perhaps so, for just when our situation was looking blackest, someone who was moved by our poverty and distress stepped forward and offered to take me in and send me to elementary school 'so that at least the elder son will have some education.'

My grandfather on my father's side died before I was born, but it was one of his former apprentices, Sato Taiji, who took pity on my family's plight and took me into his home. As a boy, Mr. Sato had been sent all the way from Hokkaido to be a live-in apprentice at my grandfather's dye works. After years of learning the trade, he had returned as a young man to his hometown of Asahikawa and set up his own dye works specializing in Kyoto dyeing techniques.

While living in my grandfather's house in Kyoto, Mr. Sato's relationship with my father was that of apprentice to master's son, but apparently they often played together, since they were about the same age.

Though I hate to say it, it was as plain as the nose on your face: If he hadn't taken me into his home and thus given my mother one less mouth to feed, our family might have faced utter ruin.

Planning for me to start elementary school the following April, at the end of November Mr. Sato himself made the long trip down from Hokkaido to take me back with him.

It was hard on me to have to leave my family at such a tender age. My heart almost burst with the pain of saying good-bye to my dear mother and my sweet little brother. Toru had always idolized me and used to run along beside me calling, 'Big brother! Big brother!' I often had to help my mother by baby-sitting for him, but he was really as much a playmate to me as anyone, and I knew even before I left that I would miss him terribly. Yes, the day I left for Hokkaido was a black day all right.

Before my father got so sick, he was hardly ever at home, so I didn't have very many happy memories of him and wasn't so torn up about leaving him. The one thing I do remember is something that happened about a year before his illness confined him to bed: I don't remember the details, but the four of us had gone to the hot springs at Kinosaki on the Sea of Japan. In my mind's eye, I can see us in our room at the inn, him lying back on the futon and bouncing me on his upraised knees. Somehow, that one happy memory has stayed with me all these years. . . .

What a terrible, sad thing it is to part from the people you're close to, the people you love and hold dearest in the world! All of the spirits who have spoken here have known the sorrow of parting; indeed, is there any person who hasn't?

You may think that the pain of parting lasts but a short time when one is young and that a child's heart soon forgets, but being separated from my family left a deep wound in my heart.

Well, Mr. Sato took me off with him. We changed trains several times before we arrived at Aomori Station, stayed one night in a cheap rooming house, crossed the Tsugaru Straits by ferry the next day, and at last arrived on the island of Hokkaido. Though Japan is a small country, I felt we had traveled quite a long distance. Everything, from the streets and houses to even the natural scenery, was utterly different from what I was used to seeing on Honshu, the main island of Japan, especially in the crowded city of Kyoto where my family lived. I felt as if I had come to a foreign country.

Mr. Sato's father was originally from Fukushima Prefecture and had come to Hokkaido in his younger years as a combination militiaman-farmer, one of thousands sent to Hokkaido by the government to cultivate the land and develop the territory. After his stint in the Army was up, he decided to stay and settled down on the outskirts of Asahikawa. Later, as Asahikawa grew, he moved into the city proper, opened a kimono shop, and sent his young son to Kyoto to learn the art of Kyoto dyeing as apprentice to a master dyer, my grandfather. When his son returned years later with the necessary knowledge and skills, he converted his shop into one that specialized in kimono made of fabrics dyed using Kyoto dyeing techniques.

While I was living in Mr. Sato's house, his father, who was still healthy and spry despite being quite old, would tell me stories about the trials he had faced as a pioneer eking out a living in Hokkaido and how he had done his best to fulfill the mission entrusted to him. He seemed to enjoy telling me these tales from his past as much as I enjoyed hearing them, and he took pains to talk in terms that a young boy could easily understand.

A few years after returning to Hokkaido from his apprenticeship in Kyoto with my grandfather, Mr. Sato was drafted into one of the infantry brigades of the 7th Army Division in Asahikawa and sent to Siberia in 1918. His first post of duty was along the route of the Manchurian Railway. Later, he was sent across the Russian-Manchurian border to the area around Lake Baikal. The Japanese troops were plagued by the guerrilla tactics characteristic of the Bolshevik partisans, who seemed able to appear out of nowhere, attack, and then disappear without a trace; on top of that, the purpose behind their combat was not very clear to them, which lowered morale and undermined their efforts. As a result, the Japanese troops lost one battle after another. The actual situation must have been tragic, but the way Mr. Sato told us about his combat experiences time after time as we ate our evening meal, he made it sound pretty funny. In those days, most young Japanese boys wanted to grow up to be a high-ranking soldier, and Mr. Sato's son Kan'ichi and I were no exception: We listened tirelessly to his war stories, our young eyes shining with joy and excitement.

When I was in my third year at elementary school, word came that my father was dying. Mr. Sato and I hurried down to Kyoto as fast as we could, but the trip took three whole days. When we finally arrived and I was ushered in to see my father, he looked as if he were at death's door. His breathing was labored and painful; he was gasping as if he were trying to take in all the oxygen in the room with each desperate breath.

His ankles and the flesh around his eyes were swollen, but the rest of his body was even more gaunt and emaciated than when I had left for Hokkaido three years before. He was nothing but skin and bones.

Even to the inexperienced eyes of a young boy like me, it was obvious that he was dying, and I thought to myself, 'So this is what death is like.'

His big, deep breaths became irregular; he skipped one completely from time to time, and the interval between breaths grew longer. And then, as if to make up for the breath he had missed, his next breath was twice as deep.

Meanwhile, his eyes would open from time to time and sweep around the room. When I brought my face into his line of vision, he stared at me with eyes full of love—love he had never shown me before—and moved his lips a little, as if he were trying to say something. Then he raised his hands in the air before him as if he were searching for something.

My mother stretched out her hand to him. He grasped it tightly, then with a great nod of his head and a look of contentment, he breathed his last.

Owing to our family's meager resources, the funeral was small and simple. Afterward, the body was taken to Mt. Kiyomizu Crematorium. When the coffin was pushed through the iron doors into the flames, my mother, who till then had fought to hold back her grief, at last let go and burst into tears, her fragile shoulders shaking with the force of her great sobs.

Suddenly, a searing wave of grief and sorrow welled up in my breast, and I clung to my mother as tears poured down my cheeks. I had not seen her since I had left for Hokkaido three years before, and tried now to show her all the love I had for her as I clung to her waist and buried my face in her black kimono.

Later, Mr. Sato and my mother had a serious talk about what to do with me now that my father was dead. In the end, they concluded that there was absolutely no way she could pay school expenses for both me and my little brother out of the small income she had from the piecework and odd jobs she could do at home. Feeling that it would be a shame to take me out of the school that I had just gotten used to, they decided that I should return with Mr.

Sato to Hokkaido and stay with him till I graduated from elementary school as originally planned.

Actually, I think Mr. Sato treated me so kindly because he felt an obligation to repay the debt of kindness he owed my father's family from his days as an apprentice to my grandfather.

So once again, I had to leave my mother and little brother, and again, the good-byes were heart-wrenching, made all the more emotional for coming so soon after my father's death.

My remaining three years at elementary school passed very quickly, in a blur.

As the end of my sixth and final year neared, Mr. Sato said he would sponsor me through at least the next stage of schooling if I wanted to continue, but I declined his generous offer and decided to return home to Kyoto in March as soon as the school year ended.

Even though I was still quite young, I guess I had begun to feel a sense of my own independence that would not let me allow Mr. Sato to continue supporting me any longer, and as the first-born son, I had also begun to feel a sense of responsibility for helping support my family in Kyoto now that my father was gone. But more than anything else, I just wanted desperately to be with my mother and little brother again.

So I said farewell to Hokkaido, where I had spent six years basking in the kindness and generosity of Mr. Sato and which had become a second home to me, and headed back to Kyoto.

This time, I made the long journey by myself. My ears, nose, and the back of my neck were black with soot and smoke from the steam engine when I got off the train at Kyoto Station. The train arrived right on schedule, and when I saw my mother and little brother waiting on the platform for me, my heart nearly burst with joy. I was home again!

A New Start in Kyoto

Through an introduction by someone my mother knew in connection with the piecework she did at home, I got a job the very next day as live-in kitchen help at an inn and restaurant called Tosaya in Fushimi. This place was famous as one of the finest restaurants in Fushimi, which was itself an area of the city noted for its fine eating establishments.

I had assumed that by living in Fushimi I would be able to see my mother and little brother often, but nothing could have been further from the truth. The work was really hard: cleaning pots and pans, unloading boxes, scrubbing down the counters and floors, taking out the garbage—all the dirty work. What's more, they had me working straight through from five in the morning till eleven at night.

The only happy hours I had were those I spent sleeping, all the more so because I had no money to spend. I got no wages, since I was a kitchen apprentice, and each month on the half-day I had off from work, I went to my mother's house and gave her every bit of what little pocket money the restaurant owner gave me as an allowance. I got three days off for the Bon Holidays each August and three days off at New Year's, that's all.

After three years there, I finally was allowed to help with the actual cooking; at first, I thought I was finally on my way to learning a trade, but this was just another period of training and hardship.

There were five chefs, whose rank was clearly determined by a seniority system and a set of rules that was in some ways even stricter than the army's. Whenever I made even a tiny mistake, one of the cooks would give me a hard knock on the head with the blunt edge of a knife. And yet, even at this stage of my training, they still wouldn't teach me how to cut up fish, season food, and the like; my work was just carrying dishes to one or the other of the five cooks and washing vegetables. Ultimately, I learned that the restaurant owner himself or the head chef did all the important work of cooking, and the only way I would ever be able to advance to the level of chef was to watch these two at work in the kitchen and learn their techniques on my own.

So I did just that, and in another three years, I became one of the middle-ranking chefs. The main reason behind my rapid advancement, however, was that the elder chefs-in-training were all being drafted for military service as soon as they reached a certain age.

About that time, there was a cook two years older than I who would soon take his draft physical. He was a mean-spirited fellow and was always on my case, teasing and harassing me. One day, he criticized the way I had arranged the food on a tray and gave me a hard poke in the head with the handle of his kitchen knife.

That was the straw that broke the camel's back. My pent-up anger and resentment flared, and I lost all control. I grabbed the knife he had just put down on the counter and slashed him on the head. Blood gushed from the wound and he collapsed to the floor, but not before his blood had spurted all over the dishes of food set on the counter. It was quite a mess, and everyone in the kitchen was yelling and screaming. They took him to a Fushimi clinic affiliated with Rakuhoku Medical School Hospital, where it took ten stitches to close the cut.

Under normal circumstances, I probably would have been dragged off by the police and charged with the serious offense of stabbing a man, but since high-ranking field officers of the 16th Army Division and the local Chief of Police and his top officers were regular patrons of the restaurant, the owner didn't want any notoriety and asked them to keep the incident quiet. So he saved me from being arrested, but fired me the very next day.

In the beginning, I had taken that live-in job to help my family economize, and I had dreamed of becoming a first-rate chef in time, but that dream was not to be realized.

Still, I couldn't just loiter around the streets and waste time regretting my mistakes. Japan had always been a poor nation, but that period was particularly hard because of the Depression. One of the songs popular then described the woes of university graduates unable to find work, so you can see that for guys like me with only a grade-school education, finding a job of any sort was not easy.

Through the help of yet another of my paternal grandfather's acquaintances, I was able to get a job in a dye works on Motoseiganji Street off Horikawa Boulevard. Perhaps there was, after all, some fated bond between myself and the Kyoto dyeing business.

I had to start at the bottom all over again, though I could hardly have expected it to be otherwise, since I had no knowledge or experience of dyeing. My fingernails constantly stained with dye, I mastered the various techniques of the dyeing process: *kirifuki*, spray-damping the cloth; *hikizome*, dye application; and *bokashi*, dye gradation. Carrying the surprisingly heavy piles of cloth before and after dyeing was backbreaking work, and having to be constantly standing up bending forward over the cloth I was dyeing was also hard on the body.

I learned the essentials relatively quickly and did unexpectedly well for a beginner, perhaps because the blood of generations of Kyoto dyers flowed in my veins. Most importantly, however, I enjoyed the work immensely. As a result, the dye works owner and senior workers thought the world of me and treated me as if I were a prize catch for their business.

Just when I thought I had found my proper course in life and my mother was rejoicing over my future prospects, the day came for my draft physical.

The Manchurian Incident in 1931 had led Japan to steadily increase its military force in China until full-fledged war broke out in 1937. More and more young men were being drafted to keep Japan's war machine running, and I was fated to join them.

Drafted into the Imperial Japanese Army

I went to take my draft physical in the spring of 1939. As you know, every Japanese youth was required to take his draft physical on turning twenty. That morning, I put on the brand-new loincloth my mother had made for me, got dressed, and went to the examination site. The examination ended with a humiliating check for venereal diseases.

'Yoneda Isamu: 1-A!' he called out to the recording clerk. Speechless with pride and suddenly a bit overwhelmed by this rite of passage, I thought to myself, 'Now I'm a real, full-fledged man!'

Just after the following New Year's holiday, in 1940, I got my orders to report for duty to the 213th Field Artillery Regiment of the Kyoto 16th Army Division.

Members of the Women's National Defense Association and our neighbors lined the narrow, mazelike streets in front of our house to see me off, waving colorful streamers and Rising-Sun flags and singing the 'Greater East Asia March' and 'Sending Our Soldiers Off to Battle.' Wearing a red sash across my chest from shoulder to waist, I picked up my duffle bag and set out to join my regiment.

My mother and my little brother Toru wanted to accompany me as far as they could, so the three of us boarded the Fushimi Line electric streetcar and rode it as far as Inari along the Takeda Road, which was so narrow in some places that you felt the car was going to scrape the roofs of the houses on either side. From there, we walked along the street called Division Road the rest of the way to regimental headquarters.

Apparently, many other new recruits had been ordered to report for duty on the same day and at the same time. As we approached the barracks gate, there was a thick crowd of recruits and their mothers, fathers, sisters, and brothers who had come to see them off. In that sea of young recruits, some looked anxious like me; some were flushed with high spirits and were obviously raring to go; and some kept their eyes on the ground and looked as if they were going to start crying any moment. I also remember seeing two people, who looked like a mother and her son, walking toward the gate and consoling each other.

We entered the barracks gate, and a noncommissioned officer led me to a yard between two barracks, where I changed into my new uniform and handed over my civilian clothes to my mother. Then it was time to say good-bye.

'Take care of yourself,' my mother said, dabbing at the tears that streamed down her cheeks, 'and don't let things get you down. Army life is hard, but I know you can do it!'

She gripped my hand tightly, encouragingly. Toru's eyes were wet, and a sob escaped his lips a time or two, though he did his best to hold them back. Then I turned and entered the barracks.

I had heard beforehand about the strictness and hardships of military life, and I was prepared for it—or so I thought. But the reality was much, much worse than I could ever have imagined. From the very first day, I learned the brutal truth: New recruits were treated as less than human. We had no idea where to get our meals; which beds were ours and how to put the sheets and blankets on them; when to take off our uniforms, how to fold them, and where to put them; and most important of all, what the day's schedule was—but the squad leader or the senior soldiers pushed us around and yelled, 'Hey! you got lead in your ass? Get a move on!'

From then on, not a day passed that I wasn't slapped. No matter how tiny or insignificant a mistake I made, the iron palm of one of the senior men came crashing down on my cheek every time without fail. Worse still, even when I hadn't done anything wrong, they'd slap me anyway for being 'insolent' in some way or for being 'rebellious' enough to look them in the eye—hit me so hard my cheek would swell up and make my face all lop-sided.

Our basic daily schedule never varied. When reveille sounded, we would fall in, then have the morning roll call, eat breakfast, have morning drill, eat lunch, have afternoon drill, eat dinner, bathe, study, have the evening roll call, and at last go to bed. But the duties of the new recruits didn't stop there; we had to take turns serving as personal attendants to the senior soldiers, cleaning the barracks inside and out, doing KP duty, standing sentry all through the night, and more—it was go, go, go all day long every day, and we never had a minute to ourselves. The only way you could manage to get it all done was to cut short the time you spent washing your face, or in the toilet, or doing your laundry and such.

But the worst part of it all was the morning and afternoon drills. Those drill instructors really put us through the wringer. Each session of basic training began like this: We would fall in, then stand motionless, and salute. Then the drill began, and it was so physically demanding that I understood clearly why none but the 1-A draftees were inducted into the Artillery Corps—only men in tip-top physical condition could survive it.

Infantrymen carried a Model 38 infantryman's rifle, which wasn't terribly heavy, or at most a machine gun or grenade launcher, but the field artillery crews had to man the big field guns such as howitzers and cannons, and that was real work, I can tell you. They were so heavy, if you took one of those babies apart and tried to lift a piece—just one piece of it!—up on your shoulder, why you'd be flat on your ass before you knew it. So there was no way a man could walk carrying a part of one of those big guns on his shoulder.

Actually, one of the infantrymen was, it turned out, fool enough to try to do just that. In the very act of lifting it up onto his shoulder, he collapsed backward under the weight and was pinned under it. It smashed his ankle to bits, and he had to go to the hospital.

The Artilleryman's Drill Manual said, 'Your gun and you will share the same fate.' The infantryman was issued his old-style Model 38 infantryman's rifle as a sacred gift from the Emperor and was trained to think of it as his own flesh and blood. Our field artillery training was much more rigorous and demanded much more of us.

The purpose, cleaning, and correct assembly of every single piece of the ten-centimeter howitzer was drummed into our heads. We also had to learn how to handle the dray horses that pulled the guns around the battlefield and practice hitching them to the howitzer drays and guiding them to position the guns where we wanted. We also had to rub down the horses after drill, care for their hooves, feed them and clean up after them, and clean out the stable. In the field artillery corps, we had all the duties of infantrymen, transport corpsmen, and cavalrymen in addition to our official duties as artillerymen. For us artillery recruits, it all added up to day after endless day of grinding drudgery.

After a few brutal days of this sort of intense drilling and being slapped around by the senior soldiers at the slightest provocation, I felt I had reached the end of my rope both physically and emotionally. Some of my fellow recruits were actually driven over the edge and were discharged as being mentally disturbed and unfit for military service; and one even hung himself.

We were always hearing that once you were stationed out on some battlefield, you could take it easy most of the time, so naturally we were eager to be sent into battle to escape the hell of basic training.

About six months after our induction, soon after completing our second review, my group of recruits was sent to Central China.

It was June, 1940, about eighteen months before the start of the Pacific War. We shipped out from Ujina harbor at Hiroshima and headed for Hubei Sheng in China. As soon as we arrived, we were sent into battle in Operation Yi Chang.

Our military training continued in the field, and it was even worse than what we'd gone through back in Japan—exactly the opposite of what we'd been told by the old hands. Even when we weren't fighting, we could always hear the metallic sound of sporadic rifle fire, the staccato of Czechoslovakia-made machine-gun fire, and the sound of trench mortar shells exploding both in the distance and nearby. With those constant reminders of war and the all-too-real possibility of sudden death all around us, we warmed to the training drills and really got down to the business of learning how to fight and kill. The attitude of the senior soldiers, who had fought in many battles, was quite different on the battlefield from the jocular bullying they'd shown us back in Japan. They told us time and again in no uncertain terms what we were up against.

'You hear that gunfire out there, you sorry grunts? You'd better listen up and learn this shit, 'cause how hard you train now will determine whether one of those bullets hits you or not, and whether you live or die!'

When they said things like that, we recruits listened up, all right, and drilled even harder.

Over the next two years, I rose in the ranks first from one-star to two-star private, then from two-star to three-star private.

About that time, I was looking over a troop of new recruits who had just arrived from Kyoto, when who did I see but my very own little brother, Toru!

'Big brother!' he cried out, a look of utter surprise on his face as if I were the last person on earth he had expected to run into there; and despite the rules of Army discipline, he ran over to me and gave me a big hug.

Toru was by nature a bit faint-hearted, and he had gotten a classification of 1-B on his draft physical. He was so puny and weak that if the war hadn't been going on for so long, he would never have been assigned to a unit as tough and physically demanding as the field artillery corps. Unfortunately, his frailty had given the drill instructors and senior soldiers even more reason to bully him. He appeared to have been the victim of some pretty vicious hazing even for a new recruit; his slightly lop-sided face, swollen on one side, told me he had been slapped around pretty badly.

On the one hand, it was wonderful to see a face so dear to me, and I was truly glad that fate had put him in my regiment; but on the other hand, in the special sphere of Army life, he was a ready target for bullies. The thought of them picking on him and pushing him around rankled in my heart; as his older brother, I made up my mind to protect and shield him from the taunts and blows of men stronger than him.

I was by nature defiant and aggressive, and by this time I had some senior ranking, so I wasn't scared of anyone in the regiment. I was a three-star private, and the raw recruits and the two-year men alike respected me as a seasoned veteran. A soldier's place in the military hierarchy depends on how long he has been in the Army; since I thought nothing of the young probationary officers with their gold stars on their collars and treated them highhandedly, they kept a respectful distance between themselves and me.

The barracks of our field artillery battalion were located in a village called Ying Shan, and an airfield had been built right next to the village.

There was no fighting going on at the time, and even though guerrillas infested the area, the infantry unit stationed nearby could always take care of them. As a result, I was able to relax and take it easy for the first time since I'd entered the service.

But it wasn't long before a new battalion commander, who had graduated from the Military Academy, arrived to take over the command, and we had to shape up and get back in the thick of the fighting. Our field artillery corps sometimes went as far as the front line around Pin Jing Guan in the secured areas of Ma Ping and Zhe He and fired our howitzers at the enemy's position.

In my fourth year of military service, I was promoted to the rank of private first class and could now wear one gold stripe on the collar of my uniform. But that doesn't mean that I was particularly interested in getting promotions; actually, the gold stripe made me feel sort of self-conscious.

Transfer to the Philippines

We were still enjoying a relatively quiet, relaxing interlude at the Chinese front when our regiment suddenly got new orders. We were to be transferred to the Philippines. It was the summer of 1944. First, we were to join the Kanto Army stationed in Manchuria, in northeastern China, but soon we were to be transferred to the Philippines to prepare for the U.S. Army's counteroffensive and defend Manila. Though soldiers at our level in the chain of command were not told anything about this at the time, those stirring days early in the Pacific War when Japan won every battle were a thing of the past, and the American and Japanese positions were just beginning to reverse. Before, we had been able to send letters home from China without restriction, but now we were forbidden to say anything about our upcoming transfer to the Philippines in our letters. Our sudden transfer and the strict order not to mention it in letters home gave us our first inkling that the war in the Pacific must be going pretty badly.

Japanese troops from many parts of China were assembled at Lüda, where we boarded about twenty troopships and set sail from China, all of us fervently wishing that the ships had been taking us home to Japan.

Even land troops like us could see that the 3,000-ton class troopships carrying us were broken-down and dilapidated. To make matters worse, about three thousand soldiers were crowded into each ship, so we were jammed together like sardines in a can. The convoy was led by an old destroyer that looked as if it might have seen action in the Russo-Japanese War of 1904-1905, and a few coastal defense ships guarded our flanks and rear. We followed a zigzag course in case of a torpedo attack by enemy submarines. As the ships sailed along slowly, the blazing sun of August beat down mercilessly. Inside the ships, it was like a steam bath; in order to escape the heat belowdecks and also because we thought it was safer to be above deck if there happened to be a torpedo attack, many of us scrambled to get a place on deck and held on to it for the duration of the voyage. Each ship contained troops from many different regiments that had been stationed in various encampments throughout China, so disputes over the choice spots were generally determined by brute force.

I don't know why, but once the ship had set sail, my thoughts drifted back over the years I had spent in China, and a variety of emotions filled my heart. I remembered the pleasant, though certainly superficial, personal contacts I'd had with the Chinese civilians at the Army post where I'd been stationed, and the poor, harmless farmers entangled in the war. I know now that Japanese troops committed atrocious acts in some parts of China, but as far as I know, our regiment maintained close military discipline. For example, First Lieutenant Yamamoto, our company commander, who was a graduate of the Military Academy, always forbade us to pillage the towns and villages we captured. The process of procuring food from the locals sometimes led to misunderstandings, because of the language barrier and the difference in customs, but we always paid them something for what we took, we didn't rob them. As a result, the children from the villages and surrounding farms often came to the Army post to play, and most of us enjoyed horsing around with them in our free moments. We naturally grew fond of them, and they of us. When our orders for the Philippines came and we pulled out so suddenly, some of the Chinese boys even cried. These thoughts that were going through my mind as the ship sailed out of the harbor; in a way, I was sorry to leave the land that had been my home for the past three and a half years, and in my heart I bid China a silent good-bye.

The convoy arrived without incident at Kaohsiung in Taiwan and stopped there for about a week to lay in a supply of food and pick up weapons and ammunition. The stopover ended up taking longer than had been planned, so we were suddenly given permission to take turns going ashore and got an unexpected chance to stretch our legs on land and unwind. Under ordinary circumstances, soldiers being transported usually had to stay cooped up on the overcrowded ships; perhaps the commanding officers took pity on us, since our convoy was continuing on to the Philippines without even stopping in Japan. Or perhaps when suddenly faced with unavoidable delays, they decided it would be less trouble to let us go ashore than to have 3,000 soldiers on each ship eating up the stored provisions.

Even though we didn't visit Japan on our way to the Philippines, we were able to get at least a taste of home in the Japanese-style meals served in the restaurants and coffee shops of Taiwan, a Japanese territory at the time, not to mention the readily available, traditional Japanese sweets. We ate our fill and really kicked up our heels.

Then the convoy set sail again, across the Bashi Channel toward the Philippines. Just one month after we left, the port of Kaohsiung was bombed. Two months later, in October and November of 1944, Japan lost naval supremacy in the East China Sea; and due to repeated attacks by U.S. submarines, the Bashi Channel, south of Taiwan, became such a dangerous place that it came to be called *Ma no Umi*—'the Devil's Sea' Close to ninety percent of Japan's transport ships were hit and sunk, and tens of thousands of our troops were swallowed up by the sea, all traces of them lost forever.

Luckily, when the convoy that took my regiment to the Philippines sailed through those waters, the torpedo attacks by American submarines had just begun; and Japan still had some aircraft left then, a few of which would circle over our convoy from time to time on patrol. Each time we looked up and saw our planes flying overhead, we felt reassured knowing that they were protecting us from enemy vessels. But there were rumors that several ships in the convoy that had set sail right before ours had been sunk by torpedoes, so we were in constant fear every day of the voyage. Without even being ordered to do so, we all kept our eyes peeled for enemy submarines.

Despite our fears and the possibility of attack, our convoy managed to cross the Bashi Channel safely, and the anxiously awaited mountains of Luzon finally came into view. They were a beautiful sight, rising up out of the sea in the distance, all covered with the lush, dark green jungle foliage characteristic of the Tropics. After dropping off some of the troops and their equipment at Aparri on the northern end of Luzon, our convoy sailed down to the southern end of the island and at last put in at our final destination, the port of Manila.

Just as I had heard, the sunset there was incredibly beautiful, surely one of the most beautiful in the world. In the evening calm, the motionless surface of the sea was a gorgeous emerald green, reflecting the burning rays of the setting sun, and the color of the sky changed from moment to moment—from red to yellow to purple to azure. It was a mysterious, affecting scene, almost otherworldly. I could hardly believe that this exquisite landscape, as near to paradise as one could hope for in this world, would soon become a bloody battlefield. As I gazed out over the shining water and thought of my dear homeland far away beyond that vast sky that seemed the very symbol of peace, I felt a pang of homesickness, made all the sharper for having been told that a decisive battle was imminent.

Our unit belonged to the 16th Army Division, whose main force had already been transferred from Luzon to Leyte Island in early April, 1944, to prepare to repel an expected American advance; but several battalions had been ordered to remain on Luzon, and our unit was placed under the command of their commanding officer.

In Manila, most of our troops came down with dengue and developed a terrible fever. A sports stadium had been requisitioned for our billet. All the big hotels and the University of La Salle, which must have been beautiful at one time, were closed and boarded up, having been ruined by Japanese troops billeted there earlier.

The people of Manila were forced to bow in the direction of the Imperial Palace in Tokyo, and the children had to exercise to Japanese radio exercise programs at their schools each morning and sing out the count in unison in Japanese, 'Ichi, ni, san!' And in the streets I saw Japanese soldiers slap Filipino civilians across the face for being 'uncooperative.'

It seemed to me that if we had to force the ideals of our Greater East Asia Co-Prosperity Sphere onto other peoples by making them repeat political slogans over and over ad nauseum, so that they were merely giving lip service to those ideals instead of really learning to accept them as their own, then those ideals had already failed.

In the beginning, I had thought our orders were to defend Manila, but to our surprise, we were commanded to set up a base of operations at Dingalan Bay on the eastern coast of the island, which would put us in a position to repel U.S. landing operations on the eastern coast of central Luzon.

We marched to the shoreline, the dray horses pulling our ten-centimeter howitzers, which had enormous firepower. Our mission was to destroy the American landing craft as soon as they attempted to land.

Of course, infantry units were also in position there and had the barrels of their rapid-fire cannons, small cannons, and machine guns aimed at the shoreline. We devoted all our thought and energy to preparing a coordinated, invincible line of firepower with which to meet the enemy.

The work of entrenchment began on September 25 and was completed about three months later at the end of December. We had built a full-scale defense position and were prepared to drive back the enemy.

Meanwhile, we received news of the war situation on Leyte Island and learned that the main force of the 16th Army Division had been annihilated in November. A pall of sadness and grim uncertainty fell over us, and our anxiety increased. In early December, U.S. troops landed on Mindoro Island. Japanese special attack units, commonly known as kamikaze, were sent out again and again on suicide missions to crash their fighter planes into enemy ships in Leyte Gulf, in a desperate attempt to stop the enemy's advance. I received this news solemnly, in awe of the supreme sacrifice these brave pilots were making.

Soon after, to our surprise, we received a report that on January 9, 1945, a large enemy force had landed on the opposite, western shore of Luzon Island in Lingayen Gulf. We were suddenly ordered to move out.

None of us could get over the fact that our three months of hard work and entrenchment had all been in vain, but an order was an order, so we hurriedly broke camp and began moving our artillery back across the island, heading for the city of San José on the central plain of Luzon.

Such a move was a lot more work for our artillery unit than it was for the infantrymen. It took us more than a week to pack up our ammunition and provisions and get the big field guns ready to move. So the infantry units, the bulk of our troops, went on ahead and were soon lost to sight, while our artillery unit trailed along behind.

Even as we were getting ready to move, we could already hear the distant gunfire of Filipino guerrilla ambushes up on the mountain paths, and we were exposed to repeated air raids by U.S. Army Lockheed fighter planes. Owing to their domination of the skies, we could only travel at night, and even at that, they often spotted us at dusk or dawn and were quick to attack. Each time they bore down on us with their bombs and machine-gun fire, several trucks of supplies and ammunition went up in flames, several dozen dray horses were slaughtered outright in a split second or wounded so badly they were rendered useless to us, and many of our men were killed or wounded.

Our information about the movements of the U.S. troops after their landing at Lingayen was sketchy at best, and as we made our way through Bongabon toward San José, we received word that the Americans had already invaded San José. We halted our advance. We were faced with the difficult and critical decision of whether or not to backtrack to Rizal.

Despite being unable to go forward, we nevertheless decided not to go back, and we set up a gun emplacement right there, concentrating all our firepower in the direction of the enemy tanks that we expected to appear at any moment.

Before long, we came under heavy bombardment and machine-gun fire from enemy fighter planes. We dived behind the nearest object for cover or hit the dirt and didn't budge an inch.

Our commanders' estimation of the situation was completely off the mark, for there wasn't a sign of any enemy tanks. Deprived of the targets we'd expected, our unit fired all its 10-centimeter howitzer shells at the city center of San José and then turned back to Rizal. We massed our troops there and two days later set out on the road to Carranglan to join up with the main force. From the piles of abandoned ammunition boxes that littered the sides of the road, we knew that the Japanese troops who had traveled this road before us had been driven to a frantic, helter-skelter retreat.

At a spot about ten kilometers northeast of Rizal, we started up into the mountains along narrow, dirt paths. We saw many trenches and defense positions built by Japanese troops in all the critical places along the road. Although we traveled under the cover of the massive, jungle trees that towered above us, we were spotted by enemy planes circling overhead; they must have reported our position to American ground troops, because it wasn't long before heavy, concentrated artillery fire rained down on us, killing or wounding many of our men. When the shelling was over, our few remaining artillery guns had been damaged beyond repair. Worse still, maddened by the exploding bombs, the dray horses had stampeded and run off a cliff, dragging howitzers, shells, and other essential equipment with them. Thus, in the wink of an eye, we were put in the sorry position of being an artillery unit without a single field gun.

We regrouped and made our way to the area locally known as the Spanish Road, which we called Suzuka Pass, in the mountainous region between Carranglan and Aritao. This area was crucial to our defense of the island, so we took up our position. In accordance with our new orders, we readied ourselves for duty as a guerrilla unit armed with small arms instead of field guns and dug in, preparing to harass the enemy's rear.

During all this fighting, my little brother Toru, who had joined my unit in China as a buck private not long before our transfer to the Philippines, was right by my side. We had both come down with dengue soon after arriving at Manila, and we had shared every hardship since. As I said before, he was weaker than me, so I always gave him part of my meager food rations. Sometimes when we encountered enemy small-arms fire or artillery, he would be so frightened and confused he didn't know which way to turn, so I'd push him down to the ground and throw myself on top of him. He was my little brother, who always looked up to me and depended on me, and he was dearer to me than life itself; I would have done anything to protect him from the dangers on those bloody battlefields.

As we lay still as the dead behind some rock or tree, we would talk to divert our minds from the terror that kept a constant, icy grip on our hearts. We'd talk about Kyoto and our mother, and the foods of home—oh, food was a big topic among us soldiers in the field. Toru and I would talk about the terrific, sweet, adzuki-bean soup with chestnuts at a shop near Kawaramachi Boulevard or the wonderful Western-style food at the Star Restaurant, and dream about the days after the war when we'd return to Japan and get rich enough to eat in high-class restaurants like Manyoken and Yaomasa.

Armed with outdated Model 38 infantry rifles and hand grenades, we would cut behind enemy lines, move in as close as thirty meters to an enemy camp, and stage an attack to create a disturbance so that we could steal some of their provisions. Other times, we'd lie hidden in foxholes all day long, waiting for the enemy to show his face, and when the Americans came close enough, we'd fire a volley in unison and send them scurrying. That's the sort of sneaky, guerrilla warfare we had to resort to.

Then we'd search the bodies of the American soldiers we had just killed for anything useful. Our rifles were old-fashioned, single-fire models, and even at that, there weren't enough to go around, so we'd take the American soldiers' repeating rifles and go through their pockets looking for cigarettes and food. Still, every time we had one of these skirmishes with the Americans, we lost five or six men to their overwhelmingly superior weaponry. Before long, our unit had dwindled down to a small, ragged band of survivors, the pitiful remnants of a defeated army.

Occasionally, we ran into groups of survivors from other regiments along the road. Judging from their behavior, the passing down of orders along the chain of command was not going smoothly. We witnessed squabbles between soldiers and noncommissioned officers; some of the soldiers were openly defiant and rebellious, ignoring orders even from their platoon leader or company commander.

From the day of my induction into the Imperial Army, this rule had been drummed into my head: 'You are to regard an order from an officer as an order from His Majesty the Emperor himself.' Those words had carried weight back during our basic training in Japan and while we were still winning every battle we fought, but among the disorderly mobs that many of our surviving troops had become, they were now just hot air. Unrest among the men was so great that the once-arrogant and the inept officers alike feared they might be beaten to death by their own men if they weren't careful.

Upon entering military service, each of us had been issued a rifle emblazoned with the Imperial chrysanthemum crest. We were taught to treasure it as an object entrusted to us by the Emperor himself and to handle it carefully and with due respect. If even a speck of dust was found on a man's rifle during inspection, our drill instructor smacked him so hard it practically knocked the man's jaw out of joint. But in combat, these single-fire rifles were so old-fashioned and inferior as to be practically useless compared with the U.S. Army's high-performance, re-peat-fire rifles; and some of the men ended up discarding their Model 38 rifles by the side of the road the minute they could get their hands on one of the dead American soldier's rifles.

The invincible Imperial Army had fought China in 1894-1895, Russia in 1904-1905, in World War I and the Manchurian Incident, and China again in 1937, and had never been defeated. We had been indoctrinated to believe in certain victory above all else; our hearts and minds had been filled with the imperative that it was our sacred duty to sacrifice everything—even our lives— for the sake of our country and His Majesty the Emperor. We had been deluded into believing that Japan was invincible. Once we started to lose the war, however, the once-unthinkable prospect of defeat pulled the blinders from our eyes, and we at last saw this half-baked war philosophy based on the presumption of Japan's invincibility for what it was—a fragile illusion.

Our commander was an exceptionally warmhearted person, both liked and respected by the men, and an officer of superior judgment and leadership ability, so he was able to maintain some degree of military discipline in our company. We trusted him and believed that our best chance for survival lay in sticking with him, though by this time there were only a few dozen of us left alive.

Mortal Combat on Luzon

We struggled on, but by mid-March, the U.S. Army had gained almost complete control of the central plain of Luzon and had started attacking Balete Pass, Sarakusaku Pass, and the Spanish Road, which we called Suzuka Pass, in order to flush out the Japanese troops that had escaped into the mountains to the north.

That life-and-death combat between our two armies was an appalling, ghastly experience more horrible than words can describe. In order to protect the main force, commanded by General Yamashita and camped quite a ways to the north, the *Tetsu* and *Geki* corps were given strict orders to stand their ground and 'retreat not a single step.' Each man dug a foxhole for himself on the side of the mountain and got inside to wait for the enemy. At night, shock troop units went out on potentially suicidal raids behind enemy lines, but our casualties were high, and the Imperial Army continued to dwindle in the face of the Americans' vastly superior weaponry and material resources.

Our suicidal 'human bullet' tactic of storming enemy tanks with hand grenades was sometimes effective in the beginning, but losing several tanks that way, the Americans learned to forestall such attacks by firing a flame-thrower methodically into our foxholes, one by one, before advancing. This reduced the effectiveness of our 'human bullet' tactic to almost zero and sent our casualties soaring. As the fighting went on day after day, I saw more and more blackened, gore-dripping corpses of Japanese soldiers lying piled in heaps or scattered on the ground.

By early May, in spite of our immense efforts, the Americans had pushed us back as far as Balete Pass. The men of our company built a new line of defense; we again dug foxholes on the sides of all the mountains surrounding Balete Pass and holed up in them to await the inevitable arrival of the enemy. But this time, too, the American heavy bombers rained their massive shells down on us mercilessly in such numbers and intensity that the very contour of the landscape was altered. Under such an onslaught, we succumbed easily; it was all we could do to hold out for a few days.

Even though we had almost nothing to eat, many of us developed diarrhea, probably caused by amoebic dysentery, and spent day after day in those wretched foxholes lying in a stinking pool of mud and our own feces. All around us, the unmistakable, sickly-sweet stench of the rotting corpses of our slain comrades hung in the air. There was nothing we could do: If we tried to move even a short distance from our foxholes during the daylight hours, we were spotted immediately and deluged with heavy gunfire, so we just had to take it—the pain in the gut, the stench from our own shit and rotting corpses, the cold-sweat terror of not knowing if the next bomb would blow us to smithereens—and sit there motionless in the foxholes until it got dark. Those days, hours, minutes, seconds were more terrible and agonizing than any hell I could imagine.

After the U.S. Army smashed through our lines of defense at Balete Pass and Sarakusaku Pass with its intense firepower and seemingly endless supply of ammunition, we started looking for a new site to set up a guerrilla-warfare base of operations in the Gadeng region on the uppermost branch of the Cagayan River. We advanced more or less aimlessly through trackless bush along a deep gorge cut into the mountains.

The rainy season had set in, and the river at the bottom of the gorge was beginning to rise. The corpses of Japanese soldiers from units that had preceded us along that route lay scattered along the path. They had collapsed from hunger, amoebic dysentery, or malaria; and since their companions had no way to care for them or help them, they had been left to die where they fell. Some of the poor wretches were still alive, though just barely: Their bodies were wasted away to skin and bones; their eyes, open just a slit, gazed lifelessly ahead without seeing; they didn't even ask us for help as we passed by—they were just waiting to die.

We had a terrible time cutting our way through the overgrown brush that blocked our way. Some days we advanced only about fifty meters. We also had to brush off the leeches that fell onto us from the overhead branches of trees and contend with swarms of mosquitoes, lice, and giant ants that bit us.

Many of the corpses we passed by were already nothing but bleached skeletons, and black mounds of hideous green-bottle flies swarmed over those that had a few shreds of carrion still clinging to them. These were hellish sights, more horrible than anything I ever dreamed I'd see in this world. I know you'll find this hard to believe, but more often than I care to remember I witnessed some of our men, transformed by hunger and terror into fiends, finish off our dying comrades-in-arms by bashing in their heads just to get their hands on the fallen soldier's last cache of rice—a mouthful or two at most! And it was a daily occurrence to see men throw away their worn-out boots and put on those removed from the bodies of the dead.

Before long, yet another tragedy beset us. Our company commander, who was the highest-ranking officer in our group, took a bad hit in the thigh from a stray bullet, probably fired by a Filipino guerrilla. We were able to stop the bleeding, but as you can imagine, he was in pretty poor condition from malnutrition and exhaustion anyway, and his resistance was low. We couldn't stop the wound from festering, and his whole body was soon shaking due to a high fever brought on by malaria or perhaps blood poisoning. He lay there stoically in that godforsaken place, gritting his teeth against the pain, and eventually died without speaking.

We dragged the body of our respected senior officer a little way off the path so that soldiers passing that way after us would not step on it or see the pathetic, horrible sight of it covered with maggots and left to rot. That was all we could do. We simply didn't have the strength or the will to dig a hole and bury him.

You probably think tropical countries have lots of wild fruits and vegetables that we could have gathered and eaten—bananas, mangoes, papayas, yams, and the like; but the fact is they grow only around populated areas. Far back in the jungle, where we were, nothing like that grows. There was absolutely nothing to eat, and we were slowly starving to death.

After losing our commanding officer, the few remaining members of our unit gradually split up and went off on their own. Toru and I were now by ourselves and simply wandered through the mountain jungle like famished ghosts, searching for something—anything—to eat. What happened to the other men of our company, whether they lived or died, was a matter of complete indifference to us.

From time to time, Toru would look as if he were about to collapse, but I urged him on, believing that we would be saved if we could just meet up with a large force of our troops, it didn't matter which unit. The only way through the jungle was littered with corpses, but we continued north toward Gadeng at a snail's pace. At times, it seemed as if we were pushing our way through a sea of rotting corpses.

In the rays of light that filtered down through the dense web of tree branches overhead, I could see my little brother, his hair and beard grown long and scraggly, his body pitifully gaunt and bony; the only sign of life left in him was the desperate, hungry gleam in his eyes as we searched in vain for something to eat. Weakened by starvation, amoebic dysentery, and malaria, he was obviously near death. He looked ghastly, almost like a walking corpse.

Finally, it seemed as if the end had come. I was holding him up as we trudged on, his arm slung across my shoulders, when suddenly I felt him go limp and he crumpled to the ground.

'Come on, Toru! You've got to keep walking!' I ordered sternly, but I knew it was useless.

I had precious little strength left myself. Too exhausted to do anything else, I slumped down beside Toru and just let my eyes lazily follow the scattered rays of light filtering down from above and gazed up at the small patch of sky above us.

I didn't even have the energy to think any more.

Toru mumbled, trying to say something. I put my ear close to his lips.

'Water, want to drink water . . .' The words, actually more a rasp, came from deep in his throat, and I could barely make out what he was saying. Then, he whispered something that for a moment froze my already hardened heart with horror.

'Please, big brother, eat my body! I can't make it out of here, but you can. Use my flesh to survive, so you can return home to Kyoto and take care of our mother. I'm done for, but part of me can live on in you, so do what I say. Please, I beg you!'

With that, his head fell to his chest. For a moment, I thought he had died, but he was still breathing, though just barely.

I summoned up what little strength I had left and cried, 'Toru! What are you saying! You've got to hang on. We'll make it back to Kyoto alive, you and me together! We promised each other we would, remember? I'm going to get you some water now. You'll be all right! You'll see!'

I struggled to my feet and stumbled off down the mountainside toward the sound of rushing water in the gorge below.

I knew he was going to die, but I wanted at least to give him the drink of water he'd begged for to ease his final moments.

It sounded as if the churning flood waters were close by, but I had a terrible time getting to them, fighting my way through the thickets of trees and dense jungle brush—half-stumbling, half-crawling on all fours because I didn't even have the strength to stand up and walk properly.

I finally slid down the steep side of the gorge and reached the bank of the river. Just as I was about to fill a makeshift bamboo-tube canteen with water, my eyes fell on the badly decomposed bodies of several Japanese soldiers floating in the water directly in front of me. When I at last recovered from my shock and revulsion enough to force myself to put my hand holding the bamboo tube into the water, I noticed for the first time more bodies on either side of me lying face down on the riverbank half in, half out of the water. They had probably used their last ounce of energy to drag themselves to the water's edge and died just as they were about to drink.

Disgusted as I was, my thirst-ravaged body was beyond caring whether the water was dirty or foul-smelling, and I gulped it down greedily. Then I filled the bamboo-tube canteen with water, summoned up my last ounce of strength and determination, and began crawling back up the slope to Toru.

It took me a good two hours of sweat and strain to get back up, and it was a terrible ordeal. But when I finally arrived back at the spot where I'd left Toru, I found a scene more hellish, more gut-wrenching than all the hideous things I'd seen so far.

I was used to seeing the piles of corpses, the bleached bones, and the rotting flesh of my fallen comrades-in-arms, and such grisly scenes no longer shocked me. But the scene that lay before me now was not just another atrocity for my benumbed mind to see without really seeing. Two men with filthy, unkempt beards were standing next to Toru. One of them had a half-torn-off sergeant major's insignia on his collar; they were apparently from one of the groups of Japanese guerrillas that were roaming the mountain jungle. They had removed my little brother's tattered uniform, and were slicing off pieces of flesh from his thigh with their swords and stuffing them into their mouths!

They had seen me crawling up over the edge of the cliff, but they didn't show any surprise; they merely kept their impassive faces turned toward me and watched me closely. Their beards around their mouths were smeared bright red with blood—my little brother's blood! In the dim light of the jungle floor, it was truly a scene out of Hell.

A wordless howl of rage and madness burst from my lips, and though I had been too weak to stand up just a few seconds before, I jumped up and charged headlong at them, ready to tear them limb from limb with my bare hands.

To my bitter regret at the time, however, I didn't stand a chance against them. It had been days since I had last eaten anything, and I was so weak it was a miracle I could stand up at all. They, on the other hand, had been feeding and surviving on human flesh and still had some strength left. Without a word they turned to meet my charge. Grabbing me by the front of my uniform, the sergeant major pushed me toward the edge of the cliff and kicked me viciously in the groin. I tumbled backwards over the edge of the cliff down the mountainside into the gorge below.

The last thing I remember was a whirl of tree trunks, bushes, and branches going round and round before my eyes as I rolled head over heels down the side of the gorge.

I rolled all the way down to the riverbank, where my fall was stopped by a corpse lying half in the water, which kept me from falling into the river where I would surely have drowned. In the moment of impact, however, I began to lose consciousness. Sunlight through the leaves danced on my closed eyelids for a moment or so, and then I blacked out.

When I came to, I could hardly believe it, but I was in an American field relief station. My head was all wrapped up in bandages, and I figured my right arm was broken because it was in a cast and anchored so that I couldn't move it. A needle was stuck into a vein in my left arm, and 500 cc or so of some liquid was dripping into my body through a tube.

'Death before the dishonor of captivity.' These words had been drummed into my head since my first day in the Army, but my first thought on regaining consciousness was, 'Thank God I'm alive!'

I guessed that some American soldiers had found me passed out but still breathing, and carried me out of the jungle with them. If they'd just left me there, I'd have died for sure. It wouldn't have surprised me if they'd just put a bullet in my head as an act of mercy, so, all things considered, I was pretty lucky.

Ironically, the field relief station was located far behind the enemy's front line, in San José, the city we'd emptied our field guns on a few weeks earlier.

The American base was laid out in an orderly fashion. Several dozen trucks and tanks were parked next to a mountain of gasoline cans. Beyond the neat rows of round-roof barracks, there were even a few tennis and basketball courts, where some off-duty soldiers were playing with their shirts off and having a good time.

I and the other Japanese prisoners had to wear shirts and slacks stamped with the letters 'PW.' There couldn't have been less than fifty of us.

As we slowly recovered from malnutrition and our various diseases and wounds, we began to remember the soldiers who had been our friends and comrades back in the mountain jungle, the ones who had starved to death, died of disease, fallen in combat, or blown themselves up with their own hand grenades in the extremity of pain and despair. Even as I lay safe in my hospital bed, there must have been many Japanese soldiers still out there, starving and wandering the mountains aimlessly like lost souls. The thought of them tore at my heart and filled me with unbearable sadness. I even began to feel guilty for being alive and well fed in the hands of the enemy. But another idea was tormenting me, too.

'Isn't there any way,' I asked myself, 'to stop this hopeless, futile war and save them?'

What I had seen in the mountain jungle just before my fall down the cliff still haunted me: the unspeakable sight of my little brother Toru and the hideous faces of the two Japanese guerrillas—cannibalistic beasts!—who were devouring his flesh. That scene had been burned into my brain with such force that I knew I would never forget it. But now, with a full belly and a calmer view of things, I realized that those two were also victims of the war, and a feeling akin to pity for them began to take hold in my heart. At the same time, I could not help thinking that what they had done to Toru was the one act of man against man that absolutely could not be forgiven, and my mind tossed fitfully in the nightmarish web of these opposing and inextricably tangled emotions.

They, too, must have abandoned their jobs and been pulled away from their families and friends back home in Japan for the sake of this 'holy war,' only to end up killing their own comrades-in-arms and wandering aimlessly through the hostile mountain jungle of a foreign land. On that battlefield, the reality was that if you didn't eat human flesh, you would die, too. It seemed to me that the soldiers who had been put in that unspeakable predicament of having to choose between death and cannibalism were the ones who suffered the cruelest fate. As I pondered these sad, perplexing matters during my recovery, I realized that the real responsibility for these atrocities lay far beyond the men who committed them, with the men in Tokyo who had started this hellish war in the first place.

The Defeat of Japan

The war ended on August 15. We Japanese prisoners of war could tell that the American soldiers at the military base were drunk with victory, and their cheers and shouts of joy rang through the base. I, too, felt relieved that the war was over, but it goes without saying that I bitterly envied the Americans their victory. The conflict of these mixed feelings drained me emotionally, and I felt exhausted to the very core of my being.

Before long, we Japanese prisoners heard the American soldiers singing in unison a song we'd never heard before, and I saw all of them bow their heads as their Army Chaplain led them in prayer. I thought they were probably giving thanks to their god for their great victory over us.

After becoming a prisoner of war, I often saw examples of their religiousness and demonstrations of the humanity inspired by that religion, the like of which I had seldom observed among my fellow Japanese comrades-in-arms.

I also gradually came to have an understanding of their concept of democracy. Utterly unlike the compulsory indoctrination based on the Emperor system of government practiced in Japan that I had been subjected to, democracy appeared to be an ideology of freedom that Americans learned naturally, without being forced to by their government. I learned that democracy is based on the principle that if each person thinks an idea or plan is good, then he casts his vote accordingly, and the majority of votes determines how the government and country will be run.

From the time I was captured by the Americans till I returned to Japan, not once was I subjected to any sort of indoctrination.

Meanwhile, many Japanese soldiers who had been hiding up in the mountain jungle heard the news of the war's end and came down and surrendered. Many other Japanese soldiers were killed even after the 15th of August by Filipino guerrillas who had not yet received word that the war was over. This sad news brought home to me once again the utter waste and tragedy of war.

In October, the other Japanese prisoners and I were transported in open trucks through the streets of Manila and put on board a Japanese coastal defense ship that had survived the war. Much of the city had been destroyed during the war and now lay in ruins, bearing mute witness to the ferocity of the battles that had been fought there.

As the trucks carrying us passed by, the Filipinos in the streets raised their fists at us and shouted, '*Japón, Japón, bakayaro!*'

'Bow toward the Imperial Palace!' some of them bawled at us contemptuously.

Once, not so long before, these people had had to put up with Japanese soldiers slapping them across the face and saying, 'Bakayaro—Fuck you!' and with being forced to sing the Japanese national anthem and worship the Emperor of Japan. Now it was their turn to vent their long-repressed resentment and hatred toward us, and they hurled back at us now the very same words of abuse that we had taught them.

Here, too, Japan's great ideal of the Greater East Asia Co-Prosperity Sphere had crumbled quickly and easily, proving that we had instilled nothing but hatred in the hearts and minds of the people we had sought to bring into our fold under Japan's rule. We Japanese had paid dearly for this war and made countless others pay dearly as well, and for what? How futile and senseless this war had been, producing nothing but sacrifice and sorrow, hatred and pain, and the deaths of countless thousands!

But that is the true nature of all wars. . . .

Before boarding the ship, we were sprayed with DDT to rid us of body lice. As we stood there looking at each other's funny-looking, powder-white heads and faces, a huge wave of relief suddenly welled up in us, and we couldn't help breaking into amused smiles and grins at the comic figures we made. The coastal defense ship at last moved away from the quay at Manila harbor and set a straight course for home, Japan.

We were baptized once again with DDT after the ship landed at Sasebo in Kyushu.

'Ahh, home at last!' my heart cried, nearly bursting with joy. I felt like kissing the ground.

The situation I found in Japan after my return was just as my fellow spirits have already told you. I took a jam-packed train to Kyoto and headed for home. It was a sad, lonely sort of homecoming, partly because it had already turned dark; but when I had walked the relatively short distance from Kyoto Station and stood before my mother's house, my legs were trembling with both joy at being home at last and tension from a new problem—namely, what to tell my mother about Toru. It pained me to think of the anguish she would suffer if I told her the true circumstances of my dear little brother's death in the mountain jungle of Luzon.

I slid open the front door, and it still stuck just as it had done the day I left to join my regiment five long years before. My mother, whose safety I had prayed for without fail throughout the long war, was sitting there in the small living room I'd yearned for and seen a thousand times in my dreams, sipping the bowl of rice-and-vegetable gruel that was her dinner.

I'll never forget her face at that moment. Though she looked up and saw me, she couldn't immediately take in the fact that her son was back from the war; but then she realized it was true, and tears of joy rolled down her wrinkled cheeks.

She had learned that Toru's and my regiment had been transferred from its original post in China to the Philippines, and later heard rumors that the Kyoto 16th Army Division had been annihilated in the Philippines, so she had half-resigned herself to the overwhelming probability that both of us were dead. I had agonized over this moment for many weeks, and there was no way I could bring myself to tell her that Toru had been killed and his flesh eaten by some of our own soldiers. Breaking the news of his death to her as gently as possible, I told her that he and I had become separated in the confusion of battle and I had later learned that he had been killed in combat.

If this were your run-of-the-mill war story, it would end here with my safe return home and reunion with my mother and the closing line 'and they lived happily ever after.' But I haven't told you yet how my body came to be one of the cadavers your class is dissecting, Yoshio.

Despite her joy and relief at having me back safe and sound, my mother was in no position to put together a special meal—even a small, plain one—to celebrate my safe return home, nor could she tell me to rest up and take it easy for a while until I got my strength back. The whole country was in economic ruin thanks to the war, and my responsibility as head of our household weighed heavily on me.

The very next day I went round to the dye works where I'd been working before the war. My former employer was a kind person, and he said he'd be glad for me to come back to work there, but at the moment there was no cloth to be had anywhere, and so there was no work to be done. His shop was open, but there was no business.

It wasn't long before I teamed up with five or six repatriated soldiers I had chanced to get acquainted with, and my new colleagues and I started our own line of work. Some of the guys had been air force pilots in a suicide attack unit, whose sole duty was to crash their planes into the side of an enemy vessel; they'd been waiting on standby for their turn to die when the end of the war came; they were what some people called 'degenerate suicide commandos,' a live-fast-die-young, nihilistic lot.

I was the group's leader because I had the longest service record and had once come face to face with death at Luzon. I used the word 'colleagues,' and that has a nice ring to it, but to tell the truth, we were just a gang of hoods; and our 'line of work' was selling illegally obtained goods on the black market, mainly army-navy surplus clothing.

As you know, rice, potatoes, sugar, alcohol—really, any sort of food at all—sold fast on the black market. But the next most-valued commodities were clothes, blankets, shoes, and the like.

We hung out around the black-market stalls behind train stations where goods from the defunct Imperial Japanese Army—brand-new army boots, blankets, uniforms, underwear, etc.—were being sold, and we inconspicuously dug up information about where the goods were coming from. There were some legitimate sources for these goods, but in most cases they could provide only one or two pieces of an item. We learned that the large lots of new, high-quality goods came to the black market by a special route.

Incredible as it sounds, some of the people who had worked as paymasters or in the accounting sections at regimental headquarters or Army posts in Japan had carried off and hidden whole truckloads of military supplies in the confusion when the war ended, and some of them sold the goods they had taken. Some high-ranking officers had even had the audacity to order some of the men under their command to transport large quantities of these supplies right to their very own houses at the time of their discharge from the Army!

Our gang searched out these people and their stolen wares in Kyoto Prefecture and parts of Shiga, Nara, and Osaka Prefectures, then fed them some story about how we were conducting an official investigation, and half-forcibly took the goods from them. Some of these guys had driven off with whole truckloads of stolen goods, and then didn't know how to dispose of them on the black market without drawing the attention of the authorities, so they were on the spot, and we obtained large quantities of merchandise from these people. It was like taking candy from a baby, and we were making money hand over fist. After all, as long as the goods had not been obtained legally, they had no legal recourse, so they were under our thumbs.

Our operation was simple: We coerced them into letting us take the goods for next to nothing and then turned right around and sold them ourselves on the black market. It was easy and lucrative work.

Making a living was not my only motivation for targeting these black-market suppliers of military goods. The truth was I couldn't stomach the idea of them sitting pretty and enjoying the good life on their ill-gotten gains after they'd let countless thousands of Japanese soldiers go out and sacrifice their young lives on the battlefields of the Philippines, China, Burma, the South Pacific, and the islands to the north. It just wasn't right. Justice demanded that they be taught a lesson, and that's where I came in. They say every evildoer has his reasons; I had mine, and it was a pretty good one, I thought.

So there I was, living the tawdry, dissolute life of a petty gangster, when one day at the black market behind Kyoto Station, I heard about this tough group of black marketeers who had recently come up from somewhere in Osaka and were there that day. Apparently, these guys were selling stolen military supplies rather conspicuously, but even more aggravating to me was their outrageous attitude and behavior: Not only did they refuse to pay the concessionaire's fee for stall space, they had the nerve to extort money from the weaker individuals running small stalls around them, disabled veterans, widows, orphans, and other victims of the war who were struggling to make a living. As a man of some reputation in the black market and boss of my own gang, I felt I couldn't allow them to get away with that. So I went round to their stall, thinking I'd teach them a thing or two, but as I approached them, I got the surprise of my life.

The man who was obviously their leader was none other than the sergeant major I'd found eating my little brother Toru's body in the mountain jungle of Luzon! His long hair had been cut short and his beard shaved off, but that was a face I would never forget! The bastard was still alive! He'd probably survived by eating the flesh of other hapless soldiers.

After that terrible day in the jungle of Luzon, at first I had felt nothing but bitter, all-consuming hatred for this bastard who had tried to kill me by kicking me off a cliff and who had eaten the flesh of my dear little brother as he lay dying. I had thought I could never forgive the beast that had done that to Toru. But as I told you earlier, during my recovery in the American field relief station as a prisoner of war, no longer starving in the jungle and free from the terror of imminent death, I had gradually come to realize that this man, too, was a victim of that abominable war, and somewhere in my heart I had been able to forgive him. Furthermore, if he hadn't kicked me down into that gorge, the Americans might never have found me and I would surely have died.

In any case, under the circumstances, I had thought that it wouldn't be long before those two Japanese guerrillas met their own deaths in the mountain jungle, so perhaps that had something to do with my inclination to pity them and forgive them.

But when I saw that former sergeant major's face and knew that he was still alive here in Kyoto, in robust health and free from care, preying on the weak—for a moment I froze in my tracks as if an electric shock had run through me from head to toe. The next instant, the old feelings of outrage flared up, and I was seized by a blinding impulse to rush over to him, grab him by his shirt front, and beat him to death with my bare hands. But the little reasoning power that still remained in my raging mind held me back.

'You can't allow this man to live!' I reasoned with myself, 'But you must plan your move carefully in order to be sure of killing him. You'll have only one chance to kill him, and you mustn't fail. You must avenge your brother's death!'

I pretended to be looking at the piles of army boots, blankets, and commissioned officers' overcoats spread out for sale and moved closer, to where I could get a good look at his face.

No doubt about it, it was him!

He was talking and joking with two or three other sinister-looking thugs who appeared to be his henchmen. This man, who had pushed me over the cliff and thought he had surely killed me, little dreamed that I was still alive and standing right there in front of him.

Even when his eyes met mine, his expression didn't change one little bit. I moved away from the stall and said to the men from my gang, who had followed me wondering what was going on, 'I'm going to kill the leader of that gang—it's a personal matter. I'm going to go get a weapon, but I'll be back soon. You keep an eye on him so I don't lose him. If by some chance he leaves before I get back, follow him and find out where he goes.'

They must have realized from my pale, emotion-contorted face that this was a serious matter, for they received my orders without a word and stayed there to watch the stall from a short distance away. I remembered there was an old Army sword in the shed nearby that we used to store our black-market goods. Since it was the same kind of sword that son of a bitch had used to cut up my brother, it struck me as a fitting weapon for my grim purpose. I grabbed it and ran back to the black market to find him.

'They're still here.' No sooner had I heard this report from my men than I drew the sword out of its scabbard and ran over to the stall, where my brother's murderer was still talking arrogantly with his men.

'You son of a bitch! You ate the bodies of dying Japanese soldiers in the Philippine jungle, didn't you! You're the filthy bastard that murdered my brother and ate his flesh. You tried to kill me, too! You don't deserve to live, and I'm going to kill you. This is for my brother!'

I lunged forward and thrust the blade into his belly.

'You . . . !' he gasped in terror and amazement. 'You're still alive!' With those few words, my suspicions were confirmed. I knew I had stabbed the right man.

I pulled the sword out of his belly and stabbed him with the blood-smeared blade again, this time aiming for his heart. With an inward shudder of satisfaction, I felt the blade strike home. I watched his convulsed body buckle and fall to the ground at my feet.

At that moment, a shot rang out, and in the split second I registered it as the sound of a pistol, pain seared through me as if a red-hot iron rod had been driven through the left side of my chest.

One of his henchmen had shot me. For a second, I thought I saw a yellow light before my eyes, but it darkened, and soon there was only blackness.

I died almost instantaneously.

As you know, the country was going through a period of utter chaos and nihilism in the wake of Japan's defeat. There was only a small article about my death in the next day's newspaper, titled 'Two Gangsters Kill Each Other in Black-Market Scuffle.'

The body of the man I killed was taken to Osaka. The local police sent my body to Rakuhoku Medical College for an autopsy; and my mother gave her consent for my body to be used for medical research, and so it was left at the college.

I lived a pretty useless life, never did anything of importance or value. Thank you for listening to my story.

On the battlefields of Luzon, every chance we got, my little brother and I would talk about going home to Kyoto someday and working together to rebuild the Kyoto dyeing business that our ancestors had established generations before. It was a nice dream, but we never got the chance to make it come true.

Perhaps Toru would have preferred me not to die avenging him and instead take care of our mother and realize our dream of rebuilding the family dyeing business.

I'm sorry I've talked so long. I meant to keep it as short as possible; I just got carried away, I guess. Again, thank you for listening so patiently.

After Hearing the Fifth Night's Tale

After the Spirit of Yoneda finished speaking, Yoshio and the other spirits remained silent. They were all completely overwhelmed by his tale of unrelenting hardship, cruelty, and ultimate horror. After a while, Yoshio finally brought himself to speak.

"I hardly know what to say after hearing such a moving tale of grief and horror. Your entire life was ruined by the war. Certainly, all of us here have been affected to some extent by this tragic war, but your experiences . . . !

"From you, I have learned something about the cruel, inhuman side of military life; the many desperate, hopeless battles the Imperial Japanese Army fought on Luzon against the better-equipped, technologically superior U.S. Army; the terrible suffering our soldiers endured from disease and hunger; and the ultimate tragedy of men forced to cannibalize their fellow men in order to survive, though it probably occurred in only a very few instances.

"This is the first time I've heard such a detailed, poignant account of the anguish and suffering our soldiers faced during the war, probably not just on Luzon Island but on the many other islands where they fought as well. I've heard bits and pieces of stories about the Imperial Army's ordeal in Burma, but the reality must have been more terrible than I can imagine. Before you died, you committed the sin of murder, but I can understand the torment that drove you to kill the man.

"But now, as one of the living, I'd like to ask all of you, who belong to the World of the Spirits, a question: The sin of murder is judged harshly in the World of the Spirits, isn't it?"

"Yes," the Spirit of Professor Yuhara softly replied, "as I have said several times, God does not overlook even the smallest of sins committed during one's life on earth. So, of course, anyone who has taken another person's life will be punished severely regardless of his reason for doing so. But I'm not talking about physical punishment, because in the World of the Spirits, of course, a spirit has no physical body. The punishment I'm referring to is an intense, soul-searing anguish that each spirit much suffer over the sins he has committed. This anguish is much more painful than any sort of physical pain, but the spirit should think of this pain as God's scourge of love and welcome it, for only through it can true penitence be realized and the spirit be prepared to enter Heaven."

"Was the Spirit of Yoneda reunited with his little brother Toru in the World of the Spirits?" Yoshio asked. "And what about the sergeant major he killed?"

The Spirit of Yoneda serenely answered, "The Spirit of Professor Yuhara knows the answers to your questions, but let me tell you. When I was killed at the black-market stall, people naturally panicked and the place went into an uproar. Similarly to what my fellow spirits have described happening to them, my spirit left my body and was lifted up into the World of the Spirits.

"Some time after entering the World of the Spirits—though I've no idea how much time that would be in the temporal realm, since there is no such passage of time in the spiritual realm of eternity—in accordance with the will of the Holy Ghost, I was permitted to see the person I most wanted to see, Toru, who was of course already in the World of the Spirits.

"When I met Toru in the World of the Spirits, he did not appear to me in the image of the emaciated, gore-spattered, cruelly mutilated body that had been my last sight of him in the Philippine jungle. We appeared to each other as we had during our happiest times together. It was wonderful being together again.

"You know that even on earth, when a person loves someone, the closer that love is to agape, that is, purely spiritual love, the more he feels indescribably peaceful, pure, and contented when he is with the one he loves. Those feelings are heightened all the more in the World of the Spirits, and the result is a spiritual contentment and ecstasy unknown on earth. That's because we wear a garment of flesh while we are alive, and our spirit cannot become completely pure and cannot experience purely spiritual love.

"To answer your second question: Yes, I met the sergeant major in the World of the Spirits, too. Along with our garments of flesh, we had also sloughed off our former hatred. We met each other with hearts full of charity, compassion, and understanding; and we forgave each other. In the World of the Spirits, both of us repented of the sins we committed during our lives, and we are now preparing to receive the Lord's salvation. And when the time comes, we will be lifted up into the Kingdom of Heaven.

"It often happens that the spirit of a person who was considered evil on earth is permitted to enter Heaven before the spirits of others who were considered not so bad or even good on earth."

When the Spirit of Yoneda finished speaking, the Spirit of Professor Yuhara brought the fifth night's meeting to a close.

"Once again, we've talked late into the night. I'm sure we could go on talking about these things all night, if we let ourselves. But we'd better let you go home, Yoshio, or else you'll be too tired to concentrate in your classes tomorrow. Be careful riding your bicycle home. We'll see you again tomorrow night."

Yoshio left the dissecting room and headed for home.

As he pedaled across Kawaramachi Boulevard and turned left onto Teramachi Street, he felt a few raindrops on his cheeks. It was starting to rain. The drops of rain felt cool and refreshing in the heavy, muggy air of the late, summer night. The horrors of war that Yoneda Isamu had experienced in his short life filled Yoshio's heart with an aching sorrow for all the soldiers who had suffered similar fates, and he pedaled as hard as he could as if trying with the force of his legs to drive those terrible images from his mind.

CHAPTER SEVEN

SIXTH NIGHT:

The Tale of a Woman Who Suffered the Hardships of Life as a Mill Girl and a Prostitute

Born in a Poor Village

The story of my life is not an interesting one like those told by my fellow spirits these past few nights. Truly, my past is a shameful one, but . . . well, you will see what I mean.

My name in the world of the living was Taguchi Fuyuko.

I was born in a small village called Noè nestled deep in the mountains of Tottori Prefecture near the Hyogo Prefecture border. There my parents made a living as tenant farmers tending several small terraced fields cut into the mountainside. The climate afforded little fine weather; there was a lot of snow in winter, and when there was no snow, there was a constant drizzle of rain; even when the sun did show its face now and then, it shone only on the other side of the peaks that kept our village hidden in their shadow. How on earth could anyone make a go of farming in such a place?

There was never much hope of an abundant harvest of rice, barley, or vegetables, and after the share of the harvest paid to the landowner was set aside, the farmers didn't even have enough rice to eat, even though they were the ones who had planted, cultivated, and harvested it.

Despite these family hardships, I managed to finish elementary school, walking the four kilometers there and back along narrow, rocky mountain paths.

When I graduated from elementary school, I had two big brothers, one little brother and one little sister. With five hungry young mouths to feed, my mother and father never were quite able to make ends meet, and we were forced to live a life that was the very picture of grinding poverty.

Moreover, my mother had a weak constitution and was always coughing, so, as I think back now, she may have had tuberculosis of the lungs. I'm sure giving birth to five children did nothing to bolster her health. I remember her as a gaunt, haggard woman with a pasty, washed-out complexion.

Since I was the elder daughter, it naturally fell to me to take the place of my sickly mother and look after my little brother and sister, of course, and my two big brothers as well.

One day, a recruiter from the Fuji Muslin spinning mill came to our isolated village and struck up a conversation with my father. I just happened to be coming back from the fields then. My father saw me and introduced me to the recruiter.

'This is my elder daughter.'

The recruiter, who was all decked out in a smart business suit and looked a proper gentleman, immediately praised me to the skies, saying what a fine daughter my father had and how I was sure to be a beauty when I grew up.

It wasn't long before he pulled out some photographs of the town of Akashi and a huge mill, which he declared was one of the foremost spinning mills in Japan and had its head office in Tokyo. He said the mill was located not far from such major cities as Himeji, Kobe, and Osaka; with a showman's flourish, he showed us photographs of streets filled with gaily decorated shops and movie theaters in those cities, and even a huge Western-style department store, the like of which we had never seen. With those flashy photographs, he had no trouble arousing the curiosity of country bumpkins like us who had never set eyes on a big city before.

He then proceeded to outline the company's generous terms of employment and all sorts of attractive fringe benefits that we would enjoy once my father had entrusted his 'precious daughter' into the company's care. He said I would live in a clean, fully furnished dormitory near the mill. I could sign up to take classes after work in a wide variety of ladylike, cultural accomplishments—tea ceremony, ikebana, etiquette, cooking, sewing—or learn to play the koto or samisen; and if I wanted to, I would even be allowed to attend a company-affiliated girls' middle school. My parents would have no cause for worry even if I got sick, he assured us, for the mill had an excellent infirmary where I could get proper medical treatment free of charge. Above all, he stressed that the work itself would be nothing like hard physical labor, but rather simply overseeing the operation of one of the machines: as long as I operated it according to instructions, the machine itself would do most of the work.

On top of all that, the recruiter's litany of enticements continued, I was guaranteed a salary, of course, with regular raises according to my years of service with the company. As my earnings grew, I would be able to start a savings account and send money home to help out my family; the recruiter said it would be easy to save up a nest-egg sufficient to pay for my own trousseau, without any financial assistance from my parents, by the time I was old enough to marry. Once I had officially agreed to work there, the company would give my parents some money to purchase clothes and incidentals for my new life at the mill and, if necessary, an advance on my salary. Last but not least—the icing on the cake, you might say—whenever my family wanted to come up from the country to the city to visit me or do some sightseeing, the company would provide them with overnight accommodations equal to a first-class inn, free of charge. The recruiter's spiel rolled off his tongue as smoothly as if he'd said it a thousand times, and my father was so impressed by it he said, 'It sure sounds like a honey of a deal. If there was a job for me at the mill, I'd go to work there myself!'

The recruiter concluded his pitch by telling us that with so many young girls wanting to work at the mill because of the excellent terms of employment, it was strictly first come, first served. When he mentioned that he'd already signed up five or six girls in a neighboring village, my father took this as a hint that if I didn't make up my mind to join the company that very day, all the positions might be filled, so he pressed me for a decision.

My mother, however, had been listening to all this as she lay in the next room. At this point, she took the trouble to get up and come into the front room to confront the recruiter with her misgivings.

'You've painted a pretty picture of life at the mill, but I wonder if it isn't too good to be true. I've heard about such companies as yours—heard that the working conditions are bad, the pay is low, and after the company takes out deductions from your pay for this and that, there isn't enough left over to put in a savings account. What's more, some people say countless young mill girls get taken advantage of by the men there and end up crying over their lost virtue. What do you have to say about all that?'

'No, no,' he glibly replied, 'such things might have happened back in the Meiji era, but even then they were the exception, not the rule. Nowadays conditions at the mills are vastly improved over what they once were. Let me explain what happened. In the old days, Japan was the world's biggest producer of raw silk and was working hard to catch up economically and industrially with the rest of the world. Our politicians were vigorously advocating the build-up of national wealth and military strength in order to win the Sino-Japanese War of 1894-1895 and the subsequent Russo-Japanese War of 1904-1905, and part of the plan was for Japan to amass great wealth through the acquisition of foreign currencies by exporting its silk to Western countries and use that

wealth to build warships and artillery. At that time, Japan had
nothing else but silk to sell abroad, and the government was
pressuring the spinning industry to produce more and more, so
working conditions at some spinning mills did get pretty bad for
a while, you see?'

Thus he dismissed all the points my mother had brought up as
regrettable faults of a past age.

Naturally, my mother was worried about sending me off alone
to work at a spinning mill far from home, but she knew she could
do nothing to help me economically in the future if I stayed there
in our village. Moreover, even though she would be losing my
help with the housework, the family would have one less mouth
to feed and have the benefit of the money I could send home, so
in the end, she acquiesced to my father's will. The recruiter
produced a parental consent form stipulating that I was to work for
the company for a minimum of three years, and my father signed
it and affixed his personal seal next to his signature.

Half of me wanted to stay with my family, but the other half
longed to live in a big city and escape from the dreary, dead-end
existence I had led up till then, so I too, in the end, was drawn by
the easy, pleasant working conditions and attractive terms of
employment described by the recruiter. He gave me about a week
to make my preparations for the journey, then returned and gave
my parents some money to cover the expense of outfitting me for
my new position and an advance payment against my earnings, as
requested by my father, the total of which was a little over three
hundred yen. Then he took me with him to the Fuji Muslin
Company's spinning mill at Akashi, where I began my new life of
employment.

The Miserable Life of Mill Girls

The Akashi spinning mill did both thread-spinning, mostly cotton
and silk, and fabric-weaving.

After arriving at the spinning mill, I was shown to the dormitory, where I got my first unpleasant surprise. True, the dormitory was fresh and newly built, but a great number of mill girls and women were crowded into each large room, where we had to sleep on skimpily stuffed futons as thin and hard as rice crackers, laid out in rows from one end of the room to the other. The dining hall was a cheerless place, packed with long tables set with cheap aluminum tableware, where we were forced to sit so close together we were constantly jostling each other as we ate; the meals were plain and tasteless, and worse still, we were given hardly enough time to eat and had to gulp our food down in a rush. The dormitory bath was a large steam bath supplied with steam from the mill; we had to bathe together many at a time, bobbing around shoulder to shoulder in the near-scalding water like potatoes being boiled in a tub.

Worst of all, the mill work was harsh and backbreaking. First, there was the deafening racket to get used to; the ear-splitting clanking and shrill whine of the big machines was so loud you could hardly hear the voice of someone speaking, even if standing right next to you. In what little sunlight entered the gloomy workplace, you could see the air was thick with swirling clouds of dust and tiny pieces of waste thread. The girls and women who worked there were further plagued by the high temperatures and humidity produced by the machines.

Because I was a juvenile worker, I was stationed in the winding section as a bobbin winder, but most other girls my age were made to work in the spinning section, on the machines known as the spinning mule and the ring frame, or in the weaving section drawing in threads for the giant looms.

After starting work each morning, the work itself became more tiring as the day wore on, of course, but there were other factors that made working there unpleasant. Occasionally serious problems arose among the women workers. And there were several ranks in the mill hierarchy—inspector, assistant foreman,

foreman, part-time technician, assistant engineer, section head, engineer, superintendent—all of which outranked us mill girls and women. We held the lowest station there, and everyone else treated us like dirt.

Another thing I learned once I started working there was that even though among the mill women, just like in the army, there was a difference between the senior workers and the newcomers, women who had been working ten or even twenty years were treated no better by the male management staff than those of us with much less seniority. No matter how long a woman worked there, she would never be treated as anything but a mill girl.

We had to work at least twelve hours a day. Since the mill operated round the clock, occasionally you had to work overtime, which really made the work horrendous: the shift changes were erratic and didn't always come when they were supposed to; but you had to keep working at your post until someone relieved you, and sometimes you'd get stuck with a double-shift and end up working straight through till the next morning.

Our rest breaks were short, and there was no room set aside as a break lounge. Since the machines went on running even during our breaks, we had to divide each break in half and take turns because the machines could never be left unattended; while some of the workers were on break, those left behind had to do twice as much work, so the breaks didn't really provide much of a rest. We couldn't even go back to the dormitory, the only 'home' we had at the mill, for a rest during our breaks; that was strictly prohibited.

We mill girls did not get a regular salary, and we were not paid by the hour or the day, but on a piece-rate basis; since our wages were calculated according to the volume of work completed, we were compelled to work as quickly and efficiently as we could. Our job performance also determined whether or not we got a bonus at the end of the year, though even when we did get one, it was no great sum of money.

I guess the life of a mill girl in those days was much worse at some spinning mills than at the Fuji Muslin mill, but I'm sure it must have been much better at others. It wouldn't be far wrong to say that the exact opposite was true of everything the recruiter told me and my family about the company when he came to my village.

All the things I'd been led to expect about the dormitory and the facilities for taking classes were nothing but lies. And even if there had been some sort of program of cultural courses available to us, we were so exhausted from work that by the end of the day all we could think of was getting a meal, taking a bath, and going to bed as soon as possible.

The recruiter had not lied about their being a company-affiliated girls' middle school, but it was hardly likely that any of us would have had the time or energy to attend classes there, let alone study or do homework in the crowded dormitory.

Going into the nearby town of Akashi or traveling over to Kobe or Himeji to have some fun or enjoy a bit of shopping—such things were the stuff of fantasy to us, idle dreams with no hope of being realized. First, I had been informed soon after my arrival at the mill that I was obliged to pay back the money the recruiter had given my parents to cover the expense of outfitting me for my new life at the mill, and of course, I had to repay the advance on my wages, both in monthly installments automatically deducted from my wages. On top of that, there were deductions for room and board, the workers' benefit fund, and compulsory savings—after which there was almost nothing left. And as long as a mill girl still owed money to the company, she was forbidden to leave the grounds. We had to live with so many restrictions, it was just like being a convict in prison or a slave.

Corporal punishment at the hands of one of the inspectors, foremen, or the mill superintendent awaited us whenever the thread or fabric we produced was of poor quality, even though that was almost always the fault of the machines, or our job performance was not up to snuff. We were often punished by having to fill a bucket with water and then stand holding it for hours on end.

The company also unscrupulously exacted unreasonable fines for work infractions and poor performance, which were also automatically deducted from our monthly wages.

In the midst of these various hardships of life at the mill, I turned fifteen and had my first period, which was a really frightening experience, being away from home.

Like it or not, I entered adolescence while living and working at the mill. Up until then I didn't know much about sexual matters, nor was I interested in them, nor did I understand the meaning of some things I saw going on in the dormitory. But as I entered adolescence, I began to understand, and this became a new source of trouble for me.

About twenty mill girls and women were crowded into each twenty-tatami-mat room at the dormitory, all sleeping on futons right next to each other. In the morning, I often noticed several pairs of women would be sleeping in each other's arms in the same futon. It came as a great shock to me when I finally realized that these women were lesbians.

Ever since I had been living in the dormitory, I had heard the muffled sobs of some of the girls and women crying in their futons at night—some because they missed their parents far away in their native villages or because of the day's hard work; others because of some spat or clash with one of their co-workers; still others shed bitter tears of chagrin over the mean, spiteful treatment they had suffered at the hands of the male bosses. The sound of their sorrow made me so sad I almost cried myself, for I could understand exactly how they felt, and there were times when I would have given anything for the solace of another person's shoulder to cry on, but honestly, I had never before realized that the comfort some of the women took in each other's arms was of a sexual nature.

Before long, I also learned that the male bosses forced some of the prettier mill girls into having sexual relationships with them. Sometimes the girls got pregnant, and being forbidden to leave the mill openly and return home, some ran away from the mill in the dead of night and were never heard of again. I also heard rumors that in an effort to abort their fetuses, some drank strange drugs so powerful they were essentially poisons and ended up dying. The older women told us that some girls couldn't bear the pain and humiliation of staying on at the mill after having been seduced and ultimately cast aside by their seducer like a dirty rag; but of course they were not permitted to leave as long as they still owed money to the company, so, driven by desperation, they waited for their chance, ran away from the mill, and ended up in the only place a ruined woman could go, the prostitution quarter.

I don't think these sexual incidents were common among all mill girls and women, they just happened to be prevalent at the mill where I was employed. But it wasn't just the men who treated us mill girls and women as sex objects: Since there was no program of wholesome amusements or cultural enrichment, some of the women sought amusement instead in sexual relationships with the people closest to hand, their female co-workers or the men at the mill. Then, too, the moral standards of some of the women at the mill were relatively low.

I, too, had problems along this line. The mill superintendent was always finding fault with my job performance for some reason or another and making sarcastic, cutting remarks. Finally, taking advantage of his authority over me, he eventually forced me to have sex with him.

With that ulterior motive in their hearts right from the start, the male bosses would make trouble for a girl even though she'd done nothing wrong on the job, drive her into a corner where she couldn't refuse, and then demand her body. That was their dirty little game.

This happened to me late one night when I had just finished a night shift. The superintendent called me over and demanded that I have sex with him in his office—of all places!—located in a corner of the mill.

We were always being urged to strive diligently to increase production for the sake of the country, and told that mill women must give their all toward that end just like soldiers in the Imperial Japanese Army who went out to lay down their lives for the sake of His Majesty the Emperor. Yet here was the mill superintendent trying to get me to have sex with him right in the mill, the very place he and the other men over us were always saying we mustn't profane with even a speck of dirt because it was the sacred site of our holy mission—it was at once unspeakably shameful and ludicrous.

I put up desperate resistance and narrowly managed to escape being raped, but as a result, his subsequent harassment of me on the job increased beyond all reason.

Shortly thereafter, unfortunately, I received word from my father that my mother was much sicker and in critical condition.

I knew that some of my co-workers in similar circumstances had not been allowed to go see a dying parent because they had not finished repaying the money they owed to the company, so I was afraid I might have trouble getting permission. When I asked the superintendent for a few days off to return home to see my dying mother, sure enough, he said, 'No.'

'But,' he continued, 'if you'll be a little more friendly to me, I don't mind asking upper management for special permission for you to go home for a visit. You scratch my back, and I'll scratch yours, see?'

Ah, what a bastard he was to put such a loathsome proposition to me when I was begging him to let me see my mother one last time before she died! I could hardly believe my ears. Are these the sort of words one human being says to another in such a situation?

Ever since I had come to work there, I had stayed locked up within the mill grounds, going nowhere, seeing no one but my partners in slavery and our male masters, and now the first time I asked for permission to visit my family, the bastard told me I could have it in exchange for sex.

Two days later, I started for home in tears, no longer a virgin.

If I had left for home immediately after receiving my father's telegram, I might have managed to reach my mother's side before she died, but I was too late. When I at last made my way to my parents' house, it was night and the simple ceremony that passed for a funeral in my village had taken place that day.

'Your mother was worried about you right up to the end,' my father said with tears in his eyes. 'It was rash of me to send you off to work at the spinning mill, but thanks to you, that advance on your wages from the mill saved our family from starvation.'

Those few words swept away from my mind the more than three years of hardship and toil I had suffered. My little brother and sister had grown much bigger. The elder of my two big brothers was now helping my father with the farming; he had already taken his army physical and would be called up for military service any time now. The younger was employed as a factory worker at the naval shipyard at Kure and would enter the Imperial Japanese Navy when he reached the proper age; he was already excited about someday sailing in the great battleships he was helping to build.

That was my first reunion with my brothers and sister in such a long, long time, and it was wonderful to see them again, but it made me terribly sad to think that this visit with them was gained at the great expense of my mother's life.

My heart brimmed with both pity and love at the sight of my little brother and sister gleefully stuffing their mouths with the sweet-bean-jam buns I had bought for the family in front of Akashi Station with some of the little pocket money I had put by, the first savings I had ever accumulated in my life.

About two days later, however, it was time for me to return to the mill at Akashi. I bid farewell to my desolate-looking father and tore myself away from my little brother and sister, who clung fast to my hands as if they would never let me go, and boarded the train that would take me back to the mill at Akashi, which was to me a living hell.

When I returned to the mill, my harsh life of backbreaking labor and sexual harassment resumed. Each day dragged by exactly the same as the day before, with no improvement in wages or working conditions.

In this way, another two years passed, but at least I had finally repaid the advance on my wages given to my parents and had now joined the ranks of skilled workers. In addition, I now got a day off about once a month.

The only part of my earnings I put into my savings account was that needed to pay off my debt to the company; every month I sent all the rest—what little remained—back home for the sake of my little brother and sister, whom I never stopped thinking of for even a single day during those long years of toil. It was no great amount of money I sent, since my wages were so low to begin with, but still, I sent it all and did what I could to help my family.

The Labor Movement

Meanwhile, a new man came to work at the mill, a trustworthy man of solid character by the name of Nakano, who urged us to stand up for our rights to a fair wage and decent working conditions.

'You women workers don't have to put up with such inferior working conditions as these given you by the company management,' he told us. 'Laborers all over Japan are starting to wake up to the fact that they've got rights, too. You've got to demand better working conditions and be prepared to go on strike to get them.'

When it came to the improvement of working conditions, at the mill where I worked absolutely everything needed to be changed. We had to work long hours in a hot and humid building amid ear-splitting noise and choking clouds of dust; rest breaks were extremely short, and there was no real place set aside for us where we could spend them in peace and quiet; and most of all, our wages were shamefully low. There was no end of improvements that needed to be made.

We made a list of them, then selected the ones we considered urgent and feasible and drew up a formal list of demands, which we circulated among as many of the mill women as possible, asking for their cooperation and support. Then we thrust our list of demands before the superintendent and had him present it to upper management, demanding an immediate response.

After my first sexual experience with the superintendent, he had come to me again from time to time demanding sex, and though I'm ashamed to say it, I had always given him what he wanted. For the first time, I went to him of my own accord and placed our petition for better working conditions in his hands.

Since I was the one who handed him the document, it was inevitable that he should look on me as the most aggressive proponent of the demands for improvement and, therefore, the ringleader, or at least one of the ringleaders.

Actually, I felt as if I were finally bursting free from years of silent submission to the company's exploitation; I was motivated by a sense of justice and at the same time, a sense of pure, disinterested mission, as if this were something I simply had to do for the sake of all my exploited co-workers.

But in light of the results it produced, our labor movement was so inept as to be hardly worthy of the name. The upper management of the mill were old hands at the business of keeping the workers in their place, and we were no match for them.

'What are you talking about, you ingrates!' they thundered, at first threatening us with dismissal, 'If you don't like working here, you can all quit and get out!'

Then, they cajoled us: 'Why must we and you, who all eat rice from the same pot and are working here for the sake of our beloved homeland, hate each other and fight with each other like this?'

They had the nerve to use some of the very words we intended to say, twisting them to serve their own purpose: 'We have cooperated with you workers with your best interests at heart, and yet now you've come to us with this list of one-sided demands. This grieves us deeply. Before you came to work at this mill, surely our recruiter talked with each of you in person and told you all about the terms of employment; surely each of you affixed your seal to the contract with a full grasp of those terms. Someone has got you all worked up and dissatisfied now, but we won't tolerate undue interference.

'We're very sorry it must come to this,' they said in conclusion, 'but it can't be helped: We must dismiss those workers who are discontented working here. Particularly the representatives and leaders of this movement must leave the company as an example to others who might be tempted to carry on this labor movement in the future. As for the rest of you, we won't hold you accountable for your involvement this time if you promise never to do anything like this again.'

On hearing those words, the vast majority of mill girls and women simply gave up. Management had played its trump card and won the game. It was all over.

Japan's downtrodden workers were beginning to rise up against their capitalist oppressors throughout the country in those days. When a strike had started recently at a silk manufacturer in Okaya near Lake Suwa, the management at most companies had refined to perfection their tactics for heading off such movements.

Policemen came and patrolled the grounds at the Fuji Muslin mill rattling their sabers; and an officer who appeared to belong to the *Tokko*, the special secret service police, who were often called in on matters of political import, started observing goings-on in the mill at the request of company management. This turn of events terrified the female and even the male workers, and they soon started back at their jobs as before.

When it was too late to save the situation, I realized that if we were planning to petition management with a list of demands and even resort to calling a strike involving the entire work force, we should have completely organized ourselves beforehand, worked out a detailed strategy, and ascertained the solidarity of our fellow workers more carefully before taking any overt action. Our half-cocked efforts amounted to, in effect, nothing more than a momentary outburst of our discontent.

I received a notice of dismissal from the company, and under the circumstances, of course, I received no severance pay.

Until the latter part of the Taisho era, around 1923 to 1926, companies and factories competed among themselves for workers of superior ability, and in the scramble for the best workers, there was quite a bit of behind-the-scenes maneuvering that included hiring employees away from other companies with the lure of better wages or working conditions and, on occasion, more violent methods that bordered on abduction.

Representatives from other spinning mills had come to me with offers of better employment elsewhere. But when the world-wide economic depression hit Japan in the early part of the Showa era, exports fell off sharply and many companies in the spinning industry curtailed their operations and sent some of their female workers back to their native villages.

I was the first to be fired by Fuji Muslin just because I had been influenced by the forces of democratization that flourished during the Taisho era and had tried to stage a strike to obtain better working conditions.

With that black mark on my employment record, no other company was likely to hire me, no matter how skilled a worker I was.

This meant that I was finished in the spinning industry. True, I was confident in my ability and the skills I had acquired through my years at the spinning mill—bobbin winding, warping, and later, the craft of weaving—but aside from those highly specialized abilities, which now I had no way of using, I wasn't qualified for anything and had no way to earn a living.

For a woman in my position, about the only work available was that of kitchen help in one of the restaurants or greasy spoons in town. I went to the superintendent who had forced sexual favors from me and begged him for help; he arranged for me to do cleaning and wash dishes at a cheap bar in the amusement and shopping quarter of Akashi, but I didn't stay there very long.

The job gave me little more than a place to sleep and my meals; the pay was so low there was no way I could send any money home to my family.

The superintendent probably thought he had handled the situation pretty well, since it would be convenient for him to have a sexually compliant woman like me working nearby in Akashi, but I was desperate to find work that would pay me enough to be able to help my family. So one night I sneaked out of the bar and left town. My closest friend among my co-workers at the spinning mill—who had come to live at the Fuji Muslin dormitory about the same time as me and who had been assigned to the same room, done the same work, and shared the same hardships—had left the mill to return to her hometown of Umezako about a year before due to poor health; before leaving, she had told me to come see her if I ever got into trouble, left the mill, and needed help. Remembering her words, I headed for Umezako. When I arrived there, what a terrible shock it was to learn that she had died of tuberculosis about a month before!

It was evident that my friend's family lived in dire poverty, and there was simply no way they could have offered me assistance. I stayed with them one night, but I left early the next morning and headed for the largest of the nearby towns, Maizuru.

I didn't know much about Maizuru then, but I knew that it ranked alongside Yokosuka, Kure, and Sasebo as one of Japan's major naval ports, and it had a large naval force stationed there, an arsenal, and lots of other Navy-related institutions and agencies, all of which made it a thriving, bustling town. I figured there would be some sort of work available in such a busy city even for the likes of me.

At that point in my life, because I had allowed myself to be sullied by having sex with the mill supervisor, I felt I had nothing left to lose. I didn't care what happened to me; I was concerned only for my family: my one desire in life was to help my little brother and sister financially as much as possible. So I had made up my mind that even if I became destitute, I would never become an economic burden to my family by returning home to live with them.

After arriving in Maizuru, I finally located a private employment agency and asked if there were any good-paying jobs to be had. After all, at the time I still had not seen much of the world, and I was childish and naïve.

'The best-paying job is selling your body in the red-light district,' the head of the employment agency said matter-of-factly. 'Now, of course, there's a licensed prostitution district in Maizuru catering to the naval men, arsenal workers, and such, and I don't mind trying to get you hired on at one of them, but there's a vacancy in a brothel in Miyazu, not far from Maizuru, so how about working there?'

He went on to tell me that Miyazu was near the famous Amanohashidate. The brothel got a lot of Navy business and kept its girls busy, and the pay was quite good. So I accepted the offer of employment in Miyazu and sank into the sordid world of prostitution.

My Descent into Prostitution

You probably think I gave in and stooped to selling my body too easily, but I did it because I truly no longer cared what happened to me. This lack of self-concern, this feeling of utter resignation ruled my actions. With no marriage or children of my own to look forward to, I really felt I had nothing to lose, and so I became a prostitute because it seemed to me at the time there was really no other way for me to make a living.

Later on, I learned that the private employment agency I had gone to had been searching high and low for girls like me to work in brothels. From time to time, men from the agency would coerce women to come with them—sometimes almost kidnapping them—and take them to one of the brothels in the red-light district, which paid the agency a tidy sum for procuring these less-than-willing recruits. To the men at the agency, I must have seemed like a foolish moth flying straight into the flame.

I signed a contract and indentured myself to the brothel for eight years, then sent almost all of the six-hundred-yen advance on my wages home to my father, along with a brief letter asking him to use the money to help my little brother and sister.

In those days, a *sho*—a little less than two liters—of rice cost only twenty-five sen, one-fourth of a yen, so six hundred yen was an immense sum of money, and I have no doubt that it spared them many hardships.

Actually, since my father was the only member of my family who knew how I had come to have such a great deal of money, he wrote me a letter saying he was sorry I had had to make such a sacrifice. But that letter with the six hundred yen was my last to him and the rest of my family—I intended to sever all connections between myself and them. No matter how humble and obscure my family was, my father and siblings could hardly be expected to be immune to feelings of shame and dishonor if it became known that their Fuyuko was a common prostitute.

In those days, there were also unlicensed prostitutes, mostly factory and mill girls who had lost their jobs, but in my case, since the brothel I was indentured to operated under the licensed prostitution system and was patronized by naval men, the police closely regulated the employment agency's procurement practices. I had to submit a letter of parental consent, a copy of my family register, and an application for a license to practice prostitution. That's why I couldn't keep my new profession a secret from my father.

For the next ten or so years, I lived a life so low and morally degrading I felt I had forfeited my very humanity. I had become a piece of meat, a prey to men who saw me only as a tool to be used for their sexual pleasure.

When I started working in the brothel, some of the more experienced women and the madam told me that a prostitute must never fall in love with one of her customers and other bits of advice. I heeded their advice, but ultimately, out of the hundreds of men that came to me, there were a few that made me think, 'How happy I would be if only I were an ordinary woman and could marry this man!' Some men treated me as tenderly and affectionately as if I had been their mother. Of course, at the opposite end of the scale, there were also many men whom I hated even to have touch me.

Then there were the young boys who, when they turned seventeen or eighteen, were brought to the brothel by an older friend for their first lay.

There was very little opposition to such practices in this country, and they were carried on more or less openly. Japanese society was rather broad-minded about such behavior, in men at least.

To give you an example, one man smugly said to me, 'In their heart of hearts, you know, all men naturally want to sleep with as many women as they can. The desire is always there—they just don't show it, or it's never put into practice, or it's just repressed by their moral views or reason.' On the other hand, conventional relations between men and women are quite restricted; in almost all cases, people get married and start families together not because they love each other, but because their parents have decided that this is the time and this is the person that they should marry.

Women in normal walks of life are valued highly for their virginity; Japanese society demands their purity, and women themselves take it for granted that they must be sexually pure. So even women who wistfully dream of romantic love usually ready themselves for marriage without ever having actually been touched by a man.

Even though Japan is a paradise for men in that male sexual promiscuity is widely tolerated, there were probably some men who wanted to come to the brothel but could not for lack of money. Then, too, there were many men who either had no interest in buying sex or took a serious view of life and felt they had things more important to do. Yes, I think most of the men who came to us prostitutes were rather lacking in earnestness in their attitude toward life.

Japan's moral climate is somewhat lax, especially where sex is concerned. After all, I've heard that the brothels in a certain district grow rich on customers who drop in on their way home from a visit to a certain famous temple nearby.

My life at the brothel was nothing but endless repetitions of the same meaningless acts, night and day, day and night.

True, the men I had sex with were different each time, but the whole time I felt I was lying at the bottom of a dark, sordid pit without a single ray of light to give me hope that someday something good would happen to me in my life. I was so empty and numb, ten years passed almost without my realizing it.

During those years, I dressed myself up in fine kimonos and Western-style clothes bought with the money I received in return for selling my body. I spent my free time shopping for expensive trinkets and adornments and treated myself to delicious foods and costly delicacies. Before I knew it, I had developed a taste for a luxurious, materialistic lifestyle. To all appearances, I lived a splendid, gay life the like of which I had never even in my wildest dreams imagined for myself during my days as a lowly mill girl.

But as Japan became ever more militarized and plunged ahead on its course toward war, daily life became increasingly difficult.

Over these past five nights, my fellow spirits have already described the harshness of living conditions in Japan during wartime, so without going into great detail, I shall give a brief summary of what I remember about that period.

In December of 1933, a son was born to the Imperial family, which till then had been blessed only with daughters. Sirens rang out to celebrate the long-awaited birth of the crown prince, Rising-Sun flags waved on every street, and people from one end of the country to the other jubilantly sang the song, 'His Highness the Crown Prince is Born.'

It wasn't long until the Manchurian Incident occurred. Despite the official government line advocating localization of the affair, the conflict escalated rapidly, and in July 1937 the Sino-Japanese War broke out, bringing with it increasingly stringent domestic rationing of food and commodities. With much fanfare, the government called for a 'spiritual' civilian mobilization, and the Japanese people's rallying cry became 'Extravagance is an enemy.'

Cotton fabrics used for making underclothes vanished from the stores; daily necessities such as sugar, miso, soy sauce, and matches were doled out to people by means of a ration-ticket system; and the distribution of rice, the staple of life in Japan, was put under government control. The luxury of personal adornment was also abandoned, and women could no longer get permanent waves in beauty salons.

Even if it had not been for these harsh restrictions on food and goods, we prostitutes still had a rough time at the hands of the righteous women in town, who were hostile toward us. In particular, groups of middle-aged women wearing white aprons and shoulder sashes that read 'Women's National Defense Association' glared at us with unconcealed contempt and made us feel ashamed of what we were.

However, Japan soon plunged into yet another war, the Pacific War, just as if inexorably following some preordained course, and as the fighting intensified, the naval servicemen came in increasing numbers to the brothels on their days off, hurrying to get a place near the head of the line. Even the military authorities apparently thought that a brothel was the only place of solace for officers and sailors who would soon be sent into battle, and many a young sailor paid his money and came to my arms because he wanted to know what it was like to lie with a woman just once before he went off to the front.

For the sake of those young men who might soon give their lives for our country, I treated them as kindly and gently as I could, with soft caresses and affection more tender than that of an older sister, almost as if I were their mother.

'Now, you watch out for yourself over there and don't go and get yourself killed, you hear?' I would say to them, words of encouragement welling up from the bottom of my heart, 'You be sure and come home safe and sound!'

I even felt it was a mission of sorts to comfort, sexually and otherwise, and cheer them as best I could, though I guess it's asking too much for anyone but another prostitute to understand such feelings.

Somehow, I felt that by sleeping with these men and boys I was helping my country, performing a patriotic act of sorts, and the warm glow of pride I felt in doing my part for Japan seemed to sweep away my former feelings of shame and servility at being a prostitute.

Before long, naval air bases were established at Kunda on Miyazu Bay and at Kanbe in the central part of the Tango Peninsula, and hundreds of officers and servicemen from these new bases started coming to the brothels in Miyazu.

As a result, we prostitutes were busier than ever before. It may sound funny for me to say so, but I was working night and day to keep the naval men satisfied, literally laying down my body in selfless devotion to my country.

The war dragged on and evidently was not going well for our side. The screaming sirens of preliminary air-raid alerts and air-raid warnings began to pierce the once-peaceful skies over Maizuru Naval Port and neighboring Miyazu with increasing frequency.

A Certain Naval Officer

It was about that time that a young naval ensign, a university upperclassman who had been pulled away from his studies by the draft and had just finished his pilot training in the Naval Air Corps at Tsuchiura, was assigned to his first real combat unit at Kunda Naval Air Base.

I met him at a farewell party for some senior officers being transferred to the front, which was held in one of the banquet rooms of the Chadani Inn in Miyazu. That inn was one of the very few places that had ample supplies of food and liquor, thanks to special rations provided by the Navy.

As the war intensified, the number of farewell parties held in such facilities increased steadily. Most, if not all, of the local young women had been pressed into labor service at the factories, and there were hardly any left to work in the restaurant and entertainment business, so occasionally prostitutes like me were called out in place of geishas to serve sakè and entertain the men at these parties.

His companions called him Ensign Shimazutsu, but traces of the student still showed in this young naval officer's face, and there was something forlorn and nihilistic about him.

It so happened that I filled his sakè cup many times, and as I knelt facing him across the low, narrow table, I naturally tried to make light conversation with him. Yet to my every comment and question, he responded with only minimal replies and never asked me anything about myself or made any effort to prolong our conversation.

Despite his reticence, I seemed to bring out something in him that his companions didn't, and I learned that he was from Takada in Niigata Prefecture. He had been studying economics at a university in Tokyo when his draft deferment had been suspended and he had been drafted into the Imperial Japanese Navy. After undergoing intense training in the Naval Air Corps at Tsuchiura, he had been assigned to his first post of actual military duty at Kunda Naval Air Base.

I suddenly thought to myself, 'He's just my type. . . .' He didn't talk very freely with any of his fellow officers at the party, almost as if a cloud of isolation hung over him, yet with me he was different. He seemed to respond to me, and he listened to my light banter with a radiant smile on his face.

As always at such parties, I sang the usual naval songs with the officers, songs that are still etched indelibly in my memory, songs of patriotism and bravado that started with lines such as 'The naval men who protect the Empire surrounded by four seas . . .' and 'However much we are buffeted by fierce gales . . .' The party finally drew to a close when they all sang loudly in unison that famous song taken from the Manyoshu: 'If we fight at sea, we will die in the water; if we fight in the mountains, we will die on the grass; but as long as we die for the sake of the Emperor, we will die without regret.'

Afterward, as he was leaving, he whispered in my ear, 'I'd like to see you again.'

About a week later he showed up at the brothel and asked for me by name, much to my surprise, for I had not told him my name or where to find me.

Of course, Miyazu was a small town with only a few brothels, so I guess it was no great task to find out where I worked. We prostitutes had an ironclad rule: Don't fall in love with the customers. Despite that, however, something about Ensign Shimazutsu attracted me in a way I had never been attracted to a man before.

He elicited feelings in me that I thought had died once and for all long before. For one thing, when I saw him that first time he came to the brothel, I suddenly felt ashamed for him to see me there selling my body for money, a feeling that was scarcely in keeping with my long years of experience in the trade.

I quickly sensed that this was Ensign Shimazutsu's first time with a woman. Feeling as I did about him, I did my best to make it a memorable experience for him.

After that, he came to see me at the brothel every chance he got.

During his visits, we talked of this and that, and I learned that my hunch about the men stationed at the Kunda base was correct: they were kamikaze, training to crash their planes head-on into enemy ships. At that stage of the war, things were going very badly for Japan, and the military had started sending out pilots on suicide missions against enemy battleships and other enemy vessels in the waters near the beachheads where American troops had started landing in the Philippines and Okinawa. Hundreds of young air force pilots were sacrificing their lives in the skies and seas to the south of Japan in a desperate bid to save their country from defeat.

Ensign Shimazutsu was one of these special attack pilots, and sooner or later his turn would come to make the ultimate sacrifice.

Partly from a sense of release after days of intense training and partly in order to escape the unrelenting stress of knowing that before long he would face death, he sought out my company with a passion so intense it bordered on desperation. And I, for my part, reciprocated his passion with equal intensity.

Sometimes the women in my profession pretended to love a customer as the occasion demanded, in order to grease the wheels of commerce, so to speak. I know I shouldn't have fallen for Ensign Shimazutsu, should have maintained a more businesslike relationship with him, but as we became closer, he would lie in my arms and talk about books he'd read at university—Kierkegaard's *The Sickness Unto Death*, André Gide's *Strait Is the Gate*, and Kurata Momozo's *The Buddhist Priest and His Disciple*. He would tell me the gist of the story and give me his interpretation of it, and as we lay thus, I listened to him and time seemed to stand still. Such talk was way over my head, me being just an uneducated country girl, but something about it fascinated me, so I listened to him attentively. I felt as if a new way of thinking, an entirely new world of people and ideas that I had never come in contact with before, were opening up before me.

'There are still so many great books I want to read. It's really too bad I won't get around to them,' he lamented one night as we lay talking.

On several occasions he discussed what could be called his philosophy of life, telling me his answers to questions I had never before given a single thought to: What is truth? What is life? For what purpose are we born? How should we prepare ourselves to meet death? Does God really exist?

'Why must people and countries hate and kill one another in the name of war?' he said one night, somewhat agitated. 'In the United States and our other enemy nations in Europe, they have what they call "conscientious objectors," who can refuse military service, telling their government that taking the life of another human being in war goes against their conscience or beliefs. Instead of going to war, if they perform some other service such as working in a Red Cross hospital, their country considers them to have fulfilled their duty as citizens. Why, oh, why doesn't Japan have such a system?

'Before the war started,' he continued, 'I saw a Charlie Chaplin movie called *Monsieur Verdoux* in a Shinjuku movie theater in Tokyo, in which he played a man who murdered rich widows to get their fortunes. As he was being led off to be executed, he said to one of the reporters, "One murder makes a villain . . . millions a hero. Numbers sanctify, my friend." He was saying that if you kill just one person, you're a murderer, but if you kill many in war, you're a hero. With those lines, Chaplin pointed out one of the great contradictions of our world, and he was right!'

At that time, the slogan 'Death before Dishonor' was on everyone's lips. Civilian training practice in fighting with bamboo spears had been going on in earnest ever since the Cabinet decided on a general armament of civilians in August of 1944, and even the women and children were getting ready for the final effort to repulse the enemy when they attempted to land on Japanese soil. At a time when the vast majority of Japanese people were prepared to die right down to the last man, woman, and child rather than face surrender or defeat, it was indeed shocking to hear such remarks from the mouth of an officer in the Imperial Japanese Navy.

I didn't know much about military regulations, but I had sense enough to realize that if other people learned of his remarks, he would be court-martialed. At the same time, however, his anguished soul-searching troubled me in another, more personal way; till then I had accepted the necessity of this war as a holy war without question and gone along with the generally accepted opinion that we must all be willing to die for our country—but Ensign Shimazutsu's questioning about the real meaning of it all began to raise serious doubts deep in my heart.

Being a naval officer, Ensign Shimazutsu probably had access to military information kept secret from the civilian population and most likely knew just how bad the war situation really was. Apparently, when faced with the meaninglessness of continuing to fight a hopeless war and, despite that, the sacrifice of the thousands of young lives of his fellow pilots—ostensibly for the sake of the Emperor, but actually, in vain—in mass suicide attacks against the enemy, he found the absurdity and waste of it all simply unbearable. From his troubled look and tone of voice as he spoke of these things, I gathered that a great conflict was being waged in his heart between those feelings and his sense of duty as an officer in the Imperial Japanese Navy, which rightfully obliged him to throw himself willingly into the jaws of death for the sake of his country, and this conflict was tearing him apart.

His next words seemed to burst from his lips, his voice choked with anguish.

'Perhaps I'm just a hopeless coward! Thousands upon thousands of my comrades-in-arms have gone off without complaint to die a heroic death in battle in the South Seas, on desert islands, on the continent of China, and far to the north—all have gone for the sake of the land of our ancestors, all have gone without asking, "Why?" Yet I, ... I don't even know why I have such thoughts that go against all sense of duty. Probably I'm just afraid of dying.

'A soldier doesn't need to think about why he does a thing; all he has to do is get his orders from his commanding officer and march off to certain death. From a soldier's very first day of military service, that's the message that's drummed into your head; it's written in the Field Service Code and in every other training manual. I know what's expected of me, what my country demands of me, and yet now, somehow, I just can't seem to go through with it.

'Ever since the naval battle at Midway Island, the American retaliation has been simply awesome: the capture and occupation of Guadalcanal Island by U.S. troops, the suicide attack by surviving Japanese troops on Attu Island, the continued retreat of

Japanese troops in the Philippines and Burma, and now American troops have even landed on Okinawa, where many civilians are also being killed in the fighting. Japan is paying dearly for this war that is costing the blood and lives of its people.

'The world's largest battleship, the *Musashi*, the pride of the Imperial Japanese Navy, is already lying at the bottom of the ocean, sunk during the Battle for Leyte Gulf in the Philippines. In order to launch a last-ditch attack against U.S. battleships and support vessels during their landing operations at Okinawa, the *Yamato* set sail with only enough fuel to get there—our resources are so depleted, the Navy wasn't even able to provide its own battleship with a supply of fuel for the return trip—and was sunk in short order April 7.

'Furthermore, even though we send our kamikaze units out on suicide missions, which were pretty successful in the beginning, the U.S. Army recently started bombarding our planes with a new type of antiaircraft shell, which contains a variable-time fuse that is detonated by a radar-firing mechanism, so that our suicide attacks are not nearly as effective now as they once were. The fact is that by the time our planes reach the enemy vessels, they're dropping like flies, shot down right and left by this new weapon.

'Germany, our strongest ally, has surrendered, and Japan now stands alone in this war against the rest of the world.

'If it comes down to a decisive battle to repulse enemy landings on the Home Islands, millions of civilians will sacrifice their lives in the name of this so-called holy war, and Japan as we know it will cease to exist.

'I don't want to die! Even if people call me a despicable coward, I don't want to die!' With those anguished words, his impassioned outburst ended.

Tokyo, Osaka, and other principal cities across the nation were staggering under the tremendous bomb and incendiary damage they suffered in repeated air raids by enemy bombers. A new type of bomb, called the atomic bomb, was dropped first on Hiroshima on August 6 and then on Nagasaki on August 9; the awesome destructive force of this new weapon literally wiped those two cities off the face of the earth. And on August 8, Russia unilaterally abrogated its nonaggression treaty with Japan and declared war, sending a massive attack force surging across the Russian border into Japanese-held Manchuria the very next day, the same day Nagasaki was bombed. One after another, blows rained down on Japan, and it seemed as if Japan's last spark of life was about to be extinguished.

It was then that the order came for the few remaining planes in Ensign Shimazutsu's special attack unit to launch a suicide attack against an enemy task force cruising in the waters off the coast of Kishu.

'The time has come,' he said when he came to the brothel the night before his departure to bid me farewell. 'Tomorrow, at last, I set off on my mission.' He had evidently just come from a final bout of drinking and carousing with his buddies, and his face was flushed from the alcohol. Suddenly, his eyes burned with a bright intensity and he spoke excitedly as if he were possessed.

'I'm going to desert and survive this crazy war. It's only a matter of time before the war ends in Japan's defeat. I've heard that the Supreme War Council is seriously discussing unconditional surrender. I was right when I told you that I thought Japan was going to lose. If I go on that mission tomorrow, from which I will certainly never return, I'll be throwing my life away for nothing!'

I couldn't let him go off alone like that. I felt somehow we could manage to find shelter together in the little village where my family still presumably lived, or even just hide out deep in the mountains far away from other people, and wait for Japan's defeat and the war's end.

Donning baggy work-pants and shirt and tying an air-raid hood padded with cotton batting over my head, I got ready for the journey. Down in the kitchen, I made rice balls for us from some leftover rice, hastily stuffed them into a bag, and quietly slipped out of the brothel.

Our immediate concern was how to get out of the area, which was full of naval servicemen and was heavily guarded by the Shore Patrol.

Flight

At first Ensign Shimazutsu was reluctant to take me along, but I was determined to share the fate of the man I loved, and in the end he yielded to my pleas. With his arm encircling my shoulders protectively, we started our escape journey from Miyazu.

I knew that if we just kept going westward, we would eventually end up somewhere near my village. Figuring it was dangerous to take the train from the Japanese National Railways station at Miyazu or Amanohashidate, we set off on foot, heading west along the highway in the dead of night.

There were no lights on because of the wartime blackout, but to our right in the distance I could make out the huge, black form of the bridge at Amanohashidate, one of the three most famous sights of Japan, stretching out in the moonlight toward the Tango Peninsula. Even though we were fleeing for our lives and had time to think of little else, I remember being struck by the great beauty of the scene: the dark surface of the sea reflecting the moonlight, and the myriad wavelets catching the light and making it dance.

We traveled across what must have been the base of the Tango Peninsula, at length passed through Mineyama-cho, and finally arrived at the town of Amino. We walked all through the night and must have covered at least thirty kilometers.

The darkness shrouded us through the night and protected us from the eyes of the shore patrolmen, but the summer dawn came quickly. Although it was only five o'clock, the gray light of early morning had begun to creep through the streets around us.

We were careful to give a wide berth to public places where people were likely to gather, since we didn't know our way around the town. By the time we noticed that the road we were walking had widened into a major thoroughfare and was passing right in front of the train station, it was too late. Several policemen and a group of shore patrolmen standing in front of the station caught sight of us just as we noticed them.

'Hey, you! Halt!' one of the policemen yelled. The policemen then started running toward us, their hands on their sabers. Accompanied by their commanding officer, the shore patrolmen followed close on the heels of the policemen, holding their guns at the ready.

We ran as fast as we could, but were soon cornered by the bank of a river that ran along the outskirts of the town and emptied into the sea. Before us to the left, there was a low hill upon which we could see a Shinto shrine, but from that direction, too, yet another party of men, who appeared to be a vigilante corps, was rushing down toward us.

Ensign Shimazutsu took my arm protectively, and we started running toward the seashore. We'd gone but a little way along the sandy beach when we saw a breakwater stretching out into the sea and, standing at its tip, the chalky white tower of a lighthouse.

We ran for all we were worth along the top of the two-meter-wide cement breakwater toward the lighthouse. The cement path ended at the lighthouse, and beyond lay jagged rocks, against which the waves of the Japan Sea crashed again and again in a spray of white foam. Ensign Shimazutsu let go of my arm and went ahead, jumping from one craggy boulder to the next. I attempted to follow him onto the rocks, but it was obvious that we'd reached the end of the chase and had no place left to run.

The policemen, the shore patrolmen, and the vigilantes all converged into a single black mass of pursuers and caught up with us.

'You can't escape, so come along quietly now!' a voice rang out from the band of men behind us.

'If you try to go any farther, we'll shoot!' another man shouted. At that instant, Ensign Shimazutsu stopped and turned to look back at me over his shoulder.

'Save yourself!' he yelled, then turned back to the ocean and dived into the frothing waves.

The shore patrolmen fired a volley after him. The deafening report of their guns seemed to echo and swell around me. The horrifying thought that those shots had probably killed Ensign Shimazutsu came like a blow to my chest, and I lost my balance and fell.

Fortunately or unfortunately, part of that craggy shore had at one time been used as a fish farm, and I happened to fall safe and uninjured into a pool of seawater nestled among the jagged rocks.

I think that if I hadn't fallen just then, I would probably have thrown myself into the sea after Ensign Shimazutsu. And maybe that would have been better for me. . . .

Anyway, the fall gave me a hard knock on the head, and for a time I was unconscious. Some of our pursuers pulled me out of the water, and as soon as I could walk they dragged me off to the police station at Mineyama-cho, all the while heaping verbal abuse on me and calling me a traitor to my country.

They pulled Ensign Shimazutsu's body, his back riddled with bullet holes, out of the sea, flung it into the back of a naval truck, and carted it off God knows where, probably to the naval base at Kunda or the bigger naval station at Maizuru.

So, the look that passed between us when he turned to me before jumping into the sea—which hardly constituted a real farewell—turned out to be the last time I saw him alive. In that brief, wild, desperate moment, I was parted forever from the only man I had ever truly loved.

At Mineyama-cho police station, detectives and special secret police officers took turns interrogating me, making me go over every detail of my acquaintance with Ensign Shimazutsu and his desertion attempt again and again.

They finally told me they would confer with the naval authorities and then decide what to do with me for the crime of aiding and abetting the desertion of a naval officer. Till then, I was to be kept in one of the detention cells at the police station.

'You've committed a terrible crime,' the interrogation officers invariably said each time they returned to have me go over the details yet again. 'You won't get off easy!'

As I sat in the dreary gloom of the detention cell, the many things that Ensign Shimazutsu had told me little by little during his visits to me at the brothel flickered and swirled through my mind like the brightly lit scenes painted on the panels of a revolving lantern.

He was such a good person, and yet just because he thought about things seriously and was, in a sense, true to himself and didn't try to make himself go along with something he believed was wrong, he was driven by his own conscience to oppose the authority of the nation and died for having done so. How he must have regretted being shot down a deserter in the face of the enemy! Desertion was an unforgivable dereliction of duty in the Emperor's army according to manuals of military conduct such as the Emperor Meiji's Imperial Rescript to Soldiers and Sailors and the Field Service Code.

Worse still, something then happened—a cruel twist of irony—that must have made his fate even harder for him to accept, and which made me wish that he had been able to live just a little while longer. On the third day of my imprisonment in the detention cell, Japan accepted the terms of the Potsdam Declaration and surrendered unconditionally to the Allies.

I could hardly believe it! Japan had accepted defeat just as he had said it would.

But I knew that he hadn't wanted to take the life of another human being, not even that of an enemy of Japan. Since he was a kamikaze pilot, even though there was a good chance he'd have been hit by antiaircraft fire before he could crash his plane into the side of a battleship, his plane still might have reached its target and killed people. So, since he was sure to die either way if he had stayed in the navy and fulfilled his military duty, I tried to think that he must have been satisfied that he had chosen a course of action where at least he was the only one who had died and glad that he had not done anything that might have resulted in the killing of another human being, even an enemy.

After the announcement of Japan's defeat, even from behind the iron bars of the detention cell, I could sense the panic and confusion among the policemen. And I was the first prisoner they released; they probably thought I was just a nuisance who might cause trouble for them at some later date and decided that, under the circumstances, it was advisable to get me out of there as soon as possible.

All I had done, in fact, was to tag along for a single night with a naval officer guilty of attempting to desert in the face of the enemy, a crime that was no longer a crime now that the war was over. With the end of the war, all branches of the Japanese military were disbanded and ceased to exist, so even if Ensign Shimazutsu had still been alive, the Navy wouldn't have been able to court-martial him for his attempted desertion.

The end of the war brought not only the defeat of Japan but the throwing off of social customs and fetters in the name of the new democracy introduced into Japan by the Americans. The Allied forces that took control of Japan after its surrender did away with the prostitute-licensing system that had bound me to my brothel in the gay quarter, and I was free to make a fresh start in my life. Yes, I was a free woman and could go wherever I wished, but what sort of work was there for me amid the lethargy and chaos of postwar Japan? I didn't dream of seeking regular employment at a company.

In early September, it was rumored that Allied troops would at last be stationed in Kyoto Prefecture, and the local government started discussing the advisability of establishing special 'recreation clubs'—their genteel euphemism for brothels—to cater to Occupation servicemen, in an attempt to protect Japanese women in general from being ravaged by the Occupation troops. I heard that they were advertising for special women to work in these clubs.

It was only natural that the government should worry about the safety of the women. The Allied soldiers had come to Japan straight from brutal, kill-or-be-killed combat in the Pacific; they had endured a long period of sexual abstinence and were now occupying Japan as the victors. The government probably figured there was no telling what might befall the women of a conquered nation at the hands of such men.

I heard that in Tokyo, bills headed 'Women of the New Japan Are Requested to Take Notice' were posted around the Ginza district, in an extensive effort to solicit women to participate in the great work of providing 'recreation,' as they so delicately put it, for the soldiers of the Occupation Army.

The job offered food, shelter, and clothing, all of which made it extremely attractive to destitute women who had lost everything during the war. War-widows, victims of bombing or other disasters, and other women in similar desperate circumstances were barely surviving, living from hand to mouth. I heard that many of them came forward in answer to the advertisements to apply for the job, desperately eager like a drowning man clutching at a straw. Then, upon learning the true nature of the work, some were shocked and turned back to the poverty of the streets rather than subject themselves to the self-degradation of prostitution. Others, however, figuring that 'Necessity knows no law,' took the job for what it was—a chance to make a new life for themselves, though not the sort of life they would have chosen under better circumstances—and agreed to work in the recreation clubs.

An organization called the Recreation and Amusement Association was established in Kyoto as well, under the sponsorship of the Ministry of Home Affairs, the police, the Association of Geisha, and the Hotel and Restaurant Owners' Association.

A Prostitute for Occupation Army Servicemen

I made my way to the city of Kyoto, where through the agency of the Recreation and Amusement Association I resumed my life of prostitution, this time with Occupation Army servicemen as my customers.

Two emotions dwelled in my heart at that time. The greater by far was utter despair at having sunk so low and feeling that now more than ever before I had absolutely nothing left to lose, and the other was a tiny bit of pride at fancying myself a sort of sexual bulwark in defense of my fellow countrywomen, servicing the conquerors to keep them from ravaging Japan's womanhood.

Luckily, the Occupation Army servicemen that came to Kyoto were kind and mild-mannered; most of them were even gentlemanly, and you almost never heard stories about bad or violent conduct on their part. Kyoto had been spared fiery destruction by bombing during the war, and a section of what had once been the gay quarter was used for the recreation clubs.

There were three types of clubs, for blacks, whites, and officers. Each club almost always had a long line of men outside waiting their turn.

I had mixed feelings about being an army prostitute, for I knew that in the past, prostitutes had been sent along with Japanese troops wherever they went, and several hundred thousand Korean women, in particular, had been forced to serve in Japanese field brothels.

It wasn't long before 'Off Limits' signs started going up in front of the entrances to all the recreation clubs, because there were just too many Occupation Army servicemen going to them and venereal diseases had started to spread.

Of course, just because the servicemen were ordered not to go to the brothels, that didn't mean prostitution stopped altogether.

Though we prostitutes had to put up with being called derogatory names like *pan-pan* and *pansuke*, the Japanese versions of the Occupation Army servicemen's term for a prostitute or 'pom-pom girl,' we took our trade out of the brothels into the streets and continued selling our bodies to Occupation Army servicemen.

At a time when the average Japanese citizen was on the verge of starving to death, I was getting plenty of nourishing food in the form of rations from the U.S. servicemen who were my customers. Feeling as if I were really somebody special, I would walk along arm in arm with the American servicemen, smoking Camel and Lucky Strike cigarettes and chewing Wrigley's gum. I would look down on the pale, malnourished faces of the Japanese we passed as we drove by in an army jeep and feel that I was somehow superior to them. It's a terrible thing to admit, but I quickly grew accustomed to that life.

In early November, I started seeing a lot of a Chicano U.S. Army sergeant named Peter Cantu. I called him Pete, and I soon became his 'only,' a term I imagine you are all familiar with: I stopped taking other customers and slept only with him.

He kept me as his mistress in a small, one-story house on a narrow back street and often came over from the Okazaki camp in his jeep. He would now and then stay overnight on the weekends.

Even as I became accustomed to the privileged life of an Occupation Army prostitute, before long I started to worry whether it was really such an enviable position. It wasn't a question of morality or a guilty conscience that bothered me: I was anxious about the future.

You see, I knew that my sham husband-and-wife arrangement with Pete couldn't continue indefinitely. He had no intention of actually marrying me, and from the start it wasn't the sort of relationship that led me to expect any such thing. Furthermore, his fighting unit had been stationed at the front right up until the end of the war, so it was a safe bet that he would be among the first troops sent back to the United States.

I had no way of knowing then that my vague anxiety about the future would soon take concrete shape in an entirely undreamt-of event. Something truly terrible was about to happen to me.

Life is so unpredictable, isn't it? You just never know what's going to happen next.

I remember it happened the night of the American Thanksgiving holiday. Pete had brought over a whole roasted turkey and a bottle of California wine, and we drank toasts to the new Japan, the

United States, and anything else we could think of. We had a sumptuous feast such as ordinary Japanese at that time could not even begin to imagine.

Later, as we lay sleeping, I suddenly awoke with a start in the middle of the night, clutching my abdomen in pain. My forehead was covered with a cold sweat. The pain was like no other I had ever experienced, as if my entire abdomen were being viciously squeezed from inside, and so intense that I was near fainting.

Even without any medical training, I could tell that something was seriously wrong with me. For a moment, I wondered if this wasn't some sort of punishment for having feasted on such fine foods the night before while other Japanese were famished and had little or nothing to eat.

My groans awakened Pete, who was sleeping beside me. He rushed out in a panic to wake up the landlord who lived next door. Pantomiming and gesturing, he managed to get the landlord to accompany him back to my house. The landlord must have taken one look at my face, white as a sheet and contorted in pain, and realized that I was in bad shape, because he flew out of my room and ran to fetch a doctor who lived nearby.

In those first few months after the war ended, the only practicing physicians left in the city were a handful of elderly doctors, since during the war most doctors had been called up for military service in the army or navy and either had not yet returned from overseas or, in the case of army or navy doctors stationed in Japan, were busy working till all hours winding up unfinished business and closing down the former military and naval hospitals.

So it was a rather old, feeble physician who plodded wearily to my house, and I felt sorry to have to get him out of bed in the middle of the night. After giving me a cursory physical examination, he said he thought it was stomach cramps or intestinal obstruction due to knotting and twisting of the bowel. But since it was late at night, he thought it best to see how I was in the morning, so he gave me an injection to relieve the pain and left.

In a short while, the pain did ease somewhat, but only a little bit, and my body continued to be wracked by terrible pain all through the night. When at last the gray light of dawn began to seep into the room, the pain was just as bad as it had been at first, and I felt as if I were going to pass out. It was simply unbearable, so Pete carried me to his jeep and drove to the Kyoto Prefectural Rakuhoku Medical College Hospital.

At first, they refused to admit me, saying that they didn't treat emergencies and there were no unoccupied hospital beds available, anyway. But probably because it was a U.S. serviceman that had brought me there, at last the doctor on duty in the First Department of Surgery agreed to examine me. He palpated my abdomen and inserted a needle through my vagina into my abdominal cavity to aspirate some fluid; when he saw that the fluid contained blood, he diagnosed an ectopic pregnancy and immediately had me transferred to the Obstetrics and Gynecology Department.

Evidently, the sudden, intense abdominal pain and shock-like symptoms that had started the night before were caused by massive internal hemorrhage and the resultant acute anemia.

They immediately prepared me for surgery. The operation was performed by an associate professor of gynecology and the doctor on duty. When they opened my abdomen, however, they found a sea of blood. My blood pressure plummeted, they couldn't feel my pulse, and I went into shock.

As you know, the administration of general anesthesia by intubation and the management of respiration and circulation during surgery—both standard procedures in the United States at that time—were almost unheard of in Japan. The surgeon or his assistant usually gave the patient a spinal anesthetic prior to abdominal surgery, and then began the operation after confirming that the patient had lost sensation in the lower half of his body.

As far as patient care during surgery was concerned, the most a patient was given was an intravenous drip of Ringer's solution or glucose through an irrigator and a rubber tube that had been sterilized in boiling water.

All the nurses usually did in those days was take the patient's blood pressure at regular intervals, but in my case, the blood pressure was already too low to be measured.

'Prepare for blood transfusion!' the doctors operating on me shouted to the nurses, their own faces white as a sheet because they were losing me. Unlike the United States, Japan did not yet have any blood banks; far from it, the very concept of such a system for supplying blood had yet to find general acceptance here, so the term 'stored blood' did not even exist then.

Since it was an emergency, two or three off-duty nurses were called in and given a simple test for blood type, after which one of the nurses assisting the doctors inserted a large syringe into the arm of each nurse and withdrew at most 50 cc of blood, which she then injected into one of the veins in my arm. The nurses who gave their blood to me were quite thin and looked as if they didn't have enough food to eat, yet their faces betrayed not the slightest reluctance at providing me with their precious blood, and they won my eternal gratitude with their selfless devotion to their professional duty to save lives. Of course, uneducated as I was, I could hardly have known what all these technical medical terms meant while I was alive, and anyway, I had long since lost consciousness when these events were taking place: all the things I have just told you about were explained to me by the spirit of a doctor, after I entered the World of the Spirits.

The desperate and valiant effort by those nurses to save me with a transfusion of their own blood, however, was like throwing a cup of water on parched soil. My blood pressure did not rise again, and I died of shock due to massive hemorrhage. The angry shouts of the doctors running this way and that in utter confusion and the shrill cries—almost shrieks—of the nurses were the last earthly sounds I heard as my spirit left my body and was lifted up into the World of the Spirits.

Looking back on all I went through while I was alive, I guess I'd have to say my life was just one hardship after another, and riddled with shameful acts.

I thank all of you for listening so patiently to my story.

After Hearing the Sixth Night's Tale

As on each previous night, the hearts of the small group of listeners were deeply moved by the tale they had heard. They sighed at the enormity of Taguchi Fuyuko's bitter experiences in life, and remained silent for a while.

Yoshio was the first to break the silence.

"Thank you for telling us your story," he said to the Spirit of Taguchi. "Your struggle through life has touched my heart to the very quick." Then, addressing the entire group, he continued.

"Taguchi was born into a period when all Japan was poor. I've heard it said that in some parts of the country even the farmers who grew the rice were so poor they lived on millet and other such inferior grains and only ate white rice a few times a year; and when they did, they thought a bit of dried fish with their bowl of rice was a rare and delicious treat. Partly in order to have fewer mouths to feed, many farming families sent their daughters off to the big cities to work at some job or other, without looking too closely at the type of work it was or what sort of working conditions it offered.

"The hardships Taguchi suffered at the spinning mill were truly terrible.

"Labor-management relations will probably improve now that democracy has truly come to Japan in the wake of our defeat in this awful war. I see now that previously militarism and totalitarianism went unchallenged under the banner of capitalism in Japan, and everything was done for the sake of the nation, including the rampant exploitation of the downtrodden workers.

"I also can well understand how Taguchi, and other women in similar predicaments, had no choice but to sink into a life of prostitution and later become a prostitute for the Occupation Army servicemen—she and other unfortunates like her did what they had to do to survive."

"In the Bible," the Spirit of Professor Yuhara said, "it is written that the prostitute who sincerely repents of her sins before God or the pauper who out of his few possessions gives his only money, a single copper coin, to carry on God's work is more blessed in God's eyes and serves God's will more truly than those who take pride in themselves before others and before God because of their own good deeds and, thinking that it will please God, make many costly offerings to Him.

"Jesus befriended the small, the weak, the sinners, and the prostitutes of the world. People such as these were given true salvation, and Jesus despised most of all the hypocrites he encountered among the religious leaders and teachers.

"So, people like Taguchi who suffer many hardships during their lives on earth and enjoy few worldly blessings will receive great consolation and solace in the World of the Spirits and in Heaven."

Yoshio turned to the Spirit of Taguchi and said, "I feel very sorry for Ensign Shimazutsu. Thousands of soldiers in the Imperial Army and Navy were young students pulled away from their university studies and thrust into mortal combat; in the face of impending death, each of them must have groped desperately for answers to their questions about the meaning of human life and death. I imagine many of them accepted the Field Service Code and the Emperor Meiji's Imperial Rescript to Soldiers and Sailors at face value and met death willingly for the sake of their country and the Emperor; and they were, in a sense, fortunate. But many of those drafted university students who were about my age did not find the Japanese military code of 'Death before Dishonor' sufficient reason to lay down their lives for a hopeless cause.

"So I can well understand Ensign Shimazutsu's frame of mind and sympathize with his emotional and spiritual plight. Recently, I read that they're going to publish a collection of wills, diaries, and letters written by university students who were called up for military service and died in the war. Their thoughts and comments about the war should make a very interesting reading.

"A friend of mine who got drafted and had to leave his university without graduating told me this story, which brought tears to my eyes, about a still boyish soldier in his mid-teens who had been taken away from his studies at a naval preliminary training school and assigned to a kamikaze unit. The night before he was to take off on a suicide mission, his squad leader noticed him laboring assiduously over some papers and asked him what he was doing. His eyes shining with the innocence of youth, he calmly replied, 'I'm working algebra problems—what with the war and all, we haven't had much time to study.'

"Now Japan must be reborn as a peaceful nation so that this young soldier and the countless thousands like him will not have died in vain.

"There's one thing I really must ask you: Were you reunited with Ensign Shimazutsu in the World of the Spirits?"

"Yes, I met him soon after he entered the World of the Spirits," the Spirit of Taguchi replied, "though, of course, since the World of the Spirits exists on the plane of eternity, it was not 'soon' in the chronological sense of your world. Naturally, in the form in which he appeared to me, there were no scars on his back from the bullets that killed him, and his face emanated an aura of sublime peace. We talked about many things, and he told me that in the World of the Spirits he had been able to read all the books he had wanted to read while he was alive, that he had learned about truth and salvation, and that he had been shown all the sins of which he must repent and was preparing himself to enter Heaven.

"And it's almost too good to be true, but in the World of the Spirits he is able to speak in person with the spirits of the great people he admired while he was alive: Kierkegaard, Schopenhauer, Kant, Hegel, Goethe, Dostoyevski, Tolstoy, Martin Luther, Nietzsche, and many other world-famous philosophers, authors, religious leaders, and thinkers. Naturally, they have all long since ascended into Heaven, but they can move freely down into the World of the Spirits to assist in the salvation of the recently arrived spirits.

"Yes, I met my Ensign Shimazutsu again, and we experienced a bliss more sublime than any we had experienced on earth.

"By the way, once Peter Cantu got his discharge from the army, he returned home to El Paso, Texas. Now he's attending Louisiana State Medical College on a U.S. Army student loan; he's studying to be a doctor."

Here, the Spirit of Taguchi paused, and the Spirit of Professor Yuhara spoke for all seven spirits.

"Well, Yoshio, again we have talked well into the night. You must be tired, staying up so late night after night. I hope these late nights aren't affecting your health.

"We'll see you again here tomorrow night, Yoshio. Tomorrow will be our last night together. The Holy Ghost has granted us only seven nights with you, and we shall not meet again in this world after tomorrow night."

Yoshio nodded good-night to each of the spirits and left the dissecting room. The midsummer night air, slightly cooler than the parched air of midday, felt good as it brushed softly across his face. The night had passed more quickly than Yoshio had realized and it was much later than he had thought, for the sky beyond the eastern mountains was starting to lighten and he could feel the first breath of morning in the air. Soon, in about two hours, the glorious face of the sun would appear at the point where the dark form of the mountains met the pale rose of the sky.

The approaching dawn stirred Yoshio's heart as never before; he felt as if he were seeing it for the first time. This perpetually recurring, natural phenomenon seemed in that moment to cradle in its vast embrace the entire gamut of worldly experience—the joys and sorrows, past, present, and future. As Yoshio pedaled his bicycle homeward, the emotions aroused by hearing the story of Taguchi Fuyuko's wretched life reverberated in his heart and deepened his awe at the complex mystery of life, nature, and God.

CHAPTER EIGHT

SEVENTH NIGHT:

The Tale of a Man Who Was a Professor of Comparative Religion and Became President of Eiko Gakuen University

A Scholar's Tale Begins

We've come at last to the final night. My six fellow spirits have told the stories of their lives, all moving and pathetic tales of human hardship and sorrow.

All of them have modestly prefaced their stories by apologizing for their uninteresting experiences, and yet, far from boring their listeners, their tales of life fraught with ups and downs and all manner of unexpected developments have gripped our hearts and minds as no mere fiction could have, and, more importantly, have clearly demonstrated the truth of the old saying, 'There is no knowing what tomorrow will bring.'

Life is not a succession of pleasant, amusing events, but a period of drudgery, suffering, and sorrow during which one occasionally catches a faint, fleeting glimpse of happiness.

My life, for example, was a happy one in that, as a scholar and educator, I attained positions of the highest status, first as a full professor at Seito University and later as the president of Eiko Gakuen University; but compared with the extraordinary experiences of my six fellow spirits, the course of my life was, on the

305

whole, quite ordinary and would certainly cause no one to exclaim, 'Fact is stranger than fiction!' When it comes to the depth and substance of my experiences and the insights I derived from them, I'm afraid I can't hold a candle to the six who have preceded me.

Because our time together is fast drawing to a close, I will make the story of my life brief.

My Childhood

My name is Yuhara Shunji, and I was born in November 1881 in a place called Nojiri far back in the mountains of Taki County in Hyogo Prefecture, near the village of Sonobe in the Tanba area of Kyoto Prefecture. I was the second-born son, and for generations my ancestors had been physicians to the Sasayama feudal clan. For some reason or other, I was called Shunnosuke as a child.

Nojiri was a pastoral paradise, fertile fields and lush gardens surrounded by mountains. After the Buddhist memorial services held at our house several times each year, I remember, we always went to visit the family grave on the side of a nearby mountain. The kanji 'Descendents of Nitta Yoshisada' were carved conspicuously in bold relief on one side of the gravestone, so I guess my ancestors must have been quite proud of being related to that famous samurai of the fourteenth century, but that never mattered much to me.

My father, Shuntatsu, had permission to carry a sword and wore his long hair in a topknot arranged in the feudal *chon-mage* style until just before I was born. The national decree that all men were to cut their hair short had been issued some time earlier, but news of it was slow in reaching the remote areas of the countryside. My father had a gentle, serene nature. He had the distinction of having gone to Osaka as a young man to study Western sciences in Dutch, but being comparatively unenterprising by nature, he was just middling in all aspects of his life, including his profession as a physician. His medical practice was never as prosperous as that of his father, my grandfather, Yuhara Shutoku, a physician of Chinese herbal medicine who had a constant stream of patients.

By way of compensation, my mother, Natsu, was strong-minded and intelligent. Unlike my father, who never expressed any opinion as to how my elder brother and I should be educated, she was fervent about our education and was determined to find the best teachers and schools for us.

It was great fun growing up in the country. I would catch dragonflies in the fields and rice paddies and go fishing in the river. My grandfather was still a spry man for his age, and I was the apple of his eye.

'Toshi! Toshi!' he would call, using a nickname taken from an alternate reading of one of the kanji in my name. I'd come running, and he'd take me along with him to the river to fish for carp and roach.

This may be difficult for someone of your generation to understand, Yoshio, but one of my childhood chores was to clean the soot from the lamp chimneys, and it wasn't until much later, after I started attending elementary school, that electric lighting came to our neck of the woods. I still remember that day as clearly as if it were yesterday: our entire family, the maid, and even the rickshaw man gathered in the kitchen excitedly and watched with rapt attention as a single, bare light bulb was switched on in our house for the first time, its brilliant light filling us, one and all, with astonishment and wonder.

Another thing I'll never forget was something that happened shortly after I started going to elementary school. Meaning no harm, I took a five-sen coin lying on top of a chest of drawers, went to a candy store a fair distance from home, and bought some rice cakes filled with sweet-bean paste that I had always wanted to eat. But five sen bought many more rice cakes than I had expected. Even though I stuffed myself with one after another in the store and all the way back home, I still hadn't finished eating all of them by the time I got home, so I hid the rest in the front fold of my kimono and entered the house as if nothing had happened. That evening I couldn't eat a bite of dinner, so at first I tried to trick my parents by telling them a lie, that I had a stomachache. Unfortunately, one of the rice cakes fell out of my kimono, and my mother saw it! She scolded me up one side and down the other, and finally threw me out of the house into the garden.

Even now, I remember every detail of that scene. That experience left an indelible impression on me, and as a result, I later came to believe that the ability to condemn as wrong an act, such as stealing or lying, as wrong is not innate in people. I think each person first learns that such things are wrong during childhood, when severely scolded on some occasion or other.

My mother must have been crying in her heart as she spanked me. Faced with my compound wrongdoing—taking the money, which, though I acted in all innocence, still amounted to stealing, and lying to my parents about having a stomachache—she devoutly wished to make me an honest, truthful person who would never again tell a lie.

Since then, I've never taken anything that belonged to another person, even if that person was a member of my own family, and I believe that single childhood experience determined my lifelong character.

When I had finished my fourth year of elementary school, my mother enrolled me at Hatsumokan, or 'School of Enlightenment,' under the direction of Inoue Hansuke Isui, who was reputed to be one of the best educators in Tanba. There I received thorough academic and moral training.

Hatsumokan was a small, private school that Mr. Inoue set up in his home in February 1864 at the age of twenty-two. The school was founded on the belief that 'An uneducated man is but one remove from the birds and animals.' The attitude expressed in that old saying, which points up so well the necessity of education, should arouse our criticism nowadays because of its rather harsh implication that the uneducated are somewhat less than human beings, but that approach to education benefited me, and the words remind me of my schooldays at Hatsumokan, which, however disciplinarian they might have been, I still remember fondly. My mother probably entrusted my education to the methods of Mr. Inoue because she believed such a school environment would be good for my character.

For many ages past, the Tanba region had produced illustrious military commanders, great doctors, master craftsmen, scholars, poets, and artists. Most of them went to Kyoto, and some went as far as Tokyo; many of them made names for themselves and achieved great success. Mr. Inoue, however, lived aloof from fame and fortune; he remained in his native countryside and dedicated his life to the education of its youth. He was also a close friend of the pioneer educator Niijima Jo, who inspired him to exert a strong Christian influence on his pupils.

After the reformation of the educational system during the Meiji Restoration of 1868, Mr. Inoue was appointed principal of the Funai County Higher Elementary School and later became principal of the Funai County Girls' High School, devoting over forty years in the service of education. During those years, however, he continued to tutor a small number of students in his home; and while living in his home as one of his private students, I also attended the Higher Elementary School.

When I later took the entrance examination for No. 5 Middle School in Kyoto Prefecture, I flunked it royally and ended up attending the privately owned Doshin English School in Kyoto.

Doshin English School was what Japanese called a 'mission school,' founded on the principles of Christian education. I loved this middle school and enjoyed my years there. My classmates included a great number of brilliantly talented persons: one became an eminent politician, one a doctor who was also president of the medical association and a city councilman, one a minister, one a professor at Tokyo University, and so on.

Each morning before the first class, we had a religious service in the Chapel, where we read the Bible, sang hymns, and listened to a sermon. As a result of Mr. Inoue's influence on my character during my education at Hatsumokan and of my years at Doshin

English School, I learned about mankind's sin and salvation, and with relatively little resistance, I received Christ as my savior and resolved to follow Christ's teachings all the days of my life.

I was baptized by Reverend Clark, a missionary, at the Doshin Church, and thus became a Christian.

I wrote to my mother and father about my conversion, and my mother wrote back these words of encouragement and support, 'You have chosen the path you believe is right; follow it stead-fastly from now on.' In the early Meiji era, amid the deep-rooted traditions of Buddhism there was considerable general opposition to Christianity—and that's still true in Japan today. This is because of the problem of who will perform the requisite Buddhist memorial ceremonies for the family's ancestors once a person becomes a Christian; this was and still is of vital importance, especially in the rural areas, where people tend to harbor a feudalistic attitude toward some things. It was not unheard of in those days for a person to be subjected to social ostracism for converting to Christianity.

Thus, it was with the greatest apprehension that I wrote to my parents about my conversion; I was so afraid they would oppose it. I was greatly relieved to read my mother's supportive reply, and I was deeply grateful for their broad-minded understanding. From then on, I prayed for the salvation of my family and that my mother, in particular, would one day convert to Christianity.

Partly because the educational system at Doshin English School permitted its students to matriculate automatically to Doshin Preparatory School and Doshin University without taking entrance examinations, the courses were not oriented toward studying to pass entrance examinations, and I was able to learn in a relaxed atmosphere. So I didn't study specifically for the entrance examination for high school, but even so, after five years of study, I was able to pass the entrance examination for the prestigious Yoshidayama High School, and I enjoyed my years there immensely.

High-school dormitory life was full of rowdy get-togethers,

eating and drinking parties where we would guzzle sakè and beer as if there were no tomorrow, and boyish roughhousing where we would dance down the halls wearing nothing but loincloths and generally run wild, our arms linked over each other's shoulders. Those were happy times, and the dormitory environment provided the perfect setting for us to expend our rough, youthful vigor in harmless ways. With our distinctive school caps perched cockily on our heads, our short capes thrown over our shoulders in winter, and our wooden geta clattering on the pavement, we sallied forth into the streets of Kyoto singing our dormitory song, strutting and swaggering, reveling in our youth.

I was still a Christian, however, and so while the other boys sometimes drank themselves under the table, I never drank to excess. In some ways, I lived an austere, upright life, as did many Japanese Christians before the war.

Although we did a good bit of reveling outside the classroom, the classes at a first-rate high school such as Yoshidayama were demanding, and I had to study hard to keep up, especially in math and foreign languages.

Principal Kurihara was a wonderful educator: he taught us the importance of freedom and equality of the spirit, and always guided our young lives in the right direction.

My Seito University Years

After finishing three productive years at Yoshidayama High School, I enrolled at Seito University, the most prestigious university in western Japan, in the Philosophy Department in the School of Literature, majoring in comparative religion. Many of Japan's current leading thinkers were studying in that department then.

After my graduation from university, I worked for several years as research assistant in the Philosophy Department. During this period, I did research on Schleiermacher's *The Feeling of Absolute Dependence*, wrote my doctoral thesis on it, and received the degree of Doctor of Literature.

About five years after I graduated from university, in 1906 soon after the end of the Russo-Japanese War of 1904-1905, I went to study abroad in Leipzig, Germany, at the recommendation of my faculty advisor, Professor Uozumi. Two years later, I went to study Christianity in the United States, at the Divinity School of Columbia University in New York City. In the field of theology, the school had the reputation of still being in its infancy. I chose to study there because Europe's leading theologians had begun flocking to the United States. I planned to stay about two years.

One of the people I became acquainted with in America was the daughter of a Japanese diplomat, Minister Ariyoshi, who was posted at the Japanese Consulate General in New York. Her name was Koto. She was a graduate of Shira'ume Women's College in Tokyo and had come to New York to audit some courses in the Literature Department at Columbia University.

Since we were both living in a foreign country that offered little contact with other Japanese, we soon became close, and it wasn't long before both of us started thinking about marriage.

The experience of living and studying in the United States was quite a change after my two years of research in Europe, where I had felt somehow stifled: the atmosphere of European countries was so authoritarian and fettered by the weight of their long history, even the paving stones in the streets seemed to oppress me with an overwhelming sense of the past. By contrast, America was a relatively young country that presented a social and academic climate where everything was new, open, and unfettered by the past. It was wonderful studying there.

In America, I had opportunities to mingle with the world's foremost theologians and hear their latest ideas first-hand, and there was much to learn. Just when I was thinking I'd like to extend my studies for another year, if possible, Minister Ariyoshi received word that he would soon be posted back to Tokyo. Koto and I thought this would be a good time to take the plunge into marriage, so we obtained Minister and Mrs. Ariyoshi's permission and were married. We had a small wedding, a simple ceremony at Riverside Church on Broadway just across from Columbia University.

Luckily, Professor Uozumi and the administration of Seito University granted permission for me to study one more year in the United States, so Koto and I were able to spend our first year of married life in America. It was a wonderful year for me, dividing my time between the research I loved at the university and pleasant hours enjoying the endless amusements and attractions of New York City with my bride. Looking back now, that was probably the most blissful and happiest time of my whole life.

The year flew by, and we returned to Kyoto, where I resumed my academic life at Seito University, this time as a married man.

Back in Japan

The Japan I returned to was much the same as when I'd left it five years earlier, but my absence seemed to have a subtle, yet undeniable and detrimental, effect on the progress of my career and my relationships at Seito University. One after another, I published papers on the knowledge I had acquired and new ideas I had picked up during my research abroad. Far from praising my work, however, my colleagues reacted in a way that was indecipherable to me: perhaps puzzlement, perhaps envy, or even a combination of the two.

Because I had lived a considerably long time outside Japan, my way of thinking and my approach to personal relations had changed without my being aware of it. It took several months for me to return to my former Japanese way of thinking and behaving. During this time, I also came to realize that during my long absence from Japan, my relations with many of my former contacts at the university had become weakened or strained; some had dropped me completely, and some had formed new contacts with other people and seemed to have little time for me.

About one year after returning to Japan, there was an opening
for a lecturer in my field, and I got the appointment; but most of
my colleagues who were about my age of nearly forty and had the
qualification of having done some research abroad were already
working at the of level associate professor. Some of them had even
gone to teach at provincial universities, where they had quickly
risen to the rank of full professor. In my case, all the positions for
associate professor in Christianity had been filled while I was
abroad, and positions at the lower levels of lecturer and research
assistant had been filled by students who had come after me, so it
was not until I had reached the age of forty-five that my promotion
to associate professor finally came. Seito University had a splendid array of talented full and associate professors in its Department of Philosophy, including such renowned names as Hatano,
Nishida, Amano, Tanabe, Kuki, Nishitani, and Hisamatsu, so I
must admit I could see why it took time for a position to open up
for a scholar of my less-than-stellar ability and accomplishments.

Now, I must explain what was happening politically in Japan.
After ending its three-hundred-year-long self-imposed isolation
from the rest of the world, our country reversed its former policy
and strove to learn everything it could from the Western nations
in its efforts to catch up with and surpass them by any and all
means, regardless of how this appeared to the rest of the world.
Japan now embraced a governmental policy that put national
wealth and military strength above all else. With the victory over
China in the Sino-Japanese War of 1894-1895, the confidence of
the Japanese people grew slowly but steadily. Encouraged by its
military successes, Japan started planning to expand its foreign
interests beyond the already-conquered Korean Peninsula as far
as Manchuria. This plan collided with Russia's policy to expand
its territory through Manchuria and seize control of the crucial
port of Lüshun in northeast China and brought about the Russo-
Japanese War, which Japan also managed to win somehow or
other. This victory secured our country a place on the world's
political stage for the first time. But in reality, the cost of waging

those wars had severely depleted Japan's meager resources, and those years of military triumph abroad were a period of devastating poverty at home.

With the death of Emperor Meiji in 1912, Japan got a new emperor and the Taisho era began. After World War I, Russia underwent a revolution, which had a great effect on some law and economics professors at Seito University, who became ardent admirers of the ideas of Karl Marx.

Both within and outside the university, social and political factions linked to the forces of militarism—which was promoting the development of Japan into a powerful nation and the Emperor system of government—rose up in opposition to the Marxist movement in Japan. The autonomy of Seito University tottered on the brink of crisis, and the entire university was in a state of turmoil.

Because I was a Christian and particularly because my academic specialty in the field of comparative religion was Christianity, these developments caused me many problems.

Oddly enough, from Japan's particular historical perspective, the thorniest problem with Christianity in Japan was where it stood in relation to the national polity based on the Emperor system. One would expect religion to belong essentially to a different order from the national polity, but in a period of history when the belief that the Emperor was a living god took precedence over all other philosophies or beliefs and became, in a word, absolute, then it became impossible for those in power to ignore the inherent rivalry between the God of Christianity and the living god of Japan, the Emperor. Actually, it's possible to think of this rivalry as a result, in part, of a simple misunderstanding arising from the translation of the English word *God* as the word for god used by the Shinto religion, *kami*, centuries ago when Christianity was first introduced to Japan.

Even in the universities, where academic freedom should be regarded as sacred, there were some unprincipled scholars under

governmental patronage who went along with the current of the
times and willingly became cat's-paws for the government; they
promoted the acceptance of militaristic ideology and beliefs on
campus and harassed those who dared to voice a dissenting
opinion. Because of my still-weakened university contacts and
my currently unpopular field of study, Christianity, I figured I was
destined to remain only an associate professor for the rest of my
career; but I kept a low profile, and after biding my time for ten
years, at last I was made a full professor in 1935, at the age of fifty-
five.

After that, I was once even selected to serve as chairman of the
annual conference of the Comparative Religion Society of Japan
when it was held in Kyoto, though admittedly it was a small-scale
conference that took place in a single classroom at the university.

My wife, Koto, was an intelligent woman, but she was also
quite vain and rather a cold person. Nevertheless, our union was
blessed with two children, a son and a daughter. Perhaps Koto was
inept at housework or simply out of her element when it came to
running a household, but whatever the reason she had absolutely
no inclination to do it and left all the household duties to our live-
in housekeeper.

When the children were old enough not to require her constant
care, about four years old, Koto began to participate actively and
ardently in a number of organizations, on the national as well as
the local level. First, she became involved in running the women's
club at our church; then she served first on the board of directors
and later as president of the Young Women's Christian Association. In time, she became president of the Modern Women's
Association, an organization dedicated to raising the status of
women in Japanese society, president of the National League of
Women for Prohibition of Alcohol and Tobacco, and head of the
Kyoto chapter of the Association for the Abolition of Licensed
Prostitution. She was always busy, rushing here and there on
business for one organization or another. I think it must have been
quite tiring and troublesome riding eight hours on the *Tsubame* or

Sakura express train to Tokyo, as she often did, but she never seemed to mind.

Because I was at the university most of the time and Koto had experienced the freedom of the American lifestyle during our years in New York, she quite naturally devoted all of her time and energy to her work for these various organizations. Though we kept up the appearance of being a normal married couple, physically and emotionally we were more or less indifferent to each other.

For example, as the years passed, I realized that Koto and I had almost no interests in common. She played the piano fairly well; she also had a beautiful alto voice, and sometimes sang at home. But I was tone-deaf, so we couldn't even sing the simple melody of a hymn together. In a similar vein, I liked to compose haiku now and then, but my wife showed absolutely no interest in these poems of mine and had no response on the few occasions when I read one to her.

The times I enjoyed most were those spent in my office at the university, reading or writing, and conducting seminars for a few students, though due to the militaristic political climate of the times, there were extremely few students majoring in such subjects as literature, philosophy, religion, and particularly Christianity. Consequently, I made a point of spending as much time as I could at the university.

The poverty that hit Japan as a result of the worldwide economic depression in the early part of the Showa era and the concurrent rise of militarism and nationalism were in head-on conflict with the socialistic ideas being advocated by those Japanese influenced by a belief in freedom of thought and the writings of Marx, so that even in the lofty seats of learning, the universities, the winds of conflicting ideologies raged incessantly. By 1933, even distinguished professors who were thought to be Communists or even merely Commie sympathizers started being ousted from their university teaching posts.

In the midst of all this dissension and controversy, it was indeed difficult for me to do research in Christianity, which believes in the existence of immutable truth.

Crisis and a Renewal of Faith

Two years after I became a full professor, on the very first day of the university's summer recess, July 24, a fire broke out in the middle of the night at our house in the Shimogamo area of Kyoto. The actual cause of the tragedy was never determined, but could have been the result of kitchen carelessness on the part of our servant, harassment by some group directed against me, or some sort of backlash resulting from interfactional strife. The house burned to the ground, and my God! I could hardly believe it, but my wife, our daughter Mariko, and the young woman who worked as our live-in maid and cook died in the fire.

I was away from home the night of the fire; I had gone to give a speech at a national Christian retreat held in Gotenba at the foot of Mt. Fuji. My son, Shin'ichi, who was majoring in chemistry at Seito University, was also away from home at the time, attending church camp in Shima.

I mentioned earlier that my marital relationship was not all that it should or could have been, but Koto's and my problems were not due to any sort of wrongdoing by either one of us, as is apt to be the case when couples drift apart, nor was our lack of success in marriage due to infidelity. Though we had been drawn to each other in the alien environment of New York, we were basically birds of a different feather, and through the years we had become indifferent to each other. Since we were both devoted to our respective jobs and had time for little else, we never had any serious problems or disagreements and lived a life of comfortable, if dull, habit.

I regretted that we hadn't made more of an effort to accommodate ourselves to each other—to discover and cultivate some interest we could share, or develop our mutual need for each other into true affection. Now that she was gone, this regret tormented me and gnawed at my heart all the more relentlessly because of the suddenness of the tragedy that took her from me, and made my bereavement all the more bitter and intense.

The grief I suffered at losing my beloved Mariko—my sweet, young daughter, who was still a student at Doshin Girls' High School, well . . . words cannot begin to describe the hopeless sorrow that enveloped my heart.

Even though I did not feel directly to blame for the fire, I could not ignore the possibility that the cause of the fire might be linked to resentment at my promotion or malice directed against me because of my beliefs, and the thought that I might have brought such tragedy upon my beloved family, even indirectly, weighed heavily on my mind and caused me unbearable anguish.

I wanted to believe that omniscient God sent His rain upon the good and the evil alike, but the reality was that the good are not necessarily blessed in this world, while the evil prosper and live comfortable, peaceful lives. My troubled heart cried out to God, 'If you really exist, why must I lose the ones I love and suffer like this?'

My wife, Koto, participated in various groups and did all she could as a woman to make the world a better place to live in, and she dedicated herself to striving toward that admirable goal with no thought to her own personal gain. My daughter, Mariko, was truly a pure, beautiful, sweet, young girl, who always earned good grades in school. She took piano lessons, and Mr. Nishi, her piano teacher, said she was quite good at it and was even talented enough to play professionally someday. And our servant, Matsu, was an honest, dutiful young woman; without her help, we could not have managed the household as well, my wife would have been unable to volunteer her time for her public-service work, and I would probably not have been able to devote as much time to my academic research.

So why did these three good people have to suffer so cruel a fate as to be burned to death? Why was human life so full of contradictions and inexplicable twists of fate?

I felt that my long-held faith as a theologian was being tested. Even though I had spent much of my life thinking about religion and talking about Christianity learnedly to others, now that this terrible personal tragedy had befallen me, I reproached God. Still worse, I had come to doubt the very existence of God.

Truly, my Christian faith, which instructed me to put my trust in God in times of pain and sorrow, was being sorely tried. Like so many others before me, I turned to the Book of Job and learned how to interpret life's suffering.

People said that Job was a blameless and upright man, who feared God and shunned evil. But great hardship and tragedy befell him, for Satan said to God, 'Does Job fear God for nothing? You have blessed the work of his hands, so that his flocks and herds are spread throughout the land.' Satan meant that people believe in religion not because they seek God purely, but because they expect some sort of divine favor in return. He challenged God to let him put Job's faith to the test: 'But stretch out Your hand and strike everything he has, and he will surely curse You to Your face.'

Then Job was stripped of all his worldly possessions—his livestock, his servants, and even his children were all killed—so that only he and his wife remained. And Job said, 'Naked I came from my mother's womb, and naked I will depart. The Lord gave and the Lord has taken away; may the name of the Lord be praised.' Despite his great losses, Job did not sin by charging God with wrongdoing and cursing Him.

Then Satan challenged God once more, saying that Job had not cursed God because God had not sent any ill against Job himself. He said to God, 'But stretch out Your hand and strike his flesh and bones, and he will surely curse You to Your face.' And God gave Satan permission to test Job's faith again.

So Satan afflicted Job with painful sores from the soles of his feet to the top of his head. Job took a piece of broken pottery and scraped himself with it as he sat in ashes.

Job's wife said to him, 'Are you still holding on to your integrity? Curse God and die!'

He replied, 'You are talking like a foolish woman. Shall we accept good from God, and not trouble?'

Though Job lost all his worldly estate, his children, and even his health, still, he trusted and believed in God absolutely. His example of true, unshakable faith buoyed my flagging spirit and kept me from sinking into the black abyss of despair.

I was further strengthened by the writings of Martin Luther, who said that the glory of God is revealed more in suffering than in anything else.

Moreover, the Apostle Paul said in his Epistle to the Philippians, 'It has been granted to you on behalf of Christ not only to believe on Him, but also to suffer for Him.'

As I pondered the meaning and ramifications of these words, my faith was restored.

God sent his only son into the world—Jesus Christ, who was without sin—that He might be crucified and die so that we might be saved. As Jesus hung dying on the cross, he cried out to God in a loud voice,

'*Eli, Eli, lama sabachthani?*' which means 'My God, my God, why have you forsaken me?'

I thought once again of the boundless suffering that the innocent Son of God endured on the cross for my sake, to atone for my sins, and my heart ached with love and gratitude and humility.

Near the end of His ordeal, Jesus lifted up His voice once more:

'Father, into your hands I commit my spirit!'

Following the example of Christ, I no longer questioned why God had seen fit to take my wife and daughter from me. My heart beat with a new cadence of absolute faith in the righteousness of God's will, and I resolved from that moment on to leave everything in God's hands.

President of Eiko Gakuen University

The tragic loss of my beloved wife and daughter in the fire naturally affected my research and seminar lectures at the university. I doubted God for a time, but through much soul-searching and reading of Scripture, I experienced a renewal of faith. But even though I gradually came to accept the deaths of my wife and daughter as a test of faith, I was still only human, and sometimes while working at my desk or giving a lecture, I caught myself staring off into space.

It was about that time that a friend by the name of Ueno, an old classmate of mine from my Doshin English School days, who had been a minister of the church and was currently president of Doshin University, came and told me that he would like to recommend me for the position of president of Eiko Gakuen University in Nishinomiya. He said the private university would be glad to get a person with my qualifications: I was, after all, a full professor at Seito University, a prestigious national university; I held the degree of Doctor of Literature; I had conducted graduate research abroad; I was active in academic societies; and I was a published author.

Considering how things stood at Seito University then, I decided to accept the position, figuring that a private, mission-sponsored university would provide a more congenial atmosphere for me to pursue my research on Christianity.

My mother was still living then, and she and a few friends of mine telephoned and wrote letters to me, cautioning me that there was no need to throw away a full professorship at Seito, one of the country's most illustrious universities, just to go work at Eiko Gakuen University, even though it was a first-rate private university. In plain terms, they thought the move would be a mistake, and this was probably how most other people saw it, too.

I also received some malicious, anonymous letters accusing me of hankering after the exalted title of university president. The environment at Seito University was not a comfortable one for me; more than anything, its repressive atmosphere hindered my research on Christianity. Furthermore, despite my renewal of faith, the Seito University campus and Kyoto streets were constant reminders of the loss of my wife and daughter, and I hoped that a change of scene would assuage the grief that still assailed my heart. For these reasons, I decided to accept the position and move into the residence in Nishinomiya that Eiko Gakuen University had prepared for me.

The times were such that the rising tide of militarism was making itself felt at Eiko Gakuen University as well, but the school seemed to have retained its atmosphere of openness and freedom so characteristic of mission-sponsored universities. I felt it had a greater sense of internationalism than the government-run schools because it had several non-Japanese missionaries teaching there.

My main purpose in leaving Seito University for Eiko Gakuen University was so that I could be free to conduct my research on Christianity as I wished without interference. I soon realized, however, that being a university president was not necessarily conducive to that purpose.

There was almost no time for me to pursue my own study and research. And though I had charge of the seminar lectures for the theology students in addition to my duties as president, my busy schedule didn't allow me to spend even half as much time on them as I had spent at Seito University.

I had to spend the majority of my time and energy on the running of the university. I had to obtain funding from the Mission Board in the United States, solicit donations from local churches, write reports, and handle a wide range of official correspondence. Due to the already worsening political relations between the United States and Japan, it was also necessary for me to explain Japan's policy regarding Asia to the Mission Board in America and resolve as best I could any misunderstandings in order to promote goodwill between our two countries. For this reason, when the Mission Board asked me to make a speech at the next annual general meeting in New York, I felt I couldn't refuse and was saddled with the additional task of undertaking a time-consuming trip abroad.

In those days a journey to America took at least six months, including the sea voyage there and back, and it was terribly difficult to get the Faculty Council and the Board of Trustees to approve such a long absence by the president of the university. However much I explained to them the importance and necessity of my going on this trip, instead of understanding, all I got from them was criticism and censure. They said I had no business going abroad and leaving the university without leadership at a time when the country was at war with China and the universities were undergoing such upheaval.

The militarization of Japan was progressing rapidly. The Manchurian Incident in 1931 ushered in a period of intermittent conflict between Japan and China, which later developed into full-scale war in 1937. Consequently, all of what I had considered to be Eiko Gakuen University's good points before accepting the position of president were now viewed by Japan's military establishment as intolerable defects and, in that sense, had paradoxically become the school's handicaps.

The Rising Tide of Militarism

Military supervision and interference in our educational institutions, from middleschool through university, became increasingly strict and oppressive as the war progressed. One or two military officers were posted at every school; moreover, once a year someone from the Imperial Army division that had jurisdiction over the school came to conduct an 'inspection,' to review the students' military training and make sure they were being instructed in the government-sanctioned dogma and exhibited the proper attitude.

Some of the teachers, especially those who had been influenced by the so-called Taisho Democracy, were resentful of this intrusion by the military into the hallowed halls of learning and expressed their displeasure openly. However, since the military rating and evaluation of each school would affect the students' entrance to high school or university and—if they were later drafted—the quality of their treatment in the military service, the teachers yielded to the incontestable power of the military. In the end, the schools were run as directed by the military officers.

Eiko Gakuen University's school policy, founded on Christianity and dedicated to providing students with moral training based on the teachings of Christ, was particularly intolerable from the standpoint of the ruling forces in Japan at that time, the ultranationalists and the militarists.

The Imperial Army's attitude toward mission-sponsored schools seemed to be this: The educators working there were traitors to Japan; if possible, such schools were to be reformed by disposing of the Christian influence so that students could get a thorough and proper education, and if such reforms could not be implemented, the schools were to be forced to close.

It was four years before the start of the Pacific War when I was invited to take up the post of president of Eiko Gakuen University, a time when the Sino-Japanese War was already in progress following the Manchurian Incident, and anti-American and anti-British sentiment in Japan was on the rise. Consequently, from the start of my career there, I had no end of trouble coping with the military personnel, who jumped to the conclusion that the university's association with Christianity constituted some sort of traitorous tie to the United States and England.

I remember an incident that occurred my very first day as president. I was in my office conferring with the head of the business office when a military officer barged right into the room without knocking.

'I am Colonel Igarashi, the military officer assigned to this university. Pleased to meet you!' he greeted me, then continued in his haughty, arrogant tone of voice, 'You probably intend to continue to run this university along Christian guidelines as before, is that right?'

'Since those are the principles upon which this university was founded, naturally that is my intention. It's more than just a job to me; I regard it as a mission,' I replied. Then, adding what I thought was obvious, I said, 'You must understand that the decision to run Eiko Gakuen University according to the moral teachings of Christianity is not based on my personal opinion as president, but on the collective opinion and will of the Board of Trustees.'

'I understand that. But you believe that Christ is the Supreme Being, don't you? Well, let me ask you this, though I hesitate to ask a question so blasphemous to His Majesty the Emperor: Do you think the Emperor is the Supreme Being, or not?' he challenged me.

Perplexed and fumbling for a reply, I nevertheless chose my words with the utmost care, for I knew the school's continued existence was at risk if I answered clumsily.

'I believe the Emperor is the Supreme Being in Japan,' I replied, adding, 'Jesus told people to "give to Caesar what is Caesar's"; the Bible teaches us to recognize and respect the authority of this world.'

The colonel appeared to be satisfied with my answer.

I felt I was being somewhat obsequious and fawning to this arrogant representative of military authority, and it disgusted me somewhat to have to kowtow to him, but at least I had managed to smooth things over for the time being.

Colonel Igarashi abruptly turned on his heel and left my office, his hand clenched around the handle of the sword at his side and the spurs on his shiny, leather boots jingling.

Then and there, I decided that the proper handling of this unexpectedly somewhat dimwitted colonel was the key to protecting the university.

From then on, whenever anything happened that displeased Colonel Igarashi, or whenever he came into my office to complain about and meddle with what was taught in a certain course, his tactic was always the same:

'If this problem is not corrected to my satisfaction, I'm leaving the school!' he would thunder. This threat wielded a terrible power, for in those days, no school was permitted to remain open without a military officer present. If he left, that was the end of Eiko Gakuen University.

Here's an example of the sort of thing I had to put up with. It had been decided that a shrine to house a photograph of the Emperor, formally called the Imperial Portrait, would be built just inside the main gate of the university. If built on the proposed site, however, the shrine would block the way into the Chapel, which was considered the symbol of the university, so I insisted that the shrine be built a bit more to one side. Well, Colonel Igarashi flew into a rage at this; as always, he announced his imminent departure from the campus unless the shrine was built exactly as he stipulated, and thus forced us to agree to build the shrine where he wanted it built.

The Chapel, just to the right as one entered the main gate, was a distinguished building of Western-style architecture and singular construction with bricks specially imported from England. Formerly, it imparted a feeling of peace, as if it stood as a symbol of the university's Christian ideals. But once the Shrine of the Imperial Portrait was built squarely in front of the Chapel, it signified clearly that the freedom of the Christian university had been supplanted by Japan's Imperial Rule.

As president of the university, I was often irritated with the Faculty Council for their spinelessness. Some of the faculty were devoted adherents of right-wing ideology; for example, whenever someone made an antimilitarist remark during a faculty council meeting, it was immediately reported to the school's military officer. Furthermore, there were indications that such remarks were passed on from the school's military officer to the higher military authorities and the Ministry of Education.

I had thought that of all the faculty the professors of the Theology Department were the ones who best understood the problems confronting me as university president, and sympathized with me and gave me their support. In time, however, I came to the bitter realization that this was not the case.

Theirs was an attitude of unquestioning compliance. In the face of military might, they shriveled into a herd of yes-men, afraid to speak up for what they believed in. Indeed, many of them seemed to me to be so lacking in moral courage that I wondered if they hadn't misinterpreted the Scripture 'Blessed are the meek' and taken it out of context as justification for their spinelessness. The Bible also tells of how Jesus Christ saw people selling things and moneychangers doing business in one of the temples; enraged that they had turned the House of God into a marketplace, he made a whip out of cords and drove them out of the temple. I wonder how the theology faculty of Eiko Gakuen would have responded if I had reminded them of that bit of Scripture, in which Jesus himself so clearly and forcibly demonstrates the importance of standing up in defense of righteousness and truth.

At any rate, after the Shrine of the Imperial Portrait had been built, then there was the problem of getting all the faculty and students to worship before it in the proper manner. If we didn't take care of it correctly, it might be construed by the military as a sign of irreverence and cause trouble for the university. Let's take the night watch as an example: Under no circumstances were we to allow any sort of unforeseen incident or mischief to happen to the shrine; and in the event of fire or earthquake, our first priority had to be to see that the Imperial Portrait was moved to a safe place. This meant that whoever was on night-watch duty could no longer catch a few hours of sleep in the duty hut, as had always been done in the past, but had to keep watch in earnest all through the night. When I appealed to the Faculty Council, 'Now that we have the responsibility of caring for the shrine and the Imperial Portrait, it's going to mean a lot more work for all of us, so I must ask for your patience and cooperation,' again one of the faculty lost no time tattling to Colonel Igarashi. With blatant disregard for the context of my remarks, the snitch twisted the true meaning of my words and reported that the university president had said, 'The Shrine of the Imperial Portrait is a nuisance.'

A similar incident had occurred at Doshin University in Kyoto: Reverend Ueno, president of the university, had been severely reprimanded by the military authorities and the Ministry of Education for what they perceived to be an incident of irreverence involving a similar shrine in that university's judo hall.

During the remodeling of part of the judo hall, the members of the school's Judo Club had set up a Shinto shrine in a conspicuous spot. When Reverend Ueno saw it, he said, 'What on earth is this doing in a Christian university!' and ordered them to remove it. The incident was reported to the military and the Ministry of Education and caused Reverend Ueno quite a lot of trouble; it was even splashed across the headlines of the local newspapers. What with all the brouhaha, the continued operation of the Doshin University was in danger.

Even though the problem of my comments about the shrine did not reach that degree of seriousness, still, I had a terrible time explaining the true meaning of what I had said and resolving the misunderstanding that ensued.

My days were taken up with these and many other utterly trivial matters, which exhausted me both mentally and physically. It was against this backdrop and at a time when relations between Japan and the United States had deteriorated to such a dangerous level that it was even feared that war was waiting in the wings, that I finally set out on my controversial trip to the United States, which had been pending for some time. The Mission Board that provided funds for our school had requested that the university send a representative to the annual general meeting without fail.

After arriving on the West Coast, I traveled through several cities in California, then on to Chicago and New York City, giving speeches at churches and meetings of local chapters of the Japanese-American Friendship Association. I also had a chance to renew my acquaintance with old friends I had known during my period of study at Columbia University and hadn't seen for many years.

Throughout the trip, I wondered sadly how Japan had come to such a pass that war with the United States was a possibility. I didn't breathe a word of this, naturally, but I felt more and more certain that if, by some chance, Japan did go to war with such a rich and powerful nation, our poor country had no chance of winning.

Actually, I had an opportunity to talk in private with an issei who was a member of the Japanese-American Friendship Association, and he told me that military attachés to the Japanese Embassy in the United States and Japanese military officers on observation trips to the United States always said, 'If we ever go to war against a country of such advanced military strength and great economic power as the United States, we will surely be defeated.' Yes, that's what they said while they were in the United States, he said, but he had heard that they sang quite a different tune once they were back in Japan; perhaps fearing to be accused by their superiors of seeing only America's strong points and being somehow remiss in their reconnaissance mission, they apparently reported with bravado that Japan had nothing to fear from the United States.

I remember that he appeared to be seriously worried as he confided to me, 'I hope these erroneous reports and misinformation don't lead Japan to make a wrong and disastrous decision.'

It was about a year after my return from the United States that Japan attacked Pearl Harbor, thus instigating the Pacific War.

Japan Rushes Headlong into the Pacific War

Since my fellow spirits have already spoken at length about the war, I'll confine my comments to the events that affected me personally. The state of affairs at the university changed utterly with Japan's entry into the Pacific War and became much, much stricter than when Japan was fighting only the one war against China. Really, there was no comparison; things were just awful.

Eiko Gakuen University was a liberal arts school with departments of literature, economics, law, commercial science, and theology, so our students did not enjoy the privilege of draft deferment. The first to be called up for military service were those students who, for some reason or other, happened to be a year or two older than the usual age of university students. The faculty and I were sad to see them go but felt helpless to prevent their untimely departure.

The war quickly escalated, as my fellow spirits have related, and in 1943, the graduation of all students of liberal arts universities was accelerated and they were drafted and sent off to war in droves. Without having properly finished their education, these young students departed for mortal combat on the Continent of Asia and the far-flung South Sea Islands, and sacrificed their precious lives on foreign soil, in foreign skies, and on foreign seas.

It was one of my duties as president of the university to send these students off to war with appropriate words of farewell.

'You are a true son of Japan! You have our blessing as you go forth into battle for the sake of our beloved country.' That's the sort of thing I said, but deep down inside, my heart wept to see them go off to such a fate.

In October that year, some 70,000 students from the Kanto region of eastern Japan were assembled in the Outer Garden of the Meiji Shrine in Tokyo for a rousing farewell ceremony. It was reported in the news that when Mr. Okada, the Minister of Education, addressed the students and called on them to give their all for the nation and make their schools and parents proud of them, a student representative replied with modest valor, 'We do not expect to come back alive.' Then the students sang in unison a military song about their willingness to lay down their lives for the Emperor and in high spirits marched on review in the pouring rain.

I had called a special meeting of the Faculty Council in order to discuss measures for coping with the tense state of affairs on our campus, and on my way from my office in the administration building to the conference room in another campus building where the meeting was to take place, something terrible happened.

I use the word 'terrible,' but it was really nothing, an utterly trivial matter, which nevertheless got blown out of all proportion by the university's military officer. As he was in the habit of doing, Colonel Igarashi was visiting me in my office—though whether for a simple chat or to keep an eye on me, I really couldn't say—when it came time to go to the meeting, so we left my office together, heading for the conference room.

Actually, since turning fifty I had developed the slightly peculiar habit of removing my shoes and instead wearing slippers during long meetings, in spite of my having lived a relatively long time abroad in countries where shoes are worn all day long. The reason behind this habit was quite mundane: My feet swelled and hurt whenever I sat in the same position for a long time, particularly since wartime conditions had worsened and I was no longer getting proper nutrition; I simply couldn't stand to leave my shoes on during long meetings. That's why, on the day in question, as Colonel Igarashi and I were walking to the conference room, I was carrying a pair of slippers in my hand.

As Colonel Igarashi and I walked out of the administration building, we were joined by five or six professors who were on their way to the meeting. I don't know whether he just wanted to flaunt his authority or whether his instinct as a high-ranking career officer prompted him to action at seeing the rest of our group walking in a disorderly manner that he considered disrespectful to the Emperor, but when we passed in front of the Shrine of the Imperial Portrait, Colonel Igarashi suddenly barked orders at us,

'Halt! Ten hut! Right face, turn! Bow!'

Thinking wearily to myself, 'Oh, no! Here we go again!' I made a deep, exaggerated bow toward the shrine without troubling to consider the possible consequences of the act.

In doing so, however, I called attention to myself and inadvertently let myself in for a severe dressing down from Colonel Igarashi on a charge so preposterous I couldn't help but think it was a pretext simply to cause trouble for me.

He said that in bowing to the shrine while holding the pair of slippers in my hand, I had demonstrated an attitude of gross irreverence toward His Majesty the Emperor.

Actually, I had been making small talk with the other professors as we walked, and when suddenly commanded to military attention as we passed before the shrine, I had thought it would be rude and disrespectful to drop my slippers to the ground and so kept them in my hand as I bowed. But the sharp-eyed colonel next to me was quick to notice this detail and pounce on what he perceived to be a serious infraction.

He had been waiting for just such a chance to bring about my downfall and have the 'traitor'—as he considered me—removed from the post of president, and you can imagine the ferocity of his verbal attack.

'Since this is the president's attitude, it's no wonder the students here show so little patriotism and respect for the Emperor!' he shrieked triumphantly, overjoyed at his petty victory.

'Please forgive my thoughtless blunder. It was wrong of me, but I certainly meant no disrespect,' I apologized profusely, trying my best to smooth things over. As I said earlier, from the very beginning of our relationship, whenever Colonel Igarashi got in a snit about something, I could not expect him to approach the matter reasonably; I knew that going through the motions of apologizing—whether I really meant it or not—was the best way to deal with him and his ridiculous accusations, so I made a point of humbling myself. Furthermore, the Faculty Council meeting was scheduled to start soon, and all I could think of was settling the matter quickly one way or another. Apologies made, I hurried on to the meeting.

The next day, however, as I had feared, I was ordered to report in person to the district Military Police Headquarters. I left my office with a sense of dread, mentally preparing myself to be raked over the coals yet again.

When I arrived at Military Police Headquarters, I was shown into the office of the commanding officer. To my surprise, he stood up as I entered and offered me a chair. This lieutenant colonel had a gentlemanly bearing and was totally unlike the military men I had come in contact with previously.

For a long time, I had thought the men in the Military Police were different from those in the other branches of military service—sinister, terrifying, and treacherous. So I was really surprised that such a gentlemanly person as the lieutenant commander who sat before me was an officer in the Military Police.

In the beginning, however, I thought he was simply more skillful than I was at this cat-and-mouse game, his strategy being to pretend to be a reasonable, understanding person and thus trick me into exposing my weaknesses and then attack me for them. But as we talked, I gradually came to realize that this mild-mannered persona was no subterfuge but, indeed, his true character.

It came as a shock to see the thick file of reports he was leafing through, reports about Eiko Gakuen University made by Colonel Igarashi. The file also contained not a few slanderous letters from a certain professor at the university, whom I had regarded as a friend but who was evidently a malicious informer. There was even a report of a trivial remark I had carelessly made during a recent blackout. In those days, students and university employees took turns at night-watch duty on the campus; and whenever a preliminary air-raid alert sounded, those on duty assembled in a designated classroom to wait for the all-clear to sound. One such night, as the students and I and other employees on duty were sitting in a blacked-out classroom, we passed the time talking of this and that. Black curtains covered the windows, and the one ceiling light that was on was draped with black cloth so that only a small cone of light fell directly below.

'You know,' I said thoughtlessly, half-musing to myself and gazing up at the light above us, 'we're at war with the country that produced Edison, the inventor of this light bulb. . . .' In those days, even a remark as innocent as that was considered unpatriotic.

As the lieutenant colonel showed me the stack of reports of the university's infractions and my own suspect behavior, he said with a wry, almost sympathetic smile on his lips, 'Being a university president must be a very hard job these days.'

His gentlemanly manner put me at ease, and his smile lulled my fears and led me to relate my side of the previous day's incident with a candor I had not intended at the start of our interview.

'No, no, what happened yesterday was simply an unfortunate misunderstanding. . . . I was so startled at Colonel Igarashi's command to stand at attention and bow that I did so at once, without thinking. I never had any military training when I was young, so maybe I am mistaken, but I am no longer agile enough to bend down and place my slippers on the ground, and I thought that would be the wrong thing to do, anyway. I thought holding my slippers at my side as I bowed was all right, you see, since on campus the students are permitted to hold their books in one arm or hold their book satchel down at their side when they stand at attention and bow in the direction of the Imperial Palace or pray in front of the Shrine of the Imperial Portrait. The only difference between them and me was that I happened to be holding a pair of slippers instead of books. Since we Japanese tend to regard shoes, slippers, or anything worn on the feet as unclean, I'm afraid Colonel Igarashi misinterpreted my action as a sign of irreverence and got quite angry. Even now I'm not sure what would have been the correct thing to have done—was I really in the wrong?'

'I'm very sorry to have summoned you here on such a trifling matter,' the lieutenant colonel said cordially, standing up and walking me to the door. 'I don't think it really matters much one way or the other whether you hold your slippers at your side when you bow in the direction of the Imperial Palace or in front of the campus shrine; at any rate, it is certainly no cause for criticism.

Since your university's military officer reported an instance of gross irreverence to His Majesty the Emperor, for the sake of formality your presence here today was unavoidable, I'm afraid, but not all of us in military service are as inflexible as Colonel Igarashi.' And with that, he opened the door for me himself and graciously saw me out.

Yes, those were indeed hard times, when such utterly trivial, ridiculous matters of no consequence as this were treated as grave affairs calling for strict censure or punishment.

The war went on, and the situation in Japan seemed to worsen daily. Frequent enemy air raids darkened the skies over Osaka and Kobe, and when bombs and incendiaries began to rain down on Nishinomiya as well, the war was literally at our doorstep, and I didn't have time to bother about the Shrine of the Imperial Portrait.

There might have been a few cases at the schools and universities in Osaka and Kobe where someone had the presence of mind during an air raid to run to get the school's Imperial Portrait and carry it to safety, but most schools had arranged beforehand to have the photograph evacuated to a safe place. It was next to impossible to carry it out of its shrine in the midst of an air raid, for once the bombing reached the school grounds, in most cases the shrine itself went up in flames or was blown to smithereens in the wink of an eye along with all the other buildings.

As my fellow spirits have already related, male university upperclassmen were being drafted into the armed forces and sent into battle. The freshmen and sophomores were not old enough to be drafted, but they were hardly free to continue their studies, since they were kept busy day and night on the home front, manufacturing weapons and ammunition in munitions factories, digging air-raid shelters, and tearing down houses to clear fire lanes.

Female students, too, were mobilized into the labor service and sent to work in factories and on farms. Even after graduation, young women were not allowed to help out with the housework at home or take homemaking courses in preparation for marriage; unless they were already employed somewhere, they were called up for labor service.

It was this situation that led one of the professors in the Law Department to speak to me on behalf of the daughter of the president of a pharmaceutical company in Rokko. She was desperate to evade being drafted into the labor service and made to do menial work, so I hired her as my secretary. Since her father was content for her to be an employee in name only, he said I needn't worry about paying her; but I couldn't let her work for nothing, so I gave her a small allowance, just a bit of my pocket money, as a token of my appreciation for her work.

Her name was Nakajima Eiko, and she had graduated from Oka Women's College in Kobe that spring. She had a beautiful face, sweet and innocent, almost doll-like. In those days, all women wore baggy work-pants and blouses and covered their heads with heavily padded air-raid hoods whenever they went outdoors. No one even dreamed of getting a permanent wave; instead, women wore their hair tied back at the nape of the neck. And none of them—the respectable ones, at least—wore any make-up. Despite all that, however, Miss Nakajima looked quite attractive in her plain, baggy work-pants and blouse, which had been stitched together from what I imagined were her mother's or grandmother's old kimonos; oddly enough, the subdued colors and sedate splashed-pattern of her makeshift clothes seemed to set the dewey freshness of her beautiful, young face to advantage.

Though I had seen the faces of a multitude of women in all my many years, when I beheld her exquisite, jet-black eyes, her delicately molded nose, her intelligent brow, and her lovely lips, I felt I had never laid eyes on anyone as beautiful.

I imagine all of you think I was a man of strict morals so strait-laced as to be insensible to the charms of an attractive young woman, but I have a confession to make: On occasion, I would suddenly find myself gazing in rapture at her exquisitely beautiful

profile as she sat at her desk just a few feet away, making entries
in the school's daily log or recording the schedule of events; and
once I became aware of my untoward behavior, my face would
flush a deep red. Miss Nakajima was just about the same age my
daughter Mariko would have been if she had not died in the fire,
so perhaps when I gazed at her thus, I was seeing in her face the
image of the daughter I might have had.

At any rate, her presence made my office an oasis amid the
bleak, desolate surroundings of life during wartime. Set against
the drabness of those four walls, to me she was like a single white
lily softly reflecting the dying light of the setting sun. Though the
harsh realities of war were all around us, the sight of her gentle
beauty would suddenly call to mind images of peace and freedom.
Perhaps these feelings had something in common with my somewhat inappropriate appreciation of the vapor trails left in the sky
by the enemy bombers; despite the hideous, strident wail of the
air-raid sirens, as I looked up at the American B-29s overhead
flying in formation to the east or the west leaving behind their
billowy, white vapor trails high in the sky and wondered which
city they were going to bomb that day, I don't know why, but I
would suddenly think to myself, 'How beautiful they are!'

By this time, the food situation in Japan was becoming critical.
Food rations were meager, and I usually went without lunch, since
I had no one to cook and prepare a box lunch for me to take to work.
Miss Nakajima, however, always brought a box lunch from home
filled with steamed sweet potatoes, fried eggs, and other hard-to-
get, nutritious foods. I had no idea where her family could have
obtained them. Often she shared half of her lunch with me. Poor
girl! she probably couldn't stand to see me going without anything
at lunchtime, or felt she couldn't very well eat her own lunch all
by herself right in front of me without giving me part of it.

Though it shames me to admit it, I did indeed avail myself of
her kindness and gladly took whatever part of her lunch she
offered me. Before long, disgraceful as it was of me, just imagining what sort of delicious goodies she would be bringing in her

lunch box that day was enough to make my stomach growl in hungry anticipation.

The war situation grew worse and worse. Germany surrendered; Okinawa fell into the hands of the Americans; and though not a soul spoke of it, everyone knew that the war was a lost cause.

About two months after Miss Nakajima had started working in my office, one day she said as she was leaving at five o'clock,

'Good-bye, Professor Yuhara. Please be careful on your way home. I'll see you tomorrow.'

As she spoke, she took my hand between hers and pressed it warmly, then left the office. Those were perilous days, when one might encounter an air raid at any time or a bomb might drop on one's house in the middle of the night, in short, when either one of us might die at any moment, so her warm good-bye was not unusual. We lived with the sobering knowledge that each '*Sayonara!*' could well be the last. Every day, people felt poignantly the truth of the old tea-ceremony saying, 'Each moment comes only once in a lifetime, so one should treasure it.' I'm sure her grasping my hand as she said good-bye carried no special significance as far as she was concerned, but to an elderly man such as myself, who secretly harbored a smoldering affection for her, this innocent gesture of human warmth was exciting and left a sweet resonance in my heart.

Yes, there were moments when my heart leapt with the hope that she might return my affection for her, but what I felt was probably just the one-sided love of an old man for a beautiful, young woman.

It wasn't long before the war reached the point beyond which things could get no worse—I had known all along we would come to this pass, and there we were. There were hardly any students left at the university, and so formal classes were not conducted. Several years before, the government had provided old Arisaka Model 1905 rifles originally used during the Russo-Japanese War. The Imperial chrysanthemum crest had been rubbed off them, since these guns were no longer intended for use in actual combat. Model 38 infantry rifles had also been provided, and both types of rifles were used for the students' military drills at school; but all of these weapons were now re-collected by the military and were once again being used to fight the enemy. I know it must sound ridiculous to send soldiers into combat armed with old training rifles, but even these outdated guns were better weapons than the bamboo spears Japanese women were being trained to fight with on the home front.

Thanks to the relative spaciousness of our campus, the university buildings survived the air raids intact except for the gymnasium, which suffered a direct hit and was totally destroyed. White or light-colored buildings provided easy targets for enemy bombers, and the Imperial Army had ordered such buildings painted in camouflage, and some had even been painted solid black. With many of its buildings thus hideously disfigured and its luxuriant, green lawns dug up and turned into potato fields, the once-beautiful campus was now so changed it pained me to look at it.

Finally, it was announced that at noon on August 15 there would be a special radio broadcast in which the Emperor himself would speak directly to the people of Japan. This was the first time in the history of Japan that the Japanese people heard the voice of their Emperor. Even at this dire stage of the war, most Japanese still expected the Emperor's statement to be one of encouragement, calling on them to carry on and fight the enemy all the harder because of recent developments—namely, the destruction of Hiroshima and Nagasaki by some new type of bomb and Russia's entry into the war against Japan.

In fact, just a few days before this momentous broadcast, partly in order to prepare people for the shocking news of the Emperor's acceptance of the Potsdam Declaration and Japan's surrender, the director of the Information Bureau made a public announcement broadcast by radio stations nationwide, but this announcement was so ambiguous that most people took it to mean the exact opposite of what it was intended to mean: 'Things have now reached the worst possible stage. All of us must now endure

even greater hardship and sacrifice in order to preserve the
integrity and continued existence of our country.' This misinter-
pretation was bolstered by a declaration by the War Minister that
was broadcast immediately afterward, in which he called on all
Japanese to rise up as one and resist the enemy to the death, as the
rousing military march 'With Swords Drawn' played in the
background.

On the day of the Emperor's broadcast, the university employees, the students, and I all stood lined up outside to hear the
Emperor's voice for the first time in our lives. Due to his unique,
somewhat peculiar way of speaking and the radio static, it was
very hard to understand what he said; as a result, it is hardly
surprising that some people mistakenly thought—on the basis of
the grave tone of his voice and the bits and pieces of his statement
that they were able to catch—that the gist of his announcement
was that the Japanese people must bear the unbearable and
continue the fight.

Some of the people around me were apparently awed that His
Majesty the Emperor himself had deigned to make a direct appeal
to his people for their continued endurance, but from what I could
make out, it sounded as if the Emperor had said that the country
and people of Japan must bear the unbearable—and accept surrender.

'Japan has lost the war . . .,' I muttered to myself without
thinking.

'What are you saying!' shouted Colonel Igarashi, who had
been standing next to me with his head bowed like the rest of us,
listening reverently to the Emperor's voice. 'His Majesty the
Emperor has just told us that it is his will that we go on fighting.
He's appealing to us to uphold the national polity and encouraging
us to endure!' And with that, he knocked me to the ground.

While listening to the broadcast, my heart had been full of
mixed emotions—relief that the long ordeal was at last over, and
sadness at the defeat of my homeland—but being knocked to the

ground freed me of this internal conflict, and in spite of myself I beamed with joy at the advent of peace.

About an hour later, it became clear to one and all that Japan had accepted the Potsdam Declaration and agreed to the terms of unconditional surrender.

That evening some fighter planes, Imperial Army aircraft which for many months had not even taken to the skies during air raids to intercept enemy planes, came flying over cities at low altitude dropping leaflets that advocated die-hard resistance to the surrender and called on the people of Japan to continue fighting to the last man, woman, and child. But, of course, this and other efforts by military extremists to continue the war were in vain.

Thus, the final curtain fell on the Pacific War, and the Japanese people had to face the harsh reality of defeat.

Postwar Japan

Even after the war ended, my duties as president of Eiko Gakuen University did not let up. Far from it, I had my hands full coping with the social changes and problems generated by Japan's defeat.

During the war years, certain professors who were somewhat hostile toward me had branded me a traitor on the pretext of working to unify public support of the war, and others had conspired with the military behind my back at every turn. Now that Japan had been defeated, those who truly believed they had been doing the right thing by opposing me had the backbone to hand in their letters of resignation and leave the university, but the others, by far the majority, changed their tune overnight and became simpering sycophants in an effort to keep their jobs.

At this point, let me say a word or two about my family back in my native village of Nojiri. My father had died before the outbreak of the war, and my elder brother had taken over his medical practice. My mother became ill right after the end of the war and died. I had prayed daily for her conversion to Christianity ever since my own baptism so many years before, and at last my prayers had been answered; she was baptized on her deathbed by the minister of the local Christian church, to my great joy and thankfulness.

In September the Allied Forces began the Occupation of Japan. I was often summoned to the Occupation Army Headquarters in Kyoto, Osaka, or Kobe and asked for my opinions and recommendations regarding Occupation policy; I was chosen for this probably because of my years of living abroad, my fluency in English, and my standing in the community as a university president.

It turned out that one of the chaplains, Colonel Coop, stationed in Kyoto with the 6th Army, was the same Reverend Coop and fellow theology student I had known so many years before at Columbia University in New York. He was living near the Kyoto Imperial Palace in a Western-style house that had been requisitioned for use as Occupation Army officers' quarters. He invited me to dinner, treated me to the first good meal I had had in a very long time, and even gave me a box of candy—an incredible luxury at the time—to take home with me.

What's more, we had a fascinating discussion about the future of Japan, its position in the world order, and how best to promote the democratization of the 'New Japan.' What a pleasure it was to converse in English again after all those years!

While discussing these things with Colonel Coop, the desire to help Eiko Gakuen University make a fresh start sprang up within my heart. And I began to envision the various paths the school might follow in the future and pray to God for help and guidance.

It was at this point that someone started circulating a reprehensible handbill around campus with the filthy story that my secretary, Miss Nakajima, and I had been lovers during the war. She was no longer at the university, having come into my office one morning about a week after the end of the war and announced that she was quitting; because she had taken the job solely to evade being drafted into the labor service, there was no longer any reason for her to continue working.

I was thunderstruck at the audacity of such a lie! It was clearly a despicable scheme to get me ousted from the post of president. The lurid headlines of the handbill read, '*Special* Relationship Between President Yuhara and His Beautiful Secretary: An Old Man's Passion.'

As I have already confessed to you, it's true that I thought she was a beautiful, sweet girl and adored her in a way unbecoming a man of my years; but even though I had taken hold of her hand or put my arm around her shoulders—in sight of other people, obviously—as we huddled fearfully in one of the air-raid shelters many times during the war, still, I never had any sort of what is commonly called an 'immoral relation' with her.

I am well aware of Jesus Christ's teaching in the Book of Matthew regarding adultery, which points up so clearly the original sin of mankind: 'Anyone who looks at a woman lustfully has already committed adultery with her in his heart.' In my case, however, it was not a question of lust; my feeling for her was a combination of a yearning for beauty and redirected love for my daughter, of whom she reminded me. I would like to think that my love for her was platonic, but since there were times when I was seized with the impulse to take her in my arms, in all honesty I really can't claim that my feeling for her was purely spiritual and transcended physical desire.

When I pondered my enemies' tactic of using my affection for her as the foundation for their outrageous lies about us just to make me leave the university, I felt like asking them, 'Who among you is without sin and thus worthy to cast the first stone?'

This sordid, contemptible accusation was a terrible shock to me, coming as it did when my mind was so full of the myriad things that had to be done to get the university back on its feet and help usher in the new era of peace and democracy.

Even though the accusation was absurd and did not merit a public refutation, it caused me to reflect that I was somehow to blame. It seemed to me that if I had been truly virtuous and had earned the esteem of my colleagues, they would not have slandered me in this way. Such thoughts and self-recriminations depressed me greatly.

In early January 1946, plans were announced to establish a new university in Osaka, which was to be called the International Culture University. When the proposal came to my attention, some concrete action had already been taken: a Christian mission in the United States had promised to provide some financial aid for the project, and a suitable prospective site had been chosen east of Senri Hill north of Osaka. Furthermore, Colonel Coop had been put in charge of the preliminary negotiations, albeit unofficially, partly because Japan was still under military occupation and he was a colonel in the U.S. Army, and partly because of his connection with the School of Divinity at Columbia University.

He selected me to head the committee in charge of the preliminary work of establishing the new university. In accepting this post, I acknowledged that I would be prepared to become the university's first president once the university opened.

As the president of Eiko Gakuen University, I was still enthusiastic about my plans for that school's future, but the slanderous handbill had filled me with anger and disappointment; most of all, it had made me keenly aware of my own shortcomings. Even though in thought and speech I had been unsupportive of our national militaristic policy during the war, so much so, in fact, that I can understand why some people called me names like 'turncoat' and 'traitor'; nevertheless, as president of a university during wartime I had yielded to military pressure and, in effect, cooperated with the war effort. My conciliatory tactics had kept the university from being closed down, but at the cost of the ideals I believed in. Day by day, I felt more strongly that I wanted to take responsibility for my actions by resigning my post as president of Eiko Gakuen University.

I became more and more excited about the work of founding this new university in Osaka, where I could implement totally new educational concepts and pursue the ideals of the new, postwar era. I even began to feel this work was my true mission in life.

After handing in my letter of resignation to the Board of Trustees, I found a place to live in the Matsugasaki district and moved back to Kyoto. From then on, I was constantly busy running here and there on business relating to preparations for the founding of the new university. I never felt I had enough to eat, for food rations were still woefully inadequate, and I had to travel to my daily meetings on overcrowded trains, taking only a small amount of rice along to eat during the day, so I found all this running around quite exhausting physically.

One cold Sunday in mid-February, I attended the morning service for Occupation Army officers and enlisted men held at St. Augustine Church near the Karasuma-Shimodachiuri intersection at the invitation of Colonel Coop, who was preaching the sermon that day.

The kerosene heaters gave off intense heat, so that the Chapel was rather hot and stuffy. I sang the hymns in English, along with the American servicemen, and then listened attentively to Colonel Coop's sermon. He probably had not written his sermon with my presence in mind, but he spoke of the tragedy of war and mentioned the atomic bombs that had been dropped on Hiroshima and Nagasaki, even going so far as to intimate that America would have to answer to God and mankind for using such a terrible weapon. As I listened, I marveled at the greatness of this nation that had conquered us: the United States, where freedom and humility were such absolutes that one of its citizens could voice such opinions to these men who had spent the last four years of their lives at war.

Another thing that impressed me about that church service was the sweet sound of music that poured forth from a miniature organ specially manufactured for use by soldiers in the field, which these men must have carted around with them from one battleground to the next.

After the service, the barrier between the conquered and the conquerors disappeared as I and the American servicemen, who had so recently been enemies, chatted amicably for a while before leaving the church.

Colonel Coop came over and offered to give me a ride home in his jeep if I could wait a bit longer, but I declined, preferring instead to cut across the parklike grounds of the Kyoto Imperial Palace and walk back to my house in Matsugasaki.

In the Chapel, I had been warm through and through, but by the time I crossed Karasuma Boulevard and entered the palace grounds, a distance of only about two or three hundred meters, I was freezing. The cold seemed to penetrate my heavy overcoat and pierce me to the bone.

Soon I began to feel very ill, as if I were going to faint. Just as I managed to stagger from the gravel path onto the grass, my vision began to fail, my right arm and leg wouldn't respond to my brain's commands, and my tongue felt thick in my mouth. I could no longer remain standing and collapsed heavily to the ground.

When I regained consciousness, I was lying in a hospital room. This drab, dimly lit room with its peeling walls and sooty ceiling seemed an all-too-faithful reflection of the dire impoverishment Japan had brought on itself as a result of rashly waging one war after another for years on end. Yet this was the reportedly first-rate Rakuhoku Medical College Hospital.

Someone had found me unconscious on the palace grounds and notified the police, who had then carried me to the nearest major hospital.

Probably because I was a past professor of Seito University and former president of Eiko Gakuen University, the hospital staff gave me special care, but hospital stays were truly an ordeal in the months right after the end of the war, especially for someone like me who had no family to come and tend to daily needs.

I had been carrying my book of food-ration tickets with me in my briefcase when I collapsed, so that helped somewhat, but, as you know, in Japan usually a member of the patient's family or an attendant hired by the family cooks the patient's meals in the hospital room over a charcoal fire in a small, portable cookstove. Furthermore, usually all the patient's bedclothes are brought from home, so taking care of me was undoubtedly an enormous burden to the hospital staff over and above their normal duties. Hospital rooms normally are furnished with only an iron bedstead, on top of which lies a worn straw mattress that sags in the middle and has its stuffing poking out in places. When a patient is admitted to a hospital, his family has to bring all the bedclothes—including a futon to put on top of the straw mattress—cooking paraphernalia, and dishes and utensils to the hospital and wheel them to the patient's room in a handcart; and when he is discharged, everything has to be carted out again. The word 'hospital' may have the same word origin as 'hospitality,' but hospitals in Japan are anything but places of hospitality. A hospital stay occasions all the turmoil and commotion of a household move.

After two weeks in the hospital, I was allowed to go home. While there, I had not undergone any particular therapeutic treatment; I simply lay in bed, resting and going over and over in my mind my plans for the International Culture University. The physician in charge of my case explained that I had not had a cerebral thrombosis or hemorrhage; I had a disease where the blood circulation to my brain was interrupted occasionally for a short time, resulting in fainting spells called transient ischemic attacks. Since this disease is believed to be a precursor symptom of stroke, he said I would have to be careful in the future and sternly cautioned me to have my blood pressure checked regularly and take my medicine as prescribed.

On the day of my discharge from the hospital, my son Shin'ichi came and escorted me home. He had joined the Imperial Navy at the rank of ensign as an engineering trainee about four months before the end of the war and had been in active service only a short time. When the war ended, he had been able to return home immediately and was now doing graduate research in chemistry and working as a lecturer in the Science Department at Seito University.

That night, I signed and affixed my seal to the consent form, which I had requested from my physician just before I left the hospital, for donating my body after death to Rakuhoku Medical College for medical research.

'I'm old now,' I said to Shin'ichi, handing him the signed consent form, 'and there's no telling when I might get sick and die. The only thing I can do to repay society for the kindness others have shown me in my life is to donate my body for medical research. Please see that my wish is carried out.'

Following my return home from the hospital, I didn't have any particular head pain, my neck wasn't stiff, and I had regained feeling and movement in my right arm and leg. I felt fit as a fiddle, so I resumed my busy schedule of activities as before, daily attending meetings and making arrangements for the opening of the new university.

Just two months after my discharge, however, on April 16, I was sitting reading the local news in the morning newspaper—a report that the cherry trees in Maruyama Park, which had been utterly neglected during the war, were now in glorious full bloom—when suddenly everything went black before my eyes and a flash of blinding pain shot through my head, after which I lost consciousness and collapsed forward onto the table.

This second attack was caused by a severe cerebral hemorrhage, probably in the important part of the brain stem, and after only a few minutes my heart stopped beating.

My soul left my body and seemed to pass through a long, dark tunnel; I felt I was being drawn into another realm of existence, utterly different but seemingly right next to this one. That was how I entered the World of the Spirits.

My body was found by the housekeeper when she came to work at eight o'clock that morning, and my son arranged for it to be transported to the Dissecting Laboratory at Rakuhoku Medical College, as he had promised he would.

Shin'ichi faithfully carried out my wishes on still another point, the matter of my funeral.

I firmly believed that the dead shouldn't be a burden to the living. A lot of people would probably have shown up for my funeral to pay their last respects, university friends and colleagues, people I had known from church, and others. Because funerals are usually held on short notice—since death comes suddenly and often unexpectedly—people always have to change their plans or daily routine in order to attend them. On hot summer days, they must stand throughout the ceremony under a scorching sun wiping the sweat from their faces, and on cold winter days, they must stand shivering in freezing winds. I wanted, at all costs, to avoid putting people to such bother. So, Shin'ichi did not hold a funeral ceremony for me. Society holds that such a ceremony is proper and necessary, so that loved ones and friends can have a chance to cherish the memory of the deceased, to confront the solemn reality of that person's death, to grieve for the deceased, and to pray for the peace of his soul. Even though it was my express wish that no funeral service be held, in view of the importance society places on such ceremonies, I think it took great courage for Shin'ichi not to hold one for me.

So, Yoshio, of us spirits you see before you, I was the last to die. I'm sure you've noticed that mine is the freshest cadaver of those lying here on the dissecting tables, and that is why.

That's the end of my story. The life of a scholar and professor doesn't make for a very interesting tale. We lovers of learning, who always seem to have our nose in a book, have but little experience of the world and often live on the fringes of life; and conversely, those who are adept in the ways of the world are usually ill-suited to a life of study.

Now, enough has been said about my boring life. Thank you for hearing me out so patiently.

As we have done each previous night, Yoshio, let's talk a bit now, shall we? Especially since this is the last time we shall meet in this world.

After Hearing the Seventh Night's Story

When the Spirit of Professor Yuhara had finished telling the story of his life, Yoshio felt deeply moved, just as he had each of the previous nights.

"Thank you for sharing the story of your life with me," he said to the Spirit of Professor Yuhara. "You prefaced your story by saying that the life of a professor and scholar is quite dull and run-of-the-mill, definitely not 'stranger than fiction,' but I think your life was full of ups and downs, and I have learned a lot from hearing about them.

"Your experiences as a boy and later as a young man were very interesting, as was your account of your years of university research, particularly the complex web of connections within the ivory tower of academia.

"I'm still just a student, so I don't know much about it, but it sounds as if being a professor is a very demanding line of work. Here at Rakuhoku Medical College, too, though you have to be intelligent and make a good showing in academic societies in order to become a full professor, political machinations of some sort seem to be involved in the appointments. I've also heard tales of some scholars purposely thwarting each other's ambitions with veiled enmity and behind-the-scenes maneuvering. It is particularly difficult to attain the post of full professor in medical colleges, which are organized so that there is only one full professor to teach each course and consequently all the associate professors must scramble over each other trying to reach the single top position in the hierarchy of their specialty. I've heard the medical colleges are organized quite differently in the United States; they have what are called 'clinical professors,' and there are many clinical professors for each course, thus greatly reducing the vicious infighting that mars the Japanese medical educational system.

"I was deeply touched by the tragedy of the fire and the loss of your wife and daughter, and your candid account of the difficult soul-searching you went through in order to overcome your anger and grief, and the subsequent renewal of your faith.

"Though I had some personal experience of the military pressure brought to bear against schools, particularly Christian schools, both before and during the war, including interference in school affairs by the school's military officer, still, I was surprised and angered at the ridiculous and outrageous behavior you had to put up with from that Colonel Igarashi.

"Just recently I read something about how the special secret service branch of the police known as the *Tokko* considered Christianity inferior to the officially approved, more traditional Japanese religions of Buddhism and Shintoism. The *Tokko* didn't single out Japanese Catholics as possible enemies of Japan for two reasons: first, because the Vatican, the headquarters of the Catholic Church, was in Italy, which along with Germany was one of Japan's allies in the Tripartite Pact; and second, because the organization of the Catholic Church itself was somewhat totalitarian. The Japanese Protestants, however, were a different story. The *Tokko* considered Protestantism an Anglo-American body of thought and dealt with its followers accordingly. As far as hardline militarists and ultranationalists were concerned, Protestantism was a religion of the enemy that harbored dangerous ideas stressing the importance of peace and individual freedom, and they considered Protestants a dangerous group indeed.

"I hope and pray that Japan never experiences a time such as that again.

"You spoke honestly about your feelings for your secretary, Miss Nakajima, and I respect you for your candor. Most men in such circumstances would try to conceal their desire for the woman instead of openly talking about it; eminent educators such as yourself, in particular, usually affect a puritanical attitude, behave as if they were incorruptible saints, and would never mention having such a human shortcoming.

"It's disheartening and troubling to think that some of your enemies, fellow colleagues at the university, no less, should have stooped to fabricating such sordid lies about you and her just to drive you to resign from the university presidency—all the more so since Eiko Gakuen is a mission-sponsored university founded on the principles of Christianity.

"Some of the points you made about funeral services were quite good, I thought, though I must admit I had never thought about funerals in that light before. What did you do when your wife and daughter and housekeeper were killed in the fire? I take it you didn't hold services for them?"

Yoshio had been talking without a break, his mind so full of impressions after hearing the story of Professor Yuhara's life, but now he finished his discourse with this question addressed to the Spirit of Professor Yuhara.

"No, I didn't have funeral services for them. At the time of their deaths, I already held the opinion that funerals were an unnecessary waste of time. Evidently, some people criticized my decision after the fact, but that's to be expected. I am well aware that my way of thinking about funerals runs counter to the commonly accepted view.

"But now, Yoshio, since you seem interested in the subject, I'll tell you a bit more about the plight of Japanese Protestants during the war. Until the beginning of the Showa era, Japanese Protestants were deeply worried about the social and political trends in Japan and were critical of Japan's war involvement in particular.

"From about the time of the Manchurian Incident in 1931 and the steadily increasing conflict with China that eventually led to the outbreak of the Sino-Japanese War in 1937, the Protestant Church in Japan issued the Proclamation of a Critical State of Affairs and began to cooperate in the war effort.

"Protestant churches began holding devotional services to pray for Japan's victory in the Greater East Asia War, and on instructions from the government, churchgoers started bowing in the direction of the Imperial Palace in Tokyo before the start of worship services.

"All the same, agents from the *Tokko* and the Military Police sometimes attended church services and arrested the minister if he uttered the word 'peace' in his sermon.

"Before long, under external pressure from the government, all the Protestant churches in Japan were consolidated into one, the United Church of Christ in Japan. Those Protestants who had been active in the movement to reunify the world's churches believed the hand of God was at work in this turn of events, but others were strongly opposed to the founding of the United Church of Christ in Japan because they thought this was merely a tactic to facilitate governmental control of the Protestant churches in Japan and would eventually lead to further militarism and war.

"Professor Yanaihara Tadao of Tokyo University, who was a close friend of mine throughout my many years at Seito University and Eiko Gakuen University, dared to speak out against Japan's colonial policy and the wars Japan waged. As a result, he was ousted from his teaching post at the university and became the victim of harassment in other ways as well. In his farewell address to the university, he said, 'The present Japan must die and be reborn!' Looking back now, his words were indeed prophetic, weren't they? Having lost the war, a ravaged and devastated Japan is now starting over on a new course.

"But many others who criticized Japan's militaristic policies did not get off as lightly as Professor Yanaihara. Ministers of the Holiness Church, Salvation Army officers, and others who dared to speak out against the wars were thrown into prison and tortured, and many of them died there.

"Yes, when I think of those courageous men and women who stood up for their beliefs, I feel guilty for not having done what I should have in my capacity as president of Eiko Gakuen University. By not taking a stand against the war, in effect I aided the Greater East Asia War effort.

"Well, be that as it may, Yoshio, you have now heard the life stories of us seven spirits over the past seven nights, and I imagine you have learned a lot about life in general from each one, for the tales related by my fellow spirits were certainly quite interesting to me even though I have already left the material world behind and now belong to the World of the Spirits. How much more so they must have been for you, who are still involved with the business of living!

"Since all seven of us lived through roughly the same period of history and died immediately following the end of the war or soon after, naturally, we experienced many of the same things—especially that nightmarish war—albeit in different places and from the various standpoints of our different walks of life, so of course, our tales contained some overlapping, but the sufferings and hardships each of us faced were uniquely trying.

"Nevertheless, since one never knows what is going to happen next, one must be prepared for anything and make the most of each and every day of life.

"One of the Old Testament poets said, 'Teach us to number our days aright, that we may gain a heart of wisdom.' How true!

"Yoshio, I'm sure that our appearing before you has dispelled your doubt about what happens to people after death, but those who belong to the World of the Spirits are hardly ever permitted to appear directly before the living in this way, let alone speak and converse as we have done. You must understand that these seven nights have been a very rare exception.

"As I explained to you the first night we met, Yoshio, God appreciated your prayer for the soul of the cadaver you were dissecting. That is why He has granted you this extraordinary opportunity.

"Actually, God tries to manifest His existence to mankind at every opportunity, but people don't notice or won't notice God's signs. So when people complain they have no proof of God's existence, this is their fault, not God's. It is precisely because God loves mankind so much that He sent his only Son, Jesus Christ, into the world as a living man to atone for the sins of all mankind, and yet many people still do not believe God even exists. . . .

"We of the World of the Spirits have never before appeared in this way to a living person, and will never do so again. As Jesus said, 'Blessed are those who have not seen and yet have believed.' Don't put your faith in only that which you can see with your eyes, but realize that it is that which cannot be seen that is eternal, and put your faith in that.

"Tonight is the last of our meetings here, but as you now know, Yoshio, this is not the last time we shall see each other. The day will come when you will enter the World of the Spirits, and then we will meet again. Having talked with you these past seven nights, we have come to feel close to you and find ourselves sorry to have to bid you farewell, but we look forward to the day when we will meet again. Of course, that's not to say we hope you will die and enter the World of the Spirits soon! As we have tried to explain many times in the course of these seven nights, the passage of time in eternity is altogether different from that which you experience on earth. You still have a lot of life ahead of you and many important things to do, so you must live a long, full life.

"God granted you this rare opportunity to speak with the spirits of those who have died because He wants you to bear witness to the existence of the World of the Spirits, the existence of Heaven, and Christ's salvation of mankind. He has given you a great mission to accomplish in your life.

"Now, since this is the last night, let's talk a bit about something I know you are quite interested in. You seem to like classical music, Yoshio, so I'll tell you about some of the musical events we have in the World of the Spirits.

"Recently, I saw the spirits of Mozart, Haydn, and Beethoven talking together and critiquing each other's works that they had

composed during their lives on earth. At one point, the spirits of
Ravel and Debussy came and joined in, and they certainly looked
as if they were having a grand time.

"Surprisingly, the Spirit of Mozart has shown a special liking
for jazz. When the members of a New Orleans jazz band entered
the World of the Spirits one by one, once they were all together
again, they gave a jazz performance, which the Spirit of Mozart
appeared to enjoy immensely, even to the point of moving his
body in time to the music. Evidently, Mozart has always been a
lively, lighthearted person. Beethoven, on the other hand, didn't
seem to care much for jazz.

"Similar events occur among the great names in art, literature,
and all other fields of human endeavor, and this makes the World
of the Spirits quite a wonderful place. There, the boundaries of
worldly time are transcended, so that the spirits of Goethe and
Schiller can discuss their writings with that master playwright of
another century, Shakespeare. Just the other day, I saw the Spirit
of Corot discussing his paintings with the Spirit of Toulouse-
Lautrec, who was just a boy when Corot died. I've also seen the
spirits of Rikyu and Toyotomi Hideyoshi, those legendary figures
of sixteenth-century Japan, enjoying a tea ceremony together,
their worldly differences having been reconciled amicably at last
in the World of the Spirits.

"All of these spirits I just named have completed their required
time in the World of the Spirits and have already entered Heaven,
but they are free to move back and forth between Heaven and the
World of the Spirits as they please.

"In the World of the Spirits, the temporal world is transcended; as it is written in the Second Epistle of Peter, 'With the
Lord a day is like a thousand years, and a thousand years are like
a day.' Things that would be impossible on earth happen in the
World of the Spirits as a matter of course.

"But we are on earth now, aren't we, and subject to the time
frame of the temporal world. Our allotted time together is passing

quickly and will soon be over. Before we go, Yoshio, I want to talk to you about the future of Japan.

"Truly, our country has undergone many severe trials and hardships. As we spirits have told you, the hardships, privations, and sacrifices endured by the Japanese both at home and in Japan's colonies abroad have been more terrible than words can express. Many people died, and countless thousands who had worked all their lives steadily building up a home and assets for their families lost all they had worked for—everything—in a single day.

"The whole of Japan was almost completely burned to the ground, destroyed, the culmination of which was the dropping of the atomic bombs on Hiroshima and Nagasaki—all told, millions of Japanese lost their lives. Some people, wounded and suffering in both body and spirit, wandered the devastated cities and countryside aimlessly, starving, until the day of defeat arrived at last. There are still many Japanese who have not yet returned from the foreign lands where they fought. Our soldiers in Manchuria have been interned by the Soviet Union, and no one knows when they will be allowed to return home. Nor have all the Japanese civilians who were living in Manchuria returned to Japan; many of them are still wandering the wild plains of Manchuria, hiding from the enemy and trying to find a way back home. Even after Japan had surrendered, Japanese there were still being hunted down and killed, so thousands of Japanese mothers fled carrying their babies in their arms; but realizing how poor their chance of survival was and wanting at least their children to live, many of these Japanese mothers tore their weeping children from their breasts and entrusted them to Chinese friends and neighbors for safekeeping and then continued their flight.

"None of us seven experienced the Pacific war in Manchuria, but there are countless tragic stories of what befell the Japanese families who were sent by the government to colonize Manchuria, stories so steeped in human misery they would bring tears to anyone's eyes.

"Living conditions in Japan are bad now not just because Japan lost the war; 1945 was the year of the worst crop failure since 1909. The rice harvest was thirty percent less than usual; the food situation in Japan has gone from bad to worse and beyond, and tens of thousands have starved to death since the war ended. In addition to the civilian population, the near-starving include demobilized soldiers returning from abroad, the repatriated colonists and their families, the homeless war orphans, and the sick and wounded soldiers in white hospital garb camped out in train stations. Even now, many people are still living in the blackened ruins of air-raid shelters. The pitiful sight of their unrelenting misery wrings my heart!

"On top of that, there have been natural disasters, floods and earthquakes. The people of Japan have been hit by tragedy after tragedy, sorrow after sorrow, just one blow after another.

"And now Japan is under military occupation by the conquering U.S. Army. . . . I know this may sound like a harsh thing to say, but all this suffering was necessary.

"But God, who loves all mankind regardless of our foolish mistakes and outright sins, will take pity on our suffering country and give Japan His blessing.

"The people of Japan were led into war by certain powerful political and military groups, at the cost of untold bloodshed and sacrifice that eventually culminated in defeat. But by virtue of their innate abilities and diligence and spirit of cooperation, the Japanese will arise from their hardship and misery and will prosper once more. Like the fabled phoenix, Japan will rise from the ashes and rubble of its near-destruction and renew itself.

"As you look at the present state of Japan, Yoshio, I know you will find this hard to believe, but the Holy Ghost has said that the dire food shortage that plagues Japan now will have completely vanished in the next quarter-century, and Japan's abundance of food will be so great that the people of the future will be worrying about how to lose weight instead of about where their next mouthful of food will come from.

"Yes, the time will come when Japanese will be able to walk into a restaurant and eat their fill of whatever sort of delicious food they like, French, Chinese, German, Italian, Indian, and, of course, traditional Japanese dishes as well. And strange as it may seem to you now, the Holy Ghost also said that Japanese cooking will become popular in the United States and Europe as a healthful, low-calorie alternative.

"The few trains that Japanese are allowed to travel on now are battered and war-scarred and can use the tracks only when the trains set aside for use by the Occupation Army are not running, but this, too, will change. In a little over a decade or so, Japan will be famous for having the fastest trains in the world, called 'bullet trains.' So streamlined in design that you'll hardly believe your eyes, these sleek, silver trains will run between eastern and western Japan at astonishing speeds.

"Almost all the present so-called national highways in Japan are narrow and unpaved, and the U.S. Army jeeps throw up choking clouds of dust whenever they drive by. The day will come when Japan-made cars and trucks will whiz along smoothly paved, four-lane expressways at speeds you would not believe possible. At present, the only good cars on the roads are U.S. Army jeeps or American makes such as Chevrolets, Fords, Buicks, and Oldsmobiles that were brought over for use by high-ranking military officers and American civilian employees of the Occupation Army; and under present circumstances, ordinary Japanese citizens don't even dream of riding in their own private automobile. In time, however, Japan will be mass-producing superbly designed and engineered automobiles that will be driven in countries throughout North America, Europe, and Asia; and the words 'Made in Japan' will become synonymous with high quality and product reliability.

"In fact, Japan's manufacturing prowess will become so great that it will cause problems in the form of trade friction between Japan and its international trading partners.

"Nowadays, Japanese look with amazement at the portable radios carried by U.S. servicemen, but before long the majority of first-rate electrical appliances will be manufactured in Japan; and the portable radios that astonish you now will be superseded by an even more amazing invention, a box with a screen to display broadcasted images and speakers to relay broadcasted sounds—sort of a visual radio—called a television. These and many other new products will be produced by Japanese electrical appliance manufacturers in mass quantities and exported all over the world.

"At present, about the only thing Japan is allowed to export to the United States is Christmas decorations, and companies are required to label each product 'Made in Occupied Japan.' When you consider that Americans regard these Japanese products as cheap, poorly made trinkets and that this is the only image Americans have of Japanese exports now, the future holds in store some truly amazing changes.

"There will be many other new scientific discoveries and technological advances, things that you cannot even imagine now; and Japan will become one of the richest nations in the world, and its people will enjoy a life of plenty and affluence.

"And how will this small country with almost no natural resources be able to achieve such great economic and technological development? Through the unflagging efforts of its people and their talent for self-sacrifice for the sake of the common good. But also thanks to God's compassionate forgiveness and divine blessing, which is all the more reason that the Japanese must take care to be humble, not arrogant, about their great accomplishments and success in future years.

"If the Japanese grow fat on their success like well-kept pigs, fall back into their arrogant, prewar way of thinking, and again start to believe blindly that they are somehow superior to other people, then the wrath of God will be visited on Japan once more to teach the Japanese the error of their ways.

"Yoshio, I charge you to do your part to see that this does not happen. Help our people to see where their true spiritual anchor lies, to respect and fear God, and to be humble about their coming economic development and worldly success. Show them how to make Japan a country that will help the other countries of the world, especially the Asian nations that Japan sinned against by invading them and waging war against them, so that Japan may one day hold a place of esteem even in the eyes of the citizens of those war-torn countries and the Western nations.

"I hope and pray that our beloved Japan will not suffer the same fate that St. John the Divine prophesied for Babylon in his Revelation, and that we will not have to lament the destruction of Japan with cries of "Woe! Woe, O great Japan, country of power! In a single hour your doom has come!'

"Finally, Yoshio, for the sake of your salvation, I want you to take these words from Revelation 1:3 to heart: 'Blessed is the one who reads the words of this prophecy, and blessed are those who hear it and take to heart what is written in it, because the time is near.'

"And now, it is time to say farewell. In a way, it feels as if we have spent a long, long time together during the few hours we have shared. Thank you for receiving us.

"The Holy Ghost has commanded that you not reveal the content of our meetings with you these seven nights until forty years have passed. Take good care of yourself, Yoshio, and study hard. Remember the lessons you have learned from the stories of our trials and hardships, that you may live a full and righteous life. Good-bye!'

Yoshio was already crying. Through tear-filled eyes, he saw the seven spirits looking at him and smiling lovingly, these seven spirits of the dead of whom he had become so fond over the last seven nights.

"Thank you, all of you. Good-bye!" That was all he could say.

Within seconds, the human forms of the spirits gradually dissolved into thousands of tiny glowing points of light, which soon faded from sight and vanished utterly.

The faint light coming into the room from outside through the windows caressed and dimly lit the dark shapes of the cadavers lying on the dissecting tables before him, which, in the sudden darkness after the luminous spirits had disappeared, now looked as unreal to Yoshio's eyes as the black figures of an afterimage.

CHAPTER NINE

A MIDSUMMER NIGHT'S DREAM

After the spirits had vanished, Yoshio stood in the midnight silence of the now empty dissecting room and became aware of the peculiar atmosphere in the closed room, a strange mingling of the midsummer night's close, muggy air seeping in from outside and the odor of the formalin emanating from the cadavers.

He felt utterly different from the way he had at the end of the previous six nights; his heart brimmed with emotion and a vague nostalgia for the seven spirits he had just parted from. As he had done each night before, he walked out of the dissecting room, got on his bicycle, and pedaled south on Teramachi Street on the eastern side of the Kyoto Imperial Palace.

Already, he felt he couldn't be sure if the events in the dissecting room over the past seven nights had been real or just a dream. The emotional strain of such an unprecedented, momentous experience—meeting and talking with the spirits of the dead—had left him drained of energy and feeling somewhat at a loss.

He even fancied he could see mischievous fairies peeping out from behind the massive, dark pine trees that lined the wall of the palace grounds and raised their uppermost branches high into the dark night sky.

Suddenly, he remembered a scene from a movie he had seen in a movie theater in Nakano while visiting relatives in Tokyo

364

during his last year of middle school, before the war—an American production of Shakespeare's *A Midsummer Night's Dream*—and wondered if he had not imagined his meetings with the spirits.

Yoshio looked up at the stars twinkling in the night sky and was once again choked with emotion as he wondered if the World of the Spirits, to which the Spirits of Shiono Yoshiko, Kim Han Sik, Nancy Masako Ito, Sumita Shogo, Yoneda Isamu, Taguchi Fuyuko, and Professor Yuhara Shunji had just returned, lay somewhere up among those distant, luminous dots of light.

Enveloped in the all-encompassing mantle of darkness, the tranquil hush of the wee hours of the morning was broken only by the piping squeak and answering echo of his bicycle pedals, which needed oiling.

When he got to Marutamachi Boulevard, a U.S. Army jeep traveling at high speed eastbound on Marutamachi roared by in front of him, and the gay laughter of the young Japanese woman sitting next to the American serviceman driving the car startled Yoshio out of his reverie and brought him abruptly back to reality.

He knew that the next day he would return to the dissecting room in the light of day and, along with the other medical students, continue his anatomical study and dissection of the cadavers, all that now remained on earth of the seven spirits who had shared the tales of their lives with him and whom he would always remember fondly.

AFTERWORD

The fundamental idea running through this novel is that in life there is really no knowing what will happen to us from one day to the next or even from one moment to the next. As I wrote, I tried to emphasize the importance of being emotionally and spiritually prepared for whatever life may bring. In addition, from the first page to the last, I wanted to bring to the reader's attention the tragic reality and absurdity of war, and the injustice of various kinds of discrimination. I also wanted to impress upon the reader how important and indispensable peace, freedom, and equality are to our society, and how crucial it is that we do everything in our power to protect and nurture them.

When I look at present-day Japan, so blessed with material riches and abundance and yet so conspicuously spiritually impoverished, it is my sincere hope that this novel will lead the reader to reflect on what is really important in life and what goals we should all strive to realize in the long run. If it does, I shall have been more than repaid for my efforts in writing it for its originally intended Japanese audience and, later, having it translated for an English-speaking audience.

Recently in Japan and the rest of the world, there has been much controversy regarding the definition of death: At what point in the physical breakdown of the various parts of body and brain does life end and death begin? Many people now advocate that it is more important to allow human beings to die with dignity than to perform medical procedures that prolong the life of the body without restoring the patient's consciousness, even though new

366

medical breakthroughs are continually making it possible to prolong life in more circumstances than previously dreamed of. Other matters such as the ethics of internal organ transplants and the question of whether doctors should tell patients when they have cancer have also become the focus of intense debate. Naturally, how physicians themselves view life and death will have great bearing on the outcome of this debate.

Without contemplating the question of eternity or having any conviction that there is an eternity and an existence beyond this material world we live in, how can a physician honestly and correctly deal with his patients? Though it is presumptuous of me to say so, I hope that my humble book will gain a wide audience and elicit comments and criticism, not least from my fellow colleagues in the medical profession, not one of whom was able to become a physician without taking a course in anatomy and dissection such as that depicted in this novel.

I chose the dissecting room in a medical college during the first year after Japan's defeat in the Pacific War as the setting for the events of this novel, and it was necessary to contrive for the principal characters—whose bodies ended up as cadavers for medical research—to die of something or other in the vicinity of Kyoto in the weeks or months following the end of the war. Each was born, lived his life, and died after experiencing the terrible ordeal of World War II.

I would also have liked to include accounts of the hardships of the Japanese who suffered internment in Siberia, escape and flight back to Japan from Manchuria, combat in Okinawa, evacuation from Kiska Island, the desperate fight against impossible odds during the Imphal operations to attack India, or any number of other ordeals that Japanese underwent during or after the war; but it took most of these aforementioned people several years to make it back to Japan after the war ended, so their stories simply did not fit into the time frame of the novel.

The life of a physician is an exceedingly busy one. I had to write this novel in the spare moments I was able to steal between patient consultations, hospital rounds, and my own continuing study to keep up with the latest advances in the field of medicine. Many a time I sat down at my desk late at night and started to write, only to be interrupted by an urgent telephone call requesting my services as a physician. Consequently, under the circumstances, it is regrettable but unavoidable that some parts of the book should perhaps have been more thoroughly researched.

I would like to express my deep gratitude to Professor Sano Yutaka, the pride of my class at medical school and internationally known anatomist, who served as president of Kyoto Prefectural Medical College until just recently, and to Professor Takenaka Masao of Doshisha University, who after getting his degree in economics at Kyoto University, took another degree after the war, this one in theology, at Doshisha University, received a doctorate degree from Yale University in the United States, and is currently regarded as one of the leading Christian theologians—both of whom were kind enough to read the manuscript of this novel and give me valuable comments and advice.

Reverend Ono Ichiro of the United Church of Christ in Japan's Kyoto Heian Church gave me invaluable instruction and enlightenment regarding the problem of discrimination, which is a subject of deep concern to him and for which he is constantly striving to find a solution.

And, of course, my heartfelt thanks also go to the late Reverend Yoshida Ryukichi, Reverend Oyama Yutaka, Reverend Uyama Susumu, and Reverend Hara Tadakazu, all of the United Church of Christ in Japan's Kyoto Church, of which I am a member, for their pastoral care and guidance.

I would like to express my thanks to Mr. Daniel Kelly who designed the book cover.

Except for historical figures, all of the characters appearing in this novel are fictitious and have no relation to any persons living or dead. Naturally, as the author of this work, I am solely responsible for its contents.

I wish to express my sincere gratitude to Ms. Brook Neal for her painstaking efforts in translating this novel from Japanese into English.